Brass Solo and Study Material
Music Guide

Compiled by
Paul G. Anderson

The Instrumentalist Company
1418 Lake Street, Evanston, Illinois

Printed in the United States of America

PREFACE

The present century has witnessed a continuous increase in the publication of music for instruments of the brass family, thus substantially increasing the accumulation of musical literature for brass performance. This index has been prepared as an extensive report on the music which is published and presently available for performance on brass instruments.

The content included within this volume encompasses information on study materials and solos published for trumpet, cornet, horn, trombone, euphonium, tuba, and various obsolete instruments normally considered to be in the brass lineage. All titles listed herein were extracted from current publishers catalogs and recorded in appropriate categories. The second volume of this index will record bibliographical information on ensemble music available for the same instruments.

It is readily admitted that this volume is incomplete in its coverage. Through the help of publishers' catalogs and the advice received from readers, subsequent revisions should improve in this respect as well as in the correction of any errors found in the present volume. Nevertheless, the extent of this listing and the division of material by categories will hopefully enhance search procedures as required by the performer, teacher, publisher, music dealer, and librarian.

Paul G. Anderson
Iowa City, Iowa
February, 1976

TABLE OF CONTENTS

PART 1: CATEGORY INDEX

Study Materials

Trumpet

Horn

Trombone

Bass Trombone

Euphonium

Tuba

Solos
Trumpet

GENERAL INFORMATION

The two main sections of this book are (1) a listing by instrument and performance categories (trumpet etudes, trumpet excerpts, trumpet methods, etc.), and (2) a composer index, listing each composer's works alphabetically. Where the composer's name is unknown (anonymous works, folk songs, etc.) the entry is listed alphabetically by title.

The main body of the book lists bibliographical information as follows:

BACH, J.S.-SAWYER. 12 ETUDES   M80

Composer-Arranger. Diverse spellings of composers' names present problems in alphabetization. When possible, the spelling of names conforms to that found in *Baker's Biographical Dictionary of Musicians, Fifth Edition with 1965 Supplement.* Names following a hyphen indicate the arranger's, editor's, or compiler's name. The ampersand (&) is used to indicate two composers' or two arrangers' names. When only the arranger's name is available, this is presented as:

BROWN, J.R.-ARR

Title. Some titles are shortened to fit the one-line format. This is accomplished by use of abbreviations or ellipses and by translation of spelled numbers into arabic numerals (i.e., "DIX ETUDES" would appear as "10 ETUDES"). When feasible, titles are recorded in the language used in the publishers' catalogs. Conditions arise, however, which require the translation of some titles into the English language. Descriptive elements (number of volumes, pitch of instrument, etc.) are recorded in parentheses following the title. It is regretted that use of diacritical markings was precluded by the computer facilities used to prepare this book.

Publisher. A complete listing of publisher codes with the appropriate names and addresses begins on page 230.

The second section of this book gives an alphabetical listing of composers together with titles of all music listed herein. Entry format is as follows:

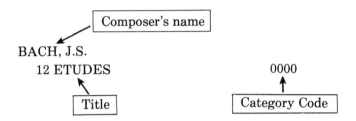

The category code refers to the section of the book where the given entry may be located (category codes are printed at the top of each page). Many titles are abbreviated in this section. Titles having more than one composer are listed under the first appearing name only. Most composer's names include initials for given names. Where it is impossible to determine a composer's first name, entries are recorded in one of two locations: (1) last-name-only, or (2) last-name-plus-initials. For example, it might be necessary to search both the SMITH and the SMITH, C. entries to locate a desired title.

DESIGNATION OF INSTRUMENTS

Cornet music is filed in the trumpet category, and baritone music is filed in the euphonium category. Music employing the phrase "for trombone or baritone" is generally filed in the trombone category. The euphonium category is usually restricted to those items specifically listed for euphonium (baritone) as the primary instrument. Abbreviations for all instruments are included in the Table of Abbreviations located on page x.

Tuba Music. The reader should be aware of the difference in the terms French tuba and bass tuba. Generally speaking, French and Belgian publications use the word "tuba" to indicate an instrument with a playing range extending upward into that of the euphonium; German, British, and American publications use "tuba" to indicate a bass instrument (bass tuba) employing a lower tessitura. Since most publishers' catalogs do not differentiate between the two instruments, it is impossible to separate such material in this index. There is one advantage to this otherwise confusing situation. Many French and Belgian publications suggest the use of bass trombone as an appropriate alternate instrument. Therefore, the tuba category offers additional materials for the bass trombone.

CLASSIFICATION OF STUDY MATERIALS

While it is sometimes difficult to determine content by title alone, the intent is to interpret the term *method* to include all instruction books which introduce elements of musical performance; the term *etude* to include musical studies designed for the improvement of technical competency; the term *excerpt* to include all publications dealing with extracted materials from orchestral, band, or other musical performing media; and the term *special studies* to include materials designed for daily drill purposes or for remedial training.

TABLE OF ABBREVIATIONS

ACC	accompaniment	(O)	orchestral accompaniment*
ARR	arranger	OB	oboe
(B)	band accompaniment*	OPT	optional
BAR	baritone	(P)	piano accompaniment*
BC	basso continuo	PA	piano
BK	book(s)	PER	percussion
BSN	bassoon	PIC	piccolo
BTRB	bass trombone	PSEUD	pseudonym
CL	clarinet	SAX	saxophone
CLAR	clarinet	SDR	snare drum
COR	cornet	ST	studies
CMPL	compiler	STR	string(s)
DB	double bass	TIMP	timpani
ED	editor	TPT	trumpet
EU	euphonium	TRANS	transcription
FL	flute	TRPT	trumpet
FR	from	TRB	trombone
(G)	organ accompaniment*	TU	tuba
HN	horn	UNACC	unaccompanied
HP	harp	VA	viola
HPCD	harpsichord	VC	violoncello
INST	instrument(s)	VN	violin
K	Köchel	VOL	volume(s)
MVMT	movement	7/3	[opus] 7, #3
NAR	narrator		

Alternatives in accompaniment are combined in one set of parentheses. For example, (OP) would indicate orchestral or piano accompaniment; (BOP) would indicate band, orchestral or piano accompaniment, etc.

STUDY MATERIALS

0000   TRUMPET ETUDES

BUTKIEWICZ, J.(CMPL). SELECTED STUDIES FOR TPT, BK 1	E72
CAFFARELLI, R. 16 ADVANCED STUDIES	D36
CAFFARELLI, R. 100 MELODIC STUDIES FOR TRANSPOSITION	E98
CALLET. BRASS POWER AND ENDURANCE	E51
CARDONI, A. LO STILE DELLA TROMBA	E98
CARNAUD. 10 EXERCISES ET 20 ETUDES	C38
CHARLIER, T. 36 ETUDES TRANSCENDANTES	D36
CHAVANNE, A.H. 25 CHARACTERISTIC STUDIES	C91
CHAVANNE, A.H. 25 ETUDES CARACTERISTIQUES	D36
CHAVANNE, A.H. 25 ETUDES DE VIRTUOSITE	D36
CHAYNES, C. 15 ETUDES	D36
CLARK, F. CONTEMPORARY STUDIES FOR TRUMPET	A03
CLARKE, H.L. CHARACTERISTIC STUDIES-THIRD SERIES	C11
CLARKE, H.L. ELEMENTARY STUDIES-FIRST SERIES	C11
CLARKE, H.L. TECHNICAL STUDIES-SECOND SERIES	C11
CLODOMIR, P.F.-FOVEAU. 20 CANTABILE STUDIES, OP.11	D36
CLODOMIR, P.F.-FOVEAU. 12 CHARACTERISTIC STUDIES, OP.12	D36
CLODOMIR, P.F.-FOVEAU. 20 CHARACTERISTIC STUDIES	C91
CLODOMIR, P.F.-FOVEAU. 20 DAINTY STUDIES, OP.18	D36
CLODOMIR, P.F.-FOVEAU. LITTLE EXERCISES, OP.158	C91
CLODOMIR, P.F.-FOVEAU. 70 LITTLE STUDIES	D36
CLODOMIR, P.F.-FOVEAU. 20 MELODIC STUDIES	C91
CLODOMIR, P.F.-FOVEAU. 20 STUDIES, OP.143	C91
CLODOMIR, P.F.-FOVEAU. 20 TECHNICAL STUDIES, OP.143	D36
COLIN, C. ETUDES MODERNE	B31
CONCONE, G.-SHOEMAKER. LEGATO ETUDES	N47
CONCONE, G.-SAWYER. LYRICAL STUDIES	M80
CONCONE, G.-REINHARDT. SELECTION OF CONCONE STUDIES	B92
CUNEO, A.F. 30 STUDIES AND 6 DUETS, OP.142B(F TPT)	E98
DALBY, C.E. DALBY ADVANCED TRUMPET STUDIES	A62
DEHERVE, A. 10 PRELUDES DE BACH	F30
DONDERER, G. KLEINE ETUDEN	E14
DONDERER, G. LITTLE STUDIES	F52
DREYER, F. 22 ETUDEN	B73
DUBOIS, P.M.-VAILLANT. 12 VARIOUS STUDIES	D36
DUHEM, H. MELODIC STUDIES, VOL.1: 81 MELODIC STUDIES	F81
DUHEM, H. MELODIC STUDIES, VOL.2: 36 MELODIC STUDIES	F81
DUHEM, H. MELODIC STUDIES, VOL.3: 24 MELODIC STUDIES	F81
DUNHAM, S. SWING RHYTHMS FOR TRUMPET	A70
ENDRESEN, R.M. ETUDES AND SOLO STUDIES	N27
ENDRESEN, R.M. SUPPLEMENTARY STUDIES	F07
ENDSLEY, G. ODD METER ETUDES	N66
ENDSLEY, G. VOLUME I FOR TRUMPET	M80
FALK, J. 20 ETUDES ATONALES	D36
FAULX, J.B. ETUDES DE DETACHE	A96
FAULX, J.B. 25 PROGRESSIVE STUDIES OF MEDIUM DIFFICULTY	A96
FONTANA, C. (CMPL). 16 ADVANCED STUDIES	B53
FRANZ, O. 10 CONCERT STUDIES	B53
FREITAG, W.F. 22 MODERN STUDIES	C46
FRIESE, E.A. NEUZEITLICHE STUDIEN...MODERNE MUSIK (2 VOL)	C75
GALLAY, J.F. 12 BRILLIANT ETUDES	D41
GALLAY, J.F. 25 ETUDES CARACTERISTIQUES, OP. 37 BIS	D41
GALLAY, J.F. 25 ETUDES CARACTERISTIQUES, OP.37	D41
GALLAY, J.F.-MAIRE. 73 ETUDES FOR TRUMPET (3 VOL)	D36
GALLAY, J.F.-MAIRE. 73 STUDIES (3 VOL)	D36
GASSIE, L. ETUDES	B66
GATES, E. MODAL ETUDES	C46
GATES, E. MOZART STUDIES (BASED ON MOZART'S MUSIC)	C46
GATES, E. ODD METER ETUDES FOR TREBLE CLEF INSTRUMENTS	C46
GATTERMANN, P. ETUDES CLASSIQUES	D41
GATTI, D.-GIAMPIERI. 10 PERFECTION STUDIES	E98
GEIER, O.-WOLF. 11 ETUDEN, OP.59	C75

```
GEIER, O.-NAGEL.  11 STUDIES, OP.59                             C91
GETCHELL, R.W.-HOVEY.  PRACTICAL STUDIES,2VOL.                  A62
GILSON.  4 ETUDES EXERCICES                                     F81
GISONDI, M.J.  BACH FOR THE TRUMPET                            D55
GLANTZ, H.  48 STUDIES FOR THE ADVANCED TRUMPETER(2 VOL)       B31
GOLDMAN, E.F.  PRACTICAL STUDIES                               C11
GOLDSTEIN, A.E.  FIRST BOOK OF ETUDES FOR TRUMPET             B44
GOLDSTEIN, A.E.  SOLOS, BK. 1                                  B44
GORNSTON, D.  PROGRESSIVE SWING READINGS(2 VOL)               C46
GORNSTON, D.-PAISNER & HUFFNAGLE.  40 RHYTHM ETUDES           C46
GRIGORIEV, B.-OSTRANDER.  56 STUDIES                           C91
HARRIS, A.  ADVANCED STUDIES                                   B31
HAUSE, W.-FREYER.  30 ETUDEN                                   B73
HERING, S.  24 ADVANCED ETUDES                                C11
HERING, S.  15 CHARACTERISTIC ETUDES                          C11
HERING, S.  ETUDES IN ALL MAJOR & MINOR KEYS                  C11
HERING, S.  28 MELODIOUS AND TECHNICAL ETUDES                C11
HERING, S.  40 PROGRESSIVE ETUDES                             C11
HERING, S.  38 RECREATIONAL STUDIES                           C11
HERING, S.  50 RECREATIONAL STUDIES                           C11
HICKMAN, D.  PICCOLO TRUMPET, THE                             M80
HUBER-ROLLINSON & ANTHONY.  25 ADVANCED STUDIES              E77
HUFFNAGLE, H.J.  23 EASY ETUDES                               C46
HUFFNAGLE, H.J.  HUFFNAGLE'S STUDIO STUDIES                   C46
HUFFNAGLE, H.J.  16 SMART STUDIES                             C46
ISRAILEVICH, L.I.  12 ETUDES ON KHIRGIZ THEMES               D71
JAMES, H.  STUDIES AND IMPROVISATIONS                         A70
JOB, M.  30 AIRS CLASSIQUES                                    D36
JOHANSON, A.W.  INSTRUCTIVE ETUDES ON RHYTHM AND TONGUING    B53
KARPA.  STYLISTIC-RHYTHMIC STUDIES FOR JAZZ TRUMPET          B69
KOLAR.  VIRTUOSENETUDEN                                        A51
KOPPRASCH, C.-HERBST.  60 AUSGEWAHLTE ETUDEN                 C75
KOPPRASCH, C.  60 ETUDES(2 VOL)                              D92
KOPPRASCH, C.-GUMBERT & HERBST.  60 SELECTED STUDIES (2VOL) C11
KOPPRASCH, C.-VOISIN.  60 STUDIES(2 VOL)                     C91
KREUTZER, R.-SCHAEFER.  10 FAMOUS ETUDES                     C09
KUCINSKI.  BRAHMS STUDIES (BASED ON BRAHMS' MUSIC)          C46
KURPAROV, P.  ETUDES ON CHARACTERISTIC TIMES AND RHYTHMS    F36
LABOLE.  ETUDES DE PERFECTIONNEMENT                          D64
LAURENT & BLAHA & ARBAN.  ETUDEN                             A51
LAURENT, R.  20 EASY AND FAIRLY DIFFICULT STUDIES           D36
LAURENT, R.  PRACTICAL STUDIES (3 VOL)                       D36
LAURENT, R.  STUDIES AND EXERCISES (DBL & TPL TONGUE)       D36
LEIDIG.  TRUMPET TODAY                                        N10
LENSELINK, W.A.  12 STUDIES                                   A78
LESTER-HERING.  60 RAMBLES                                    C11
LONGINOTTI, P.  STUDIES IN CLASSICAL AND MODERN STYLE       C91
LUBIN, E.  TSCHAIKOVSKY STUDIES (BASED ON HIS MUSIC)        C46
MAGGIOLINI, E.  12 DIFFICULT STUDIES                         G38
MANCINI, A.  15 DIVERTISSEMENTS                               A07
MANCINI, A.  TRUMPET STUDIES WITH MODERNISTIC RHYTHMS        D84
MANTIGLIA, V.U.  20 NEUE STUDIEN FUR FORTGESCHRITTENE        G38
MARCHAL, A.  16 ETUDES DE VIRTUOSITE                         F30
MAXIME-ALPHONSE.  ETUDES NOUVELLES (3 VOL)                  D36
NAGEL, R.  RHYTHMIC STUDIES                                   D73
NAGEL, R.  SPEED STUDIES                                      C25
NUTEN, P.  6 STUDIES                                          D80
PAISNER, B.-GORNSTON.  BEETHOVEN SONATAS(ETUDES ON ORCH.MUSIC) C46
PAISNER, B.-GORNSTON.  CHOPIN STUDIES (BASED ON HIS MUSIC)  C46
PAISNER, B.  MORE STUDIES IN SWING                           C46
PAISNER, B.  30 STUDIES IN SWING                             C46
PAISNER, B.  19 SWING ETUDES                                 C46
```

```
PAUDERT, E.   24 ETUDES                                              F52
PAUDERT, E.-GOLDMAN.   24 MODERN VIRTUOSO STUDIES                    C11
PERRIN, C.   33 DIFFICULT ETUDES                                     B66
PERRIN, C.   15 STUDIES & 6 PRELUDES OF HIGH VIRTUOSITY              D36
PETIT, A.S.   25 ETUDES MELODIQUES                                   C38
PETIT, A.S.   15 ETUDES TECHNIQUES ET MELODIQUES                     D36
PETIT, A.S.   15 EXERCISES                                           C38
PETIT, A.S.   GRAND STUDIES FOR EXAMS OF PARIS CONSERVATOIRE         D36
PETIT, A.S.   16 GRANDES ETUDES ARTISTIQUES                          C38
PICAVAIS.   20 ETUDES ELEMENTAIRES DE STYLE ET DE TECH               A71
PIETZSCH, H.-MAGER.   22 VIRTUOSITY STUDIES                          F60
PIETZSCH, H.   22 VIRTUOSO STUDIES                                   B53
PILAT, F.   EXERCISES FOR FLUGELHORN                                 A33
POPOVA, T.   SELECTED ETUDES                                         F36
PORRET, J.   24 DECHIFFRAGES MANUSCRITS                              B17
PORRET, J.   25 DECHIFFRAGES-MANUSCRITS A                            D64
PORRET, J.   24 DECHIFFRAGES-MANUSCRITS B                            D64
PORRET, J.   24 ETUDES MELODIQUES ET PROGRESSIVES, OP.518            D64
REINHARDT, D.S.   SELECTION OF CONCONE STUDIES                       B92
REYNOLDS, V.   48 ETUDES                                             F23
RUGGIERO.   8 ETUDES ATONALES                                        D36
SABARICH, R. & J. THILDE.   10 ETUDES                                F39
SACHSE, E.-HERBST.   100 ETUDES (TRANSPOSITION METHOD)               A56
SACHSE, E.-NAGEL.   28 STUDIES(2 VOL)                                C91
SACHSE, E.-HERBST.   100 STUDIES                                     C91
SACHSE, E.-HERBST.   100 TRANSPONIER-ETUDEN (E-FLAT TPT)             C75
SAINT-JACOME.   12 CHARACTERISTIC ETUDES                             C38
SAMBATARO, D.   STUDI(2 VOL)                                         H26
SARO, H.   24 STUDIES                                                B53
SAUVEUR, T.   20 AUSGEWAHLTE TECHNISCHE STUDIEN(2 VOL)               A90
SAUVEUR, T.   20 AUSGEWAHLTE TECHNISCHE STUDIEN(2 VOL)               C75
SCHAEFER, A.H.   KREUTZER'S 10 FAMOUS ETUDES                         C09
SCHANTL, J.-POTTAG.   PREPARATORY MELODIES TO SOLO WORK              A62
SCHNEIDER, W.   ERSTES TROMPETENSPIEL (1,2, OR 3 TPT)                F31
SCHNEIDER, W.   SPIELSTUECKE UND ETUEDEN                             E51
SCHUBERT, F.P.-MUSSER.   UNACCOMPANIED SONG STUDIES                  A03
SEMLER-COLLERY, J.   ETUDES MELODIQUES (OPTIONAL PIANO)              C01
SEMPRONI, U.   24 STUDI NEL SETTICLAVIO                              E98
SLAMA, A.-DREYER.   50 NEUE ETUDEN...TRANSPONIERENS                  B73
SMALL, J.L.   27 MELODIOUS AND RHYTHMICAL EXERCISES                  C11
SMITH, C.   VARIETY ETUDES                                          D18
SMITH, C.B.   CORNET VARIETY ETUDES                                 D18
SMITH, L.C.   EXERCISES FOR MRS.SMITH                                E68
SMITH, W.S.   BOOK OF STUDIES, A                                     E51
SMITH, W.S.   TOP TONES FOR THE TRUMPETER                            C11
SOLOMON, J.   12 STUDIES                                             F52
STANKO.   10 STUDIES OF JAZZ                                         E81
THILDE, J. & SABARICH.   10 ETUDES                                  F39
TOMASI, H.   6 ETUDES                                                D36
TYRRELL, H.W.-HOVEY.   40 ADVANCED STUDIES                           A78
VANDERCOOK, H.A.   VANDERCOOK ETUDES                                 F07
VANNETELBOSCH.   DEBUTANT TROMPETTISTE, LE (2 BKS)                   D36
VANNETELBOSCH.   20 ETUDES MELODIQUES ET TECHNIQUES                  D36
VERHEYEN, J.   CONCERT STUDIES                                       D92
VOISIN, R.L.   STUDIES                                               C91
VOLOTSKY, P.   SELECTED ETUDES                                       E19
VOXMAN, H.   SELECTED STUDIES                                        F07
WALTERS.   POPULAR STYLE PLAYING                                     F07
WERNER, F.-SEYFFARTH.   40 ETUDEN UND AKKORDSTUDIEN(2 VOL)           C75
WERNER, F.-HERBST.   40 STUDIES                                      C91
WIDMER.   18 FINE ETUDES                                             C46
WIGGINS.   FIRST TUNES & STUDIES                                     E51
```

WILLIAMS, E.   PROGRESSIVE ELEMENTARY SOLOS & DUETS   B31
WILLIAMS, E.   SUPPLEMENTARY STUDIES FOR ADVANCED STUDENTS   B31
WIMMER, J.   100 STILISTISCHE UBUNGEN   G18
WURM, W.   AUSGEWAHLTE ETUDEN   C75
WURM, W.   20 DIFFICULT ETUDES   B53
WURM, W.   40 STUDIES   F52
WURM, W.-VOISIN.   40 STUDIES   C91

0001   TRUMPET EXCERPTS

BACH, J.S.-PACHNICKE & ZSCHOCH.   BACH-STUDIEN   C75
BACH, J.S.-FOVEAU. LITTLE TPT IN THE WORKS OF J.S.BACH, THE   D36
BACH, J.S.   ORCHESTRAL STUDIES(2 VOL)   E14
BACH, J.S.-PACHNICKE & ZSCHOCH.   STUDIES, VOL.2: CANTATAS   C75
BANDMAN'S TRUMPET REPERTOIRE (2 VOL).   C11
BARTOLD (CMPL). ORCH. EXCERPTS (CLASSICAL & MODERN)(5 VOL)   C91
BROILES, M.   ORCHESTRAL INTERPRETATIONS   N21
BROILES, M.   TRANSPOSITION FOR ORCH. TPT   D55
FOVEAU, E.(CMPL). DIFF PASSAGES ORCH & DRAMATIC WORKS(5VOL)   D36
GURDEV, A.(CMPL). EXTRACTS FR BULGARIAN ORCHESTRA WORKS   F36
HALL, E.(CMPL). DIFFICULT PASSAGES FOR TRUMPET (2 VOL)   A78
HANDEL, G.F.-MINTER. COMPLETE TRUMPET REPERTOIRE (4 VOL)   E14
HANDEL, G.F.-ZSCHOCH & SIBER. HANDEL-STUDIEN(2 VOL)   C75
HANDEL, G.F.-GLASENAPP & ZSCHOCH.   STUDIES(2 VOL)   C75
HERBST, F (CMPL). ORCHESTER-STUDIEN   D78
HOEHNE (CMPL). ORCHESTRAL STUDIES FR R.WAGNER'S WORKS(2 VOL) C91
JOHNSON, G.   20TH CENTURY ORCHESTRA STUDIES   F23
JONES & BOUSTAD (CMPL). ESSENTIAL REPERTOIRE   F97
LUTAK, L. (CMPL). ORCHESTRAL STUDIES   E72
MAHLER, G.   SYMPHONIES #1-5   M68
MANCINI, A. (CMPL). SYMPHONIC HIGHLIGHTS   B31
MC GREGOR. ORCHESTRAL REPERTOIRE   M68
NEWHAUS, H. (CMPL). AUSFURLICHE ORCHESTERSTUDIEN (5 VOL)   C41
NEWHAUS, H. (CMPL). ORCHESTRA STUDIES (5 VOL)   A70
PROKOFIEV, S. & SHOSTAKOVICH-YEREMIN. ORCHESTRAL EXCERPTS   D81
REICHE, H. (CMPL). ORCHESTERSTUDIEN (2 VOL)   G43
SHOSTAKOVICH, D.-KRUMPFER. ORCHESTERSTUDIEN (VOL 10, HOFM)   C75
SHOSTAKOVICH, D.-KRUMPFER. ORCHESTERSTUDIEN   C75
STEGMANN. ORCHESTERTROMPETER, DER   N05
STRAUSS, R. COMPLETE FIRST TRUMPET PARTS   M68
STRAUSS, R.-ROSSBACH. ORCHESTRA STUDIES FROM SYMPHONIC WORKS E65
STRAUSS, R.-ROSSBACH. ORCHESTRAL STUDIES FROM SYMPHONIC WORKS C91
TCHAIKOVSKY, P.I.-YEREMIN. EXCERPTS FROM SYMPHONIC WORKS, BK. D81
VOISIN, R.L. EXCERPTS FR CLASSICAL & MODERN WORKS(9 VOL)   C91
WAGNER, R.-GUMBERT & HERBST. ORCHESTERSTUDIEN(VOL MA, HOFM)   C75
WAGNER, R.-HERBER. ORCHESTRA STUDIES(2 VOL)   C75
WOLF. ORCHESTERSTUDIEN (VOL 4, 6-9)   C75
WOLF (CMPL). ORCHESTERSTUDIEN (6 VOL)   C75
ZEYER. ORCHESTERSTUDIEN (VOL. 1, 2, 4, 5)   C75
ZEYER (CMPL). ORCHESTERSTUDIEN   C75

0002   TRUMPET METHODS

ADKINS, H.E.   METHOD FOR CORNET   A78

PETIT, A.S.   GRANDE METHODE (2 VOL)   C38
PETIT, A.S.   TRAITE MODERNE ET COMPLET   C38
PLUVINAGE, A.   JE COMMENCE EN DO MAJEUR   D67
POPULAR METHOD.   E98
PORRET, J.   METHODE PROGRESSIVE   D64
PROKOFIEV, P.   PRACTICAL TOOLS FOR PLAYING THE TRUMPET   E19
REINHARDT, D.S.   PIVOT SYSTEM   B92
RICKSTAL.   SCALE STUDIES   F21
RIVERA.   METODO ELEMENTAL   F95
ROBINSON, A.F.   RUBANK ELEMENTARY METHOD   F07
ROETSCHI, H.   ANFANGERSCHULE   C80
ROLLINSON, T.H.   MODERN SCHOOL   B72
RONKA, E.   STARTING CORRECTLY (2 VOL)   F62
RUDDICK, J.L.   MILLS' ELEMENTARY METHOD   D84
SAINT-JACOME.   GRAND METHOD (2VOL)   C11
SCHEIE, E.   SCHULE FUR FANFARE ODER SIGNAL-TROMPETE   F31
SCHNEIDER, W.   SCHULE   F31
SEREDY (CMPL).   WORLD'S METHOD (3 VOL)   C11
SHAPIRO, A.   MODERN UNIVERSAL METHOD (3 VOL)   B53
SHUEBRUK, R.   FIRST BOOK   C11
SKORNICKA, J.E.   MASTER METHOD   A78
SKORNICKA, J.E.   RUBANK INTERMEDIATE METHOD   F07
SPERTI, J.   ELEMENTARY METHOD   E80
STEGMANN.   ELEMENTARE TROMPETENSCHULE (2 BKS)   N62
STOLC, E.   ENSEMBLE SCHOOL FOR WIND INSTRUMENTS   A33
STRAND, A.   TRUMPET TUTOR   D11
STUART, H. & HERFURTH.   SOUNDS OF THE WINDS (2 VOL)   C11
STUART, W.   LESSONS IN RHYTHM AND SYNCOPATION   B31
SZODI, L. & LUBIK,I.   TRUMPET TUTOR (2VOL)   B84
TOENNIGES, C.F.   MUSIC MASTER, THE   B34
VAN BODEGRABEN, P. & CHRISTOPHER.   ADVENTURES IN COR PLAYING   F64
VANCE.   DEVELOPMENTALS   N57
VESSELLA.   PRACTICAL METHOD FOR WIND INSTRUMENTS   E98
VOXMAN, H. & GOWER.   RUBANK ADVANCED METHOD (2 VOL)   F07
WARD, N.   ELEMENTARY SCHOOL BEGINNER'S METHOD   B41
WEBER, F.   BELWIN INTERMEDIATE BAND METHOD   A62
WEBSTER, M & F. HARRIS.   LUDWING ELEM. CORNET INSTRUCTOR   D52
WHISTLER, H.S.   MODERN ARBAN-ST. JACOME   F07
WILLIAMS, E.   MODERN METHOD (3 VOL)   B31
WINSLOW, R.   TRUMPET PLAYING (2 BKS)   N10
WOLF, J.E. DE.   METHODE   J39
YOUNG, L.E.   ELEMENTARY METHOD (2VOL)   C11

0003   TRUMPET TECHNIQUES (Special Studies)

ALBUS, J.-SABARICH.   ETUDES TRANSPOSITRICES   F39
ALLARD, J.   ADVANCED RHYTHMS   B31
ALLARD, J.   JAZZ RHYTHMS   B31
ALLARD, J.   MORE ADVANCED RHYTHMS   B31
APPLEBAUM.   HOW TO IMPROVISE   B31
ARBAN, J.J.B.L.-VANASEK.   ARBAN'S DAILY GYMNASTICS   C46
ARBAN, J.J.B.L.   EXERCICES JOURNALIERS   D36
EAKER.   CONTEMPORARY TECHNIQUES   B31
EAKER.   JAZZ IMPROVISATION   B31
BELLAMAH.   44 MELODIC WARMUPS   F60
BENZINGER, K.   TAGLICHE STUDIEN   C67
BERIGAN, R.B.(BUNNY).   DAILY EXERCISES   A70
BERNINGER, H.   BLASERUBUNGEN, TONLEITERN UND TAGLICHE STUDIEN   C75

0010   HORN ETUDES

ANDRAUD, A.J. & M.POTTAG (CMPL). 335 MELODIOUS...STUDIES	F60
ARTOT, J.D. 19 ETUDEN	C75
ARTOT, J.D. ETUDES MELODIQUES (4ME SUITE)	F31
BACH, J.S.-FAULX. 20 ETUDES DE VIRTUOSITE	A96
BARBOTEU, G. 20 ETUDES CONCERTANTES	B24
BARBOTEU, G. LECTURES EXERCICES	B24
BARBOTEU, G. STUDIES (2 VOL)	B24
BELLOLI, A. 6 ETUDEN	C75
BELLOLI, A. 12 ETUDES	F60
BELLOLI, A. 24 ETUDES	F60
BELLOLI, A. 8 ETUDES	F60
BELLOLI, A.-CHAMBERS. 8 STUDIES	C91
BITSCH, M. 12 ETUDES	D36
BLUM, O.-OUSSOV. 12 ETUDES, BK.2	D81
BORRIS, S. UBUNGS-UND SPIELSTUCKE	F53
BOUTRY, R. FLASHING STUDIES	D36
BOZZA, E. 18 ETUDES EN FORME D'IMPROVISATION	B92
BOZZA, E. 18 ETUDES EN FORME D'IMPROVISATION	D36
BRAHMS, J. 10 ETUDEN	C61
BRAHMS, J.-LELOIR. 10 ORIGINAL HORN STUDIES, OP.POSTH.	D11
BREMOND, F. 252 EXERCISES POUR LE COR DE DAUPRAT	D41
BRIGHTMORE, V. 43 EASY MELODIC STUDIES	B20
BRIGHTMORE, V. LEGATO STUDIES	B20
BRIGHTMORE, V. 25 MELODIC STUDIES	B20
BUESSER. 12 ETUDES MELODIQUES	D36
CECCAROSSI, D. 10 CAPRICES	D36
CHAYNES, C.-THEVET. 15 ETUDES	D36
CONCONE, G.-SHOEMAKER. LEGATO ETUDES	A62
CONCONE, G.-SAWYER. LYRICAL STUDIES FOR HORN	M80
CONCONE, G.-SAWYER. LYRICAL STUDIES	M80
CONORD, C. 45 ETUDES DE DECHIFFRAGE ET DE TRANSPOSITION	B92
CONORD, C. 45 ETUDES DE DECHIFFRAGE ET DE TRANSPOSITION	D41
COPE, D. BTRB (THEATRE PIECE)	M80
CORRADINI, C. 8 ETUDES BRILLANTES	G38
CUGNOT, A. 30 ETUDES MELODIQUES (3 VOL)	A71
DAUPRAT, L.F. 12 ETUDES (EXTRAITES DE LA METHODE)	D41
DAUPRAT, L.F. 330 ETUDES (2 VOL)	D41
DEVEMY, J. 2 SIGHT-READING STUDIES AND 9 EXAMINATION STUDIES	D36
DUBOIS, P.M. 12 ETUDES	D36
DULSKY, N. 18 ORCHESTRAL ETUDES	D81
ENDRESEN, R.M. SUPPLEMENTARY STUDIES	F07
FALK, J. 20 ATONAL STUDIES	D36
FAULX, J.B. ETUDES DU DETACHE	A96
FAULX, J.B. 25 PROGRESSIVE STUDIES OF MEDIUM DIFFICULTY	A96
FAULX, J.B. 20 VIRTUOSO STUDIES AFTER BACH	A96
FONTANA, C.(CMPL). 16 ADVANCED STUDIES (GALLAY & OTHERS)	B53
FRANZ, O.-SCHAFFRATH. ETUDEN UND "CONCERT-ETUDEN"	C75
FREHSE, A. 100 EASY STUDIES	C75
FREHSE, A. 14 ETUDEN ALS NACHSTUDIEN	C75
FREHSE, A. 34 ETUDEN FUR TIEFES HORN	C75
FREHSE, A. 22 ETUDEN	C75
GABLER. 40 NATURHORN-ETUDEN	B73
GALLAY, J.F. 18 ETUDES MELODIQUES, OP.53	A38
GALLAY, J.F.-LELOIR. 18 ETUDES MELODIQUES, OP.53	F52
GALLAY, J.F. 12 ETUDES POUR SECOND COR, OP.57	D41

```
GALLAY, J.F.   12 ETUDES POUR SECOND COR, OP.57              F60
GALLAY, J.F.-THEVET.   12 ETUDES POUR SECOND COR             D36
GALLAY, J.F.   22 ETUDES, FANTAISIES MELODIQUES,OP.58        A38
GALLAY, J.F.   22 ETUDES, FANTAISIES MELODIQUES,OP.58        F52
GALLAY, J.F.-THEVET.   28 ETUDES, OP.13                      D36
GALLAY, J.F.   30 ETUDES, OP.13                              B92
GALLAY, J.F.   30 ETUDES, OP.13                              F60
GALLAY, J.F.-CHAMBERS.   30 ETUDES, OP.13                    C91
GALLAY, J.F.-LELOIR.   30 ETUDES, OP.13                      F52
GALLAY, J.F.   30 ETUDES, OP.3                               A38
GALLAY, J.F.-CHAMBERS.   12 ETUDES, OP.57                    C91
GALLAY, J.F.   24 EXERCICES DANS TOUS LES TONS, OP.37        D41
GALLAY, J.F.-BREMOND.   EXERCICES ET ETUDES                 D41
GALLAY, J.F.-THEVET.   22 EXERCISES, OP.37                   D36
GALLAY, J.F.-CHAMBERS.   12 GRAND CAPRICES, OP. 32           C91
GALLAY, J.F.   12 GRAND CAPRICES, OP.32                      F60
GALLAY, J.F.-THEVET.   12 GRAND CAPRICES, OP.32              D36
GALLAY, J.F.-CHAMBERS.   12 GRAND ETUDES BRILLANTES, OP. 43  C91
GALLAY, J.F.   12 GRAND ETUDES BRILLANTES, OP.43             D41
GALLAY, J.F.   12 GRAND ETUDES BRILLANTES, OP.43             F60
GALLAY, J.F.-THEVET.   12 GRAND ETUDES BRILLANTES, OP.43     D36
GALLAY, J.F.-JANETZKY.   12 GRAND ETUDES, OP.43              C75
GALLAY, J.F.-CHAMBERS.   40 PRELUDES, OP. 27                 C91
GALLAY, J.F.-SANSONE.   40 PRELUDES, OP.27                   F60
GALLAY, J.F.-CHAMBERS & CERMINARO.   24 STUDIES, OP. 37      C91
GETCHELL, R.W.-HOVEY.   FIRST BOOK OF PRACTICAL STUDIES      A62
GETCHELL, R.W.-HOVEY.   SECOND BOOK OF PRACTICAL STUDIES     A62
GOLDSTEIN, A.E.   FIRST BOOK OF ETUDES, A                    B44
GOLDSTEIN, A.E.   SECOND BOOK OF ETUDES, A                   B44
GRAVE, F.DE.   ETUDES FOR MODERN VALVE HORN(2 VOL)           G28
GUGEL, H.   12 ETUDES                                        F60
GUGEL, H.-CHAMBERS.   12 STUDIES                             C91
HORNER, A.   PRIMARY STUDIES                                 B92
HUTH, F.   TONLEITER-STUDIEN                                 C75
HUTH, F.   18 VORSCHUL-ETUDEN UND 48 AKKORD-STUDIEN          F31
KAREL, K.   ETUDES(2 VOL)                                    F36
KAUCKY, E.   HEROIC STUDIES, OP. 9                           A78
KAUCKY, E.   HEROIC STUDIES, OP.9                            A33
KAUCKY, E.   HEROISCHE ETUDEN, OP.9                          A51
KAUCKY, E.   KLEINE ETUDEN                                   A51
KAUCKY, E.   LITTLE STUDIES                                  A33
KLING, H.-SANSONE.   40 CHARACTERISTIC ETUDES               F60
KLING, H.-CHAMBERS.   40 STUDIES                             C91
KOPPRASCH, C.-FREHSE.   60 AUSGEWAHLTE ETUDEN(2VOL)          C75
KOPPRASCH, C.   ETUDES                                       E19
KOPPRASCH, C.-FRANZ.   50 ETUDES                             F60
KOPPRASCH, C.   60 SELECTED STUDIES(2 VOL)                   D81
KOPPRASCH, C.-FREHSE.   60 SELECTED STUDIES(2 VOL)           C11
KOPPRASCH, C.   60 STUDIES (2 VOL)                           B53
KOPPRASCH, C.-CHAMBERS.   30 STUDIES(2 VOL)                  C91
KREUTZER, R.-REYNOLDS.   16 STUDIES                          F23
KROL, B.   10 KONZERT-ETUDEN                                 C59
KROL, B.   NATURHORNSTUDIEN FUR DAS B-WALDHORN               C59
KROL, B.   STUDIES(ELEMENTARY GRADE)                         F52
LAMBERT, E.   12 ETUDES PROGRESSIVES                         D41
LEWY.   10 SELECTED STUDIES                                  C75
LIEBERT, H.   25 SPEZIALSTUDIEN FUR TIEFES HORN              C75
MARCHI.   12 CAPRICCI                                        G95
MAXIME-ALPHONSE.   200 NEW STUDIES (6 VOL)                   D36
MIERSCH.   MELODIOUS STUDIES                                 C11
MULLER, B.E.-FREHSE.   ETUDEN, OP.64(2 VOL)                  C75
MULLER, B.E.   12 ETUDES                                     F60
```

```
MULLER, B.E.-CHAMBERS.  34 STUDIES(2 VOL)                          C91
NAUBER.  30 LEICHTE MELODISCHE UBUNGEN                             G43
NEULING, H.  30 SPEZIAL-ETUDEN FUR TIEFES HORN                     C59
NEULING, H.  15 TECHNISCHE ETUDEN FUR HOHES HORN                   C59
PARES, G.P.C.  GAMMES ET EXERCICES                                 D41
PAUDERT, E.  60 ETUDEN ZUM ERLERNEN DES TRANSPONIERENS             B73
PAUDERT, E.  50 MELODISCHE ETUDEN                                  B73
PAUDERT, E.  32 STUDIES                                            F52
PAUDERT, E.  100 TECHNISCHE ETUDEN                                 B73
PAUL, E.  WALDHORNSCHULE, BAND 2: 50 ETUDEN                        B73
PAUL, E.  WALDHORNSCHULE, BAND 3: 100 ETUDEN                       B73
PAUL, E.  WALDHORNSCHULE, BAND 4: 60 ETUDEN                        B73
PLOYHAR, J. & WEBER,F.  STUDIES AND MELODIOUS ETUDES               A62
POTTAG, M.P. & ANDRAUD (CMPL).  335 MELODIOUS...STUDIE(2 VOL)      F60
RANIERI, V.  30 INSTRUCTIVE AND MELODIC EXERCISES                  B53
REYNOLDS, V.  48 ETUDES FOR FRENCH HORN                            F23
REYNOLDS, V.  16 STUDIES                                           F23
RIGHINI, P.  6 STUDI SERIALI                                       E98
ROSSARI, C.  12 STUDIES, OP. 4                                     E98
SCHANTL, J.-POTTAG.  PREPARATORY MELODIES TO SOLO WORK             A62
SCHMOLL, J.B.  MODERN STUDIES IN 20TH-CENTURY STYLE               F60
SCHULLER, G.  STUDIES FOR UNACCOMPANIED HORN                       E51
STARI, K.  ETUDES                                                  E19
STARI, K.  ETUDES FOR FRENCH HORN                                  E19
STRAUSS, F.  CONCERT STUDIES FOR VALVE HORN                        B53
STRAUSS, F.-R.STRAUSS.  17 CONCERT STUDIES: BEETHOVEN THEMES       E65
THEVET, L.  65 ETUDES-DECHIFFRAGES                                 D36
THEVET, L.  20 ETUDES                                              D36
THEVET, L.  50 EXERCISES FOR HORN WITH CHANGE OF KEY              D36
THEVET, L.  65 SIGHT-READING STUDIES                              D36
THEVET, L.  60 STUDIES (2 VOL)                                     D36
THEVET, L.  TRAITS DIFFICILES                                      B92
TONEV, N.  ETUDES FOR HORN                                         F36
VANDER WOUDE, M.  ADVANCED VIRTUOSO WORKS (2 BKS)                 B31
VANDER WOUDE, M.  ATONALISM FOR FRENCH HORN                        G70
VANDER WOUDE, M.  FRENCH HORN STUDIES                              F72
VUILLERMOZ.  10 PIECES MELODIQUES (TRANS)                          D36
WEBER, A.-THEVET.  13 STUDIES                                      D36
ZIMOLAG, M.(CMPL).  SELECTED STUDIES & EXERCISES (2 VOL)          E72
```

0011   HORN EXCERPTS

```
BACH, J.S.-JANETZKY.  BACH-STUDIEN (2 VOL)                         C75
BIEHLIG.  ORCHESTERETUDEN                                          C75
BOOSEY & HAWKES.  214 PASSAGES (R. STRAUSS)                        A78
BRAHMS, J.-MEREWETHER.  COMPLETE HORN PARTS, SYM. 1-4             E59
BRAHMS, J.  COMPLETE 1ST HN PARTS TO BRAHMS' MAJOR ORCH WORKS     G28
BRUCKNER, A.-SCHAFFRATH.  ORCHESTRAL STUDIES (2 VOL)              C75
CHAMBERS, J. (CMPL).  ORCH. EXCERPTS (8 VOL)                       C41
EGER.  ORIGINAL FRENCH HORN SOLOS                                  B41
FARKAS, P. (CMPL).  ORCHESTRA PASSAGES FROM MODERN FRENCH REP.     B81
FONTANA, C.  COLLECTION OF PRINCIPLE & SOLO PASSAGES              E98
GEBHARDT, W.  ORCHESTRA STUDIES (5 VOL)                           B53
GUMBERT, F.A.  ORCHESTRAL AND OPERATIC EXCERPTS (10 VOL)          F60
HANDEL, G.F.-JANETZKY.  HANDEL-STUDIEN (2 VOL)                    C75
HOFMEISTER (PUB).  ORCHESTERSTUDIEN (15 VOL)                      C75
JONES, M.  TWENTIETH-CENTURY ORCHESTRA STUDIES                     F23
MAHLER, G.-MEREWETHER.  SYMPHONIES 1 AND 2                         E59
```

```
MEEK, H.L.  ORCHESTRA PASSAGES                                       B92
MOORE, R.  OPERATIC FRENCH HORN PASSAGES                            E77
POTTAG, M.P. (CMPL).  FRENCH HORN PASSAGES (3 VOL)                  A62
STOSSER, O. (CMPL).  ORCHESTERSTUDIEN (4 VOL)                       C75
STRAUSS, R.-PLOTNER.  ORCHESTERSTUDIEN (3 VOL)                      C75
STRAUSS, R.  ORCHESTRA STUDIES FROM SYM. WORKS                      B53
STRAUSS, R.-CHAMBERS.  ORCHESTRAL EXCERPTS                          C91
STRAUSS, R.-WIPPERICH.  RICHARD STRAUSS ORCHESTERSTUDIEN            E65
TCHAIKOVSKY, P.I.-FARKAS.  COMPLETE 1ST HORN PARTS TO ORCH...       G28
THEVET, L. (CMPL).  DIFFICULT PASSAGES (8VOL)                       D36
WAGNER, R.-CHAMBERS.  ORCHESTRAL EXCERPTS                           C91
```

0012 HORN METHODS

```
BEELER, W.R.  PLAY AWAY!                                            F23
BENZINGER, K.  SCHULE FUR FURST PLESS HORN                          C67
BIANCHINI, F.-GIAMPIERI.  POPULAR METHOD                            E98
BLANC, J.  METHODE COMPLETE                                         D41
BOS, I.  METHODE COMPLETE                                           D41
BUCHTEL, F.L.  BUCK ELEMENTARY METHOD                               D18
BURDEN.  HORN PLAYING                                               E58
CECCARELLI, M.  SCUOLA D'INSEGNAMENTO DEL CORNO                     E98
CECCAROSSI, D.  ECOLE COMPLETE (4 VOL)                              D36
CHARLIER, T.  METHODE COMPLETE                                      D41
CLEVENGER-MC DUNN & RUSCH.  CLEVENGER METHOD (2 BKS)                D18
COSCIA.  MODERN FRENCH HORN PLAYER                                  A56
DAUPRAT, L.F.-BREMOND.  METHODE COMPLETE                            D41
DEVEMY, J.  METHODE DE COR CHROMATIQUE                              D36
EBY, W.M.  SCIENTIFIC METHOD                                        A70
EIDSON, A.D.-HOVEY.  FRENCH HORN METHOD (3 VOL)                     A62
EISENHAUER.  LEARN TO PLAY THE FRENCH HORN                          A10
ERDMAN, R.W.-SKORNICKA.  MASTER METHOD                              A78
FEARN, W.O.  FRENCH HORN FOR BEGINNERS                              B92
FOX, F.A.  SIGHT AND SOUND METHOD                                   N10
FRANZ, O.  COMPLETE METHOD                                          A78
FRANZ, O.-GEBHARDT.  COMPLETE METHOD                                B53
GALLAY, J.F.  METHODE                                               D41
GARRIGUE, J.  GRANDE METHODE DE COR A PISTONS                       C38
GETCHELL, R.W.  1ST BOOK OF PRACTICAL STUDIES                       A62
GETCHELL, R.W.  2ND BOOK OF PRACTICAL STUDIES                       A62
GETCHELL, R.W.  SECTION STUDIES                                     A62
GOLDSTEIN, A.E.  1ST BOOK OF EXERCISES                              B44
GOLDSTEIN, A.E.  2ND BOOK OF EXERCISES                              B44
GOLDSTEIN, A.E.  EXERCISES, BK. 1                                   B44
GORNSTON, D.  VERY 1ST METHOD                                       A37
GOUSE.  LEARN TO PLAY THE FRENCH HORN                               A10
GOWER, W. & VOXMAN.  RUBANK ADV. METHOD (2 VOL)                     F07
HAAG.  WALDHORN-SCHULE                                              E98
HAUSER, E.  FOUNDATIONS TO FRENCH HORN PLAYING                      C11
HERFURTH, C.P.  A TUNE A DAY                                        A81
HERFURTH, C.P. & STUART.  SOUNDS OF THE WINDS (2 VOL)               C11
HORNER, A.  PRIMARY STUDIES                                         B91
HOWE, M.  METHOD                                                    E93
HUTH, F.  SCHOOL FOR HORN                                           E89
KAREL, K. & TOMOV.  SCHOOL                                          F36
KAUCKY, E.  SCHULE FUR WALDHORN                                     A51
KIETZER, R.  ALTHORN SCHULE, OP. 83 (2 VOL)                         G43
KINYON, J.L.  BREEZE-EASY METHOD (2 VOL)                            G31
```

```
KLIMENT, H.   ANFANGERSCHULE FUR WALDHORN                        D20
KLINGER, R.   SCHULE FUR JAGDHORN                                D46
KROL, E.   ERGANZUNGSCHULWERK FUR WALDHORN                       C75
KROL, B.   SOLOBUCH (2 VOL)                                      E89
LAMBERT, E.   METHOD                                             B92
LAMBERT, E.   METHODE COMPLETE ET PROGRESSIVE                    D41
LANGEY, O.   LANGEY-C. FISCHER TUTORS                            C11
LANGEY, O.   PRACTICAL TUTOR                                     A78
LHUILLIER, G.   METHODE COMPLETE                                 D41
MARIANI, G.   METHOD POPOLARE                                    E98
MARIANI, G.-GRIGOLATO.   POPULAR METHOD                          E98
MUSSER & DELBORGO.   MODES IN CONTEMPORARY MUSIC                 A10
MUSSER & DELBORGO.   RHYTHM OF CONTEMPORARY MUSIC                A10
MUSSER & DELBORGO.   TONALITY OF CONTEMPORARY MUSIC              A10
NEULING, H.   GROSSE F- UND B- HORNSCHULE (2 VOL)                C59
NIESSEL.   METHODE COMPLETE                                      D41
CNOZO, J.   HORN TUTOR (2 VOL)                                   B84
PARES, G.P.C.   ELEMENTARY METHOD                                E98
PARES, G.P.C.   METHODE ELEMENTAIRE                              D41
PAUL, E.   SCHOOL OF THE FRENCH HORN (4 VOL)                     B73
PEASE, D.J.   PRO ART METHOD (2 VOL)                             E80
PEASE, D.J.   UNIVERSAL'S FUNDAMENTAL METHOD                     F98
PILAT, F.   FRENCH HORN SCHOOL                                   A33
PLUVINAGE, A.   JE COMMENCE EN DO MAJEUR (2 VOL)                 D67
POTTAG, M.P.-HOVEY.   METHOD (2 VOL)                             A62
PREE, A.-JANETZKY.   THEORETISCH-PRAKTISCHE WALDHORNSCHULE       C75
RATTNER, D.-SATZ.   ELEMENTARY METHOD                            B20
REGER, W.   TALKING FRENCH HORN                                  B31
RIVERA.   METODO DE TROMPA                                       F97
ROBINSON-FARKAS.   ILLUSTRATED ADVANCED METHOD                   G28
ROBINSON, W.C.-FARKAS.   ILLUSTRATED METHOD                      G28
ROETSCHI, H.   ANFANGERSCHULE                                    C80
ROMERO.   METODO DE TROMPA                                       F97
SANSONE, L.   MODERN FR. HN METHOD (2 VOL)                       F60
SCHANTL, J.   GRAND THEORETICAL AND PRACTICAL METHOD             G28
SCHMUTZIG.   COMPLETE METHOD (HUMOROUS BOOK)                     B44
SCHOLLAR, F.   WALDHORNSCHULE (2 VOL)                            G43
SCHOLLUM.   RUFE FUR HORN, OP. 81E                               B73
SKORNICKA, J.E.   MASTER METHOD                                  A78
SKORNICKA, J.E.   RUBANK ELEMENTARY METHOD                       F07
SKORNICKA, J.E.   RUBANK INTERMEDIATE METHOD                     F07
STERN, H.-SCHNEIDER.   SCHULE                                    F31
STOLC, E.   ENSEMBLE SCHOOL FOR WIND INSTRUMENTS                 A33
STUART, H.   SOUNDS OF THE WINDS                                 C11
THEVET, L.   METHOD COMPLETE (2 VOL)                             D36
TYNDARE-GRUYER.   METHODE COMPLETE (TROMPE DE CHASSE)            D41
VANDER WOUDE, M.   PRE-VIRTUOSO STUDIES                          B31
VOXMAN, H. & GOWER.   RUBANK ADVANCED METHOD (2 VOL)             F07
YANCICH, M.   METHOD (2 VOL)                                     G28
```

0013   HORN TECHNIQUES (Special Studies)

```
BERNINGER, H.   BLASERUBUNGEN...TAGLICHE STUDIEN                 C75
COLLINS, F.L.   DAILY EMBOUCHURE DRILLS                          A81
DAVIES, J.   SCALES AND ARPEGGIOS                                A78
FEARN, W.O.   EXERCISES FOR FLEXIBLE HORN PLAYING                B92
GATES, E.   ODD METER ETUDES                                     C46
GORNSTON, D. & MUSSER.   FRENCH HORN DAILIES                     D18
```

0020 TROMBONE ETUDES

ALLARD, L. & COUILLAUD. 26 TECHNICAL STUDIES AFTER BORDOGNI		D36
ARBAN, J.J.B.L.-ALLARD. CHARACTERISTIC STUDIES		D36
BACH, J.S.-LAFOSSE. SUITES DE J.S.BACH		D36
BACH, J.S. 6 SUITES		A71
BACH, K.P.E.-OSTRANDER. 3 ADVANCED STUDIES		B85
BAUMFAERTEL. RHYTHMISCH...STUDIEN FUR JAZZPOSAUNE (2 VOL)		B69
BELLSTEDT, H.-SIMON. 12 FAMOUS TECHNICAL STUDIES		F60
BITSCH, M.-MASSON. 15 RHYTHMICAL STUDIES		D36
BLANGENOIS, J. 10 GRANDES ETUDES CLASSIQUES		F81
BLAZHEVICH, V.M.-HUNSBERGER. CLEF STUDIES		D36
BLAZHEVICH, V.M.-OSTRANDER. CLEF STUDIES		C91
BLAZHEVICH, V.M. 42 ETUDES		D37
BLAZHEVICH, V.M. LEGATO STUDIES		C91
BLAZHEVICH, V.M.-SHUMAN. LEGATO STUDIES		F62
BLAZHEVICH, V.M. SEQUENCES		C91
BLAZHEVICH, V.M. SEQUENCES (2 VOL)		C11
BLAZHEVICH, V.M. 26 SEQUENCES		D36
BLEGER, M. 10 ARTISTIC RECREATIONS		B53
BLEGER, M. 31 BRILLIANT STUDIES		B53
BLEGER, M.-COUILLAUD. 10 CAPRICES		D36
BLEGER, M.-OSTRANDER. 10 CAPRICES		C91
BLEGER, M.-COUILLAUD. 31 ETUDES		D36
BLEGER, M.-OSTRANDER. 31 STUDIES		C91
BLCKKER, C. ETUDES		D92
BLUME, O. 16 SELECTED ETUDES		D81
BLUME, O. 36 STUDIES (3 VOL)		C11
BLUME, O.-BROWN. 36 STUDIES (3 VOL)		C91
BOKHOVE, J. 56 ORIGINELE ETUDES		F81
BONA, P. RHYTHMICAL ARTICULATION		C11
BORDOGNI, G.M.-BROWN. 24 LEGATO STUDIES		C91
BORDOGNI, G.M.-ROCHUT. MELODIOUS ETUDES (3 VOL)		C11
BORDOGNI, G.M.-ALLARD & COUILLAUD. 26 THECHNICAL STUDIES		D36
BOUTRY, R. 12 ETUDES DE HAUT PERFECTIONNEMENT		D36
BOZZA, E. 30 CAPPRICCIO STUDIES		D36
BOZZA, E. 11 ETUDES SUR DES MODES KARNATIQUES		D36
BRIGHTMORE, V. 43 EASY MELODIOUS STUDIES		B20
BRIGHTMORE, V. 25 MELODIOUS STUDIES		B20
CAMPBELL. 30 CONTEMPORARY ETUDES		C25
CHARLIER, T. 32 ETUDES DE PERFECTIONEMENT		D41
CIMERA, J. 221 PROGRESSIVE STUDIES		A62
CLODOMIR, P.F. DEEL (ETUDES)		D92
COLIN, C. & BOWER. RHYTHMS		B31
CONCONE, G.-MILLER. 40 LEGATO STUDIES		B98
CONCONE, G.-REINHARDT. SELECTION OF CONCONE STUDIES		B92
CONCONE, G.-CRAMER. 15 VOCALISES, OP. 12		N70
CORNETTE, V. 20 ELEMENTARETUDEN		A51
CORNETTE, V. 6 GRAND ETUDES		B53
COUILLAUD, H. 10 CAPRICES		D36
COUILLAUD, H. 12 ETUDES MELODIQUES		D36
COUILLAUD, H. 24 PIECES MELODIQUES		D36
COUILLAUD, H. PROGRESSIVE EXERCISES		D36
COUILLAUD, H. (CMPL). 20 FINISHING STUDIES		D36
COUILLAUD, H. & ALLARD. 26 TECHNICAL STUDIES		D36
DELEM, R. 25 STYLED ETUDES		F36
DELISSE, P.-COUILLAUD. 30 MODERN STUDIES		D36

```
DHELLEMMES, R.   25 ETUDES DE PERFECTIONNEMENT              D41
DHELLEMMES, R.   25 ETUDES METHODIQUES                     D41
DHELLEMMES, R.   25 ETUDES POLYPHONIQUES                   D41
DIEPPO, A.G.  9 PROGRESSIVE STUDIES                        B53
DREYER, F.  22 ETUDEN                                      B73
DUBOIS, P.M.  14 ETUDES DE MOYENNE DIFF                    D36
DUFRESNE-VOISIN.  SIGHTREADING                             B31
ENDRESEN, R.M.  ETUDES AND SOLO STUDIES                    N27
ENDRESEN, R.M.  SUPPLEMENTARY STUDIES                      F07
FINK, R.H.  INTRODUCING THE TENOR CLEF                     A02
FINK, R.H.  STUDIES IN LEGATO                              C11
GAETKE, E.  ETUDENSCHULE                                   G43
GAETKE, E.-OSTRANDER.  60 STUDIES                          C91
GALLAY, J.F.-DAX.  12 ETUDES, OP. 57                       C42
GLANTZ, H.  ADVANCED STUDIES                               B31
GORNSTON, D.  PROGRESSIVE SWING READINGS (2 VOL)           C46
GRIGORIEV, B.  ETUDES FOR SLIDE TRB                        F36
GRIGORIEV, B.-KWIATKOWSKI.  STUDIES                        E72
GRIGORIEV, B. (CMPL).  COLLECTED ETUDES                    E19
HADRABA, J.  150 STUDEN (3 VOL)                            D20
HADRABA, J.  UBUNGSMATERIAL (5 VOL)                        D20
HARRIS, A.  25 CHARACTERISTIC STUDIES                      B31
HARVEY, R.  HARVEY METHOD                                  A78
HAUSE, W.  30 ETUDEN                                       C75
HERING, S.  32 ETUDES                                      C11
HERING, S.  40 PROGRESSIVE ETUDES                          C11
HUFFNAGLE, H.J.  STREAMLINED ETUDES (2 VOL)                C46
IRONS, E.D.  27 GROUPS OF EXERCISES                        F60
JENNEY, J.-ARNOLD.  MODERN TROMBONE STUDIES               F01
JOB, M.  30 AIRS CLASSIQUES                                D36
KAHILA, K.  ADVANCED STUDIES (CLEFS)                       D16
KING, R.D.  FIRST YEAR PRACTICE MATERIAL                   D16
KOPPRASCH, C.-SEYFFARTH.  60 AUSGEWAHLTE ETUDEN (2 VOL)    C75
KOPPRASCH, C.  60 STUDIES (2 VOL)                          B53
KOPPRASCH, C.  60 STUDIES (2 VOL)                          C11
KOPPRASCH, C.  60 STUDIES (2 VOL)                          C91
KREUTZER, R.-SCHAEFER.  10 FAMOUS ETUDES                   C09
KREUTZER, R.-BROWN.  16 SELECTED STUDIES                   C91
KWIATKOWSKI, F.  SELECTED STUDIES AND EXERCISES            E72
LACEY, J.  SWING RHYTHMS                                   A70
LAFOSSE, A.  SCHOOL OF SIGHT READING (5 VOL)               A56
LAFOSSE, A.  VADE MECUM DU TROMBONISTE                     D36
MAENZ, O.  12 STUDIEN                                      C75
MANTIA, S.  TROMBONE VIRTUOSO                              C11
MARSTELLER, R.L.  ADVANCED SLIDE TECHNIQUE                 F60
MASSON, G. (CMPL).  12 ETUDES VARIEE                       D36
MAXTED, G.A.  20 STUDIES                                   A78
MILLER, R.-LYON.  SCHOOL FOR TROMBONE                      F62
MULLER, R.  TECHNICAL EXERCISES #1                         B53
MULLER, R.  TECHNICAL STUDIES (3 VOL)                      C11
MULLER, R.  TECHNISCHE STUDIEN (3 VOL)                     C75
PAISNER, B.  MORE STUDIES IN SWING                         C46
PAISNER, B.  30 STUDIES IN SWING                           C46
PAISNER, B.  19 SWING STUDIES                              C46
PAUDERT, E.-SEYFFARTH.  24 ETUDEN                          C75
PAUDERT, E.-OSTRANDER.  24 STUDIES                         C91
PEDERSON, T.  ETUDES FOR TENOR TROMBONE (3 VOL:ELEM. TO ADV)  M93
PFLEGER, C.-OSTRANDER.  9 STUDIES                          C91
PICHAUREAU.  20 ETUDES ATONALES                            D36
PICHAUREAU, G.  30 RECREATIONS EN FORME D'ETUDES           D36
PICHAUREAU, G.  30 STUDIES IN EVERY TONALITY               D36
PICHAUREAU, G.  20 STUDIES                                 D36
```

PICHAUREAU, G. 21 STUDIES	D36
PORRET, J. 25 DECHIFFRAGES MANUSCRITS	D64
RAPH, A. DIVERSIFIED ETUDES	M70
REUTER, F.-OSTRANDER. 5 CONCERT STUDIES, OP. 23	C91
ROCHUT, J. MELODIOUS ETUDES	C11
RONKA, E. STUDIES AND LIP DRILLS	C11
RUSSO, W. DUETS-21 ETUDES	B31
SEIDEL, E. 24 STUDIES, OP. 108	B53
SHOEMAKER, J. LEGATO STUDIES (CONCONE VOCALISES)	C11
SHUMAN, D. 5 PREPARATORY STUDIES	D71
SIEBACH, K. (ARR). STUDIEN	C75
SLAMA, A. 66 ETUDEN IN ALLEN TONARTEN	B50
SLAMA, A. 66 ETUDEN IN ALLEN TONARTEN	C75
SLAMA, A. 50 ETUDEN	B73
SLAMA, A. 66 ETUDES	C11
SLAMA, A. 66 STUDIES IN ALL KEYS	C91
SMITS. 24 ETUDES (2 BKS)	D67
STACEY, C.E. SUCCESSFUL STUDIES (3 VOL)	C09
STACEY, C.E. TECHNICAL STUDIES (2 VOL)	B72
STEFANISZIN, K. POSAUNEN-ETUDEN	C59
STEFANISZIN, K. POSAUNEN-ETUDEN	E81
STEFANISZIN, K. 40 POSAUNEN-ETUDEN	C59
STEFANISZIN, K. 55 POSAUNEN-ETUDEN	C75
TAYLOR, C.H. 20 MELODIC STUDIES	C09
TEAGARDEN, W.J.-GOTTSCHALK. MODERN TRB STUDIES	A70
TODOROV, G. ETUDES	F36
TODOROV, G. TECHNICAL ETUDES	F36
TODOROV, G. & IAKOVTCHEV. ETUDES FOR TROMBONE	F36
TYRRELL, H.W. 40 PROGRESSIVE STUDIES	A78
UBER. CHOICE COLLECTION OF SONGS	A03
UFFELEN, P.C.V. CONCERT STUDIES	D82
VANDER WOUDE, M. PRE VIRTUOSO STUDIES	B31
VANDERCOOK, H.A.-WELKE. ETUDES	FO7
VOBARON, F. ETUDEN	A52
VOBARON, F. 34 ETUDES MELODIQUES SUIVIES (2 TRB)	A71
VOBARON, F. 34 ETUDES MELODIQUES	D64
VOBARON, F. 34 ETUDES	B53
VOBARON, F. 40 ETUDES	A71
VOBARON, F. 4 LECONS ET 27 ETUDES	A71
VOBARON, F. 4 LESSONS AND 17 STUDIES	B53
VOBARON, F. STUDIES	A33
VOXMAN, H. SELECTED STUDIES	FO7
WAGNER, A. 27 PROGRESSIVE STUDIES	B53
WERNER, F.-SEYFFARTH. 38 ETUDEN UND AKKORDSTUDIEN	C75
WERNER, F.-BROWN. 38 STUDIES	C91
WOUDA, P. CONCERT STUDIES	D92
YAUS, G.C. RHYTHMICAL STUDIES IN UNISON	A62

0021   TROMBONE EXCERPTS

BROWN, K. ORCHESTRAL EXCERPTS (10 VOL)	C91
CLARKE, E. ORCHESTRAL STUDIES	C11
COUILLAUD, H. DIFFICULT PASSAGES	D36
FERRARI, B. PASSI DIFFICILI E "A SOLO" (4 VOL)	E98
GRIGORIEV, B. ORCHESTRAL DIFFICULTIES (VOL 2,4,5)	D81
HOFMEISTER (PUB). ORCHESTERSTUDIEN (17 VOL)	C75
MENKEN, J. ANTHOLOGY OF SYMPH & OPERATIC EXC. (2 VOL)	C11
MUELLER, H. INTONATION BOOK	C75

SMITH, H.C.   20TH CENTURY ORCH. STUDIES   F23
STEBACH, K.   HANDEL STUDIEN (2 VOL)   C75
STONEBERG, A. (CMPL).   MODERNE ORCHESTERSTUDIEN (8 VOL)   C41
STRAUSS, R.-BERTHOLD.   ORCHESTRA STUDIES (TRB & TUBA)   E65
STRAUSS, R.   ORCHESTRAL STUDIES   C91
WAGNER, R.-HAUSMANN.   ORCHESTRAL STUDIES   C91

0022   TROMBONE METHODS

ARBAN, J.J.B.L.-EBY.   EBY'S ARBAN METHOD (2 VOL)   A70
ARBAN, J.J.B.L.-RANDALL MANTIA.   FAMOUS METHOD (2 VOL)   C11
ARBAN, J.J.B.L.-PRESCOTT.   FIRST & SECOND YEAR   C11
ARBAN, J.J.B.L.   KOMPLETE METHODE (3 VOL)   D92
ARNOLD-RUTAN.   PLAY IN 6 WEEKS   B31
AUDIO-PLAY.   ORIGINAL RECORDED SYSTEM   A41
BAMBULA, A.   DIE POSAUNE (3 VOL)   C75
BARNES, C.P. & M. MC DUNN.   TROMBONE ARTISTRY   D34
BEELER, W.R.   METHOD (2 VOL)   E93
BERR, F. & DIEPPO.   COMPLETE METHOD   D36
BERT, E.   METHOD   B31
BIANCHINI, F.-GIAMPIERI.   METODO POPOLARE   E98
BIDDLECOME, J.   THE BEGINNER, THE TRB, AND MUSIC   B44
BLAZHEVICH, V.M.-WOLFSON.   ADVANCED METHOD   A38
BLEGER, M.-JOG.   METHOD   D36
BLODGETT, F.L.-GOLDMAN, MANTIA.   FOUNDATIO   C11
BOLTZ, E.G.-SKORNICKA.   MASTER METHOD   A78
BORDNER, G.   FIRST BOOK   A62
BRIGHT.   INTRODUCTION TO B-FLAT & F TROMBONE   A78
BUCHTEL, F.L.   ELEMENTARY METHOD   D18
BURGER, M.   SCHULE   F31
CARBONE, E.   METODO TEORICO--PRATICO   B07
CERONI.   INVITATION TO THE TROMBONE   M76
CHRISTOPHER, G.A. & VAN BODEGRAVEN.   ADVENTURES IN TRB PLAYING   F64
CIMERA, J.-HOVEY.   CIMERA-HOVEY METHOD   A62
CIMERA, J.   SECOND YEAR TECHNIC COURSE   D18
CLARKE, E.   METHOD   C11
CLODOMIR, P.F.   COMPLETE METHOD (2 VOL)   D36
CORNETTE, V.-PROCTER.   METHOD   B53
COUILLAUD, H.   METHOD   D36
DALBY, C.E.   ALL MELODY METHOD   F80
DAVIS, R.N.-SMITH.   NEW IMPERIAL METHOD   B26
DIEPPO, A.G.   COMPLETET METHOD   C11
DIEPPO, BERR, & VOBARON.   COMPLETE METHOD   D36
DORSEY, T.   POSAUNENSCHULE   C41
EBY, W.M.   EBY'S ARBAN METHOD   A70
EIDSON, A.D.-HOVEY.   TROMBONE METHOD (3 VOL)   A62
EISENHAUER.   ELEMENTARY SUPPLEMENT, BK 1   A10
FLANDRIN, G.   METHOD FOR TROMBONE   C38
FUHLISCH, G.   NEW METHOD FOR TROMBONE, A   F50
FUNOLL.   METODO COMPLETO   F95
GATTI, D.-GIAMPIERI.   GRAN METODO   E98
GORNSTON, D.   ADVANCED METHOD   A37
GORNSTON, D.   INTERMEDIATE METHOD   A37
GORNSTON, D.   VERY 1ST METHOD   A37
GOUSE.   LEARN TO PLAY THE TROMBONE (2 BKS)   A10
GOWER, W. & VOXMAN.   RUBANK ADVANCED METHOD (2 VOL)   F07
GRIGORIEV, B. & VOSTRYAKOV.   BEGINNING SCHOOL   D81
HADRAEA, J.   150 STUNDEN   D20

VOSTRYAKOV & GRIGORIEV. BEGINNING SCHOOL   D81
VOXMAN, H. & GOWER. RUBANK ADVANCED METHOD (2 VOL)   F07
WESLER, A.G. MILLS ELEMENTARY METHOD   D84
WILLIS, S. LUDWIG TRB INSTRUCTOR   D52
WINSLOW, R. TROMBONE PLAYING (2 VOL)   N10
YOUNG, L.E. ELEMENTARY METHOD   C11

0023   TROMBONE TECHNIQUES (Special Studies)

ALLARD, J. ADVANCED RHYTHMS   B31
ALLARD, J.-BOWER. ADVANCED RHYTHMS   B31
ARBAN'S MADE EASY.   B31
BAKER. JAZZ STYLES & ANALYSIS   N23
BLAZHEVICH, V.M.-OSTRANDER. ADV. DAILY DRILLS   B85
BLAZHEVICH, V.M. CLEF STUDIES   D36
BOWER, B. BASS CHORDS & PROGRESSIONS   B31
CARNIVAL OF VENICE MADE EASY.   B31
CIMERA, J. TRIPLE TONGUE COURSE   D18
COHN, A. JAZZ WORKSHOP   B31
COLIN, C. EAST COAST JAZZ SCENE   B31
COLIN, C.-YANS. EASY STEPS TO RHYTHM   B31
COLIN, C. LIP FLEXIBILITIES (2 VOL)   B31
COLIN, C. MELODIOUS FUNDAMENTALS   B31
COLIN, C. 100 ORIGINAL WARM-UPS   B31
COLIN, C. PROGRESSIVE TECHNIQUE   B31
COLIN, C.-BOWER. RHYTHMS   B31
COLIN, C. WARM-UPS WITH VITAL BRASS NOTES   B31
COLLINS, F.L. DAILY EMBOUCHURE DRILLS   A81
DAVIES, J. SCALES & ARPEGGIOS   A78
DAVIS, M. COOL SOUNDS   B31
DAVIS, M. MILES DAVIS COMPLETE   B31
DAVIS, M. SCHETCH ORCHS   B31
DUPRESNE & VOISIN. DEVELOP SIGHT READING   B31
EDMONDS, H. MORE OF MILES DAVIS   B31
FILLMORE, H. JAZZ TROMBONIST   C09
FINK, R.H. INTRODUCING THE ALTO CLEF   A02
FINK, R.H. INTRODUCING THE TENOR CLEF   A02
GAETKE, E.-BROWN. SCALE STUDIES   C91
GAETKE, E. 32 TAGLICHE ZUNGEN   G43
GARCIA, M.B. ESCALAS Y EJERCICIOS PARA TROMBON   F95
GIBBS. BASS CHORD CONSTRUCTION   B31
GILLESPIE, D. DIZZY BLOWS KEROUAC   B31
GIUFFRE. JAZZ PHRASING & INTERPRETATION   A38
GOLDMAN, E.F. DAILY EMBOUCHURE STUDIES   C11
GORNSTON, D. FUN WITH SCALES   D71
GORNSTON, D. TRB MECHANISMS   D71
GORNSTON, D.-REINHARDT. TRB MECHANISMS   C46
GORNSTON, D. & MUSSER. TROMBONE DAILIES   C46
HARRIS, A. DAILY ROUTINE   B31
HIGGINBOTHAM, J.C. WARM-UP BOOK   D71
HINTON & PETTIFORD. MILT MEETS OSCAR   B31
HUFFNAGLE, H.J.-GORNSTON. YOUR CONCERT READER(RHYTHM STUD.) C46
KARLIN, F. JAZZ PHRASING (DUETS)   B31
KENFIELD, L.S. 36 DAILY EXERCISES   B53
KING, T.H. DAILY EXERCISES   G10
KLEINHAMMER, E. ART OF TRB PLAYING   F72
LA PORTA. GUIDE TO IMPROVISATION   M77
LAFOSSE, A. TROMBONE PLAYER'S VADE MECUM   D36

```
LAMITOLA & SPEAR & STEIN.  BASIC SYNCOPATION                   E80
LANE, G.B.  CONCISE DAILY ROUTINE FOR TRB                      M80
LITTLE, L.  EMBOUCHURE BUILDER                                 E80
MANGELSDORFF, A.  ANLEITUNG ZUR IMPROVISATION                  F31
MANTIA, S.  ADV. DAILY STUDIES                                 B31
MARSTELLER, R.L.  ADVANCED SLIDE TECHNIQUE                     F60
MARSTELLER, R.L.  BASIC ROUTINES                               F60
MC DUNN, M. & BARNES.  TROMBONE ARTISTRY                       D34
MUSSER, W.I.-GORNSTON.  TRB. DAILIES                           D18
MUSSER, W.I.-GORNSTON.  TROMBONE DAILIES                       C46
OSTRANDER, A.  F-ATTACHMENT & BASS TRB                         B31
OSTRANDER, A.  20 MINUTE WARM-UP                               B31
PAISNER, B.-GORNSTON.  FUN WITH SCALES                         C46
PARES, G.P.C.  DAILY EXERCISES AND SCALES                     C11
PARES, G.P.C.-WHISTLER.  PARES SCALES                          F07
PARKER, C.  PARKER ORIGINALS                                   B31
PARKER, C.  YARDBIRD ORIGINALS                                 B31
PETTIFORD-HINTON.  GREAT JAZZ LINES                            B31
P & R.  SCHETCH ORCHS                                          B31
RAPH, A.  DANCE BAND READING & INTERP                          C25
REINHARDT, D.S.  PIVOT SYSTEM                                  B92
REINHARDT, D.S.-GORNSTON.  TRB. MECHANISMS                     D37
ROGERS, S.  SCHETCH ORCHS                                      B31
RONKA, E.  STUDIES & LIP DRILLS                                C11
SALVO.  240 DOUBLE & TRIPLE TONGUING EXERCISES                 E80
SCHAEFER, A.H.  PROFESSIONAL'S KEY TO DOUBLE...TONGUING        C09
SCHLOSSBERG, M.-C.K. SCHLOSSBERG.  DAILY DRILLS               A56
SHINER, M.  LIP BUILDING                                       B31
SHUEBRUK, R.  GRADED LIP TRAINERS                              C11
SHUMAN, D.  5 PREPARATORY STUDIES                              D37
SMITH, H.  JAZZ BEATS                                          B31
SMITH, R.  F-ATTACHMENT & BASS TRB                             B31
SPEAR & STEIN & LAMITOLA.  BASIC SYNCOPATION                   E80
STACEY, C.E.  SUCCESSFUL STUDIES (3 VOL)                       C09
STEIN & LAMITOLA & SPEAR.  BASIC SYNCOPATION                   E80
STRETTON.  UNISON SCALE BOOK                                   A78
STUART, W.  FAKE BOOK FOR THE CLUB DATE MUSICIAN               B31
STUART, W.  JAZZ AD LIB                                        B31
STUART, W.  JAZZ IMPROVISING                                   B31
STUART, W.  JAZZ SCALES                                        B31
TANNER, P.  PRACTICE WITH THE EXPERTS                          D71
WEDDING FAKE BOOK.                                            B31
WHISTLER, H.S.  MODERN PARES                                   F07
WHITE, W.C.  UNISONAL SCALES, CHORDS & RHYTHMICAL STUDIES      C11
WILLIAMS, E.-SCHAEFFER.  METHOD OF SCALES                      B31
WILLIAMS, E.  TRB HIGH TONES                                   B31
WILSON & VIOLA.  CHORD STUDIES                                 M77
```

0030   BASS TROMBONE ETUDES

```
BLUME, O.-FINK.  36 STUDIES                                      C11
BORDOGNI, G.M.-ROBERTS.  43 BEL CANTO STUDIES                    D16
DELGIUDICE, M.  12 ETUDEN "RHYTHMIK UND MELODIK"                 C01
GILLIS, L.  20 ETUDES                                           F60
GILLIS, L.  70 PROGRESSIVE STUDIES                              F60
GRIGORIEV, B.-OSTRANDER.  24 STUDIES                             C91
HARRIS, A.  SCALES & ETUDES                                      B31
KOPPRASCH, C.-FOTE.  SELECTED STUDIES                            D14
MAENZ, C.  20 STUDIEN                                            C75
OSTRANDER, A.  MELODIOUS ETUDES                                  C11
OSTRANDER, A.  SHIFTING METER STUDIES                            D16
PEDERSON, T.  ETUDES FOR BASS TROMBONE (3 VOL: ELEM TO ADV)      M93
RAPH, A.  26 ETUDES                                              M70
RODE-BROWN.  15 CAPRICES                                         C91
STEFANISZIN, K.  20 SPEZIAL-ETUDEN                               C59
STEFANISZIN, K.  20 SPEZIAL-ETUDEN                               E81
STEPHANOVSKY, K.-BROWN.  20 STUDIES                              C91
```

0031   BASS TROMBONE EXCERPTS

```
MENKEN, J. (ED).  ANTHOLOGY (2 VOL)                              C11
```

0032   BASS TROMBONE METHODS

```
BERNARD, P.  METHODE COMPLETE                                    D36
BIANCHINI, F.-GAIMPIERI.  METODO POPOLARE                        E98
KIETZER, R.  POSAUNE, BASS-VENTILPOSAUNE IN B, OP. 82            G43
KLIMENT, H.  ANFANGERSCHULE                                      D20
KLIMENT, H.  F-ES-BASS SCHULE                                    D20
LANGEY, O.  PRACTICAL TUTOR                                      A78
MAENZ, O.  20 STUDIEN                                            C75
MARIANI, G.-ANDREONI.  METODO POPOLARE                           E98
RAPH, A.  DOUBLE VALVE BASS TRB                                  C11
ROBERTS, G. & TANNER.  LET'S PLAY BASS TRB                       A03
SCHUBERT, O.  SCHULE                                             D46
TANNER, P. & ROBERTS.  LET'S PLAY BASS TRB                       A03
```

0033   BASS TROMBONE TECHNIQUES
(Special Studies)

```
COLIN, C. & BOWER-SCHAEFFER.  RHYTHMS FOR F ATTACHMENT B.TRB     B31
DUFRESNE-SCHAEFFER.  SIGHTREADING STUDIES                        B31
GILLIS, L.  70 PROGRESSIVE STUDIES                              F60
HOFFMAN, E.  TRIGGER TROMBONE                                   F60
```

0040   EUPHONIUM ETUDES

BERNARD, P. 12 PIECES MELODIQUES	D36
CHARLIER, T. 32 ETUDES DE PERFECTIONNEMENT	D41
DUHEM, H. 81 ETUDES MELODIQUES	F81
GALLAY, J.F.-DAX. – 12 ETUDES, OP. 57	C42
HOFMANN, H. MELODISCHE UBUNGS, OP. 36	C75
KOPPRASCH, C.-SEYFFARTH. 60 AUSGEWAHLTE ETUDEN (2 VOL)	C75
MULLER, R.-ROSCHER. 30 LEICHTE ETUDEN	C75
PETIT, A.S. GRANDES ETUDES	D36
UFFELEN, P.C.V. ETUDES	D92
VOXMAN, H. SELECTED STUDIES	F07

0042   EUPHONIUM METHODS

ADKINS, H.E. MODERN METHOD	A78
ARCHIMEDE, A. & GOLDMAN. FOUNDATION TO BARI PLAYING	C11
BEELER, W.R. METHOD FOR BARITONE (2 VOL)	E93
BEELER, W.R. PLAY AWAY!	F23
BLEGER, M. METHODE COMPLETE	D36
BRASCH. EUPHONIUM & 4-VALVE BRASSES	N06
BUCHTEL, F.L. BUCK ELEMENTARY METHOD	D18
BURGER, M. SCHULE FUR TENORHORN ODER ALTOHORN	F31
CARBONE, E. METODO	B07
FALCONE & BERNDT. METHOD (2 BKS)	D34
FINK, R.H. FROM TREBLE CLEF TO BASS CLEF BARITONE	A02
GATTI, D.-GIAMPIERI. GRAND METHOD FOR BARITONE (3 VOL)	E98
GOUSE. LEARN TO PLAY THE BARITONE, BK. 1	A10
HINDSLEY, M.H. CARL FISCHER BASIC METHOD FOR BARITONE	C11
KIETZER, R. TENORHORN SCHULE, OP. 81 (3 VOL)	G41
KLIMENT, H. ANFANGERSCHULE FUR EUFONIUM	D20
KLIMENT, H. SCHULE FUR FORTGESCHRITTENE	D20
LANGEY, O.-SEREDY. TUTOR FOR BARITONE (3 VALVES)	C11
LANGEY, O.-SEREDY. TUTOR FOR BARITONE (4 VALVES)	C11
MESTDAGH, P.-MOREAU. METHODE VOOR CORONET EN BARYTON	D80
MICHALEK, J. METHOD	A33
ROSSARI, C. METHOD (2 VOL)	E98
STOLC, E. ENSEMBLE SCHOOL FOR WIND INSTRUMENTS	A33

0050   TUBA ETUDES

ARBAN, J.J.B.L.-PRESCOTT. FIRST & SECOND YEAR	C11
BACH, J.S.-BIXBY & BOBO. BACH FOR THE TUBA (2 BKS)	M79
BELL, W.J.-COLIN. DAILY ROUTINE	F31
BERNARD, P. ETUDES ET EXERCICES	D36
BERNARD, P. 40 ETUDES	D36
BERNARD, P. 12 MELODIC PIECES	D36
BERNARD, P. 12 PIECES MELODIQUES	D36
BERNARD, P. 40 STUDIES AFTER FORESTIER	D36
BLAZHEVICH, V.M. 70 STUDIES (2 VOL)	D16
BLEGER, M.-COUILLAUD. 31 BRILLIANT STUDIES	D36
BLEGER, M.-COUILLAUD. 10 CAPRICES	D36
BOBO, R. (ED). BACH FOR THE TUBA	G21
BORDOGNI, G.M.-ROBERTS. 43 BEL CANTO STUDIES	D16
BRUGGEN, P. VAN. ETUDES	D92
CIMERA, J. 73 ADV. STUDIES	A62
COLLECTED ETUDES.	E19
CONCONE, G.-SHOEMAKER. LEGATO ETUDES	C11
DELGIUDICE, M. 12 ETUDEN "RHYTHMIK UND MELODIK"	C01
DELGIUDICE, M. 10 KLEINE TEXTE	C01
DUBOIS, P.M. 12 SOLI EN FORME D'ETUDES	D36
ENDRESEN, R.M. SUPPLEMENTARY STUDIES	F07
FINK, R.H. STUDIES IN LEGATO	C11
GALLAY, J.F.-DAX. 12 ETUDES, OP. 57	C42
GETCHELL, R.W.-HOVEY. 1ST BOOK OF PRACTICAL STUDIES	A62
GETCHELL, R.W.-HOVEY. 2ND BOOK OF PRACTICAL STUDIES	A62
HEJDA, M. ETUDEN	A52
HEJDA, M. STUDIES	A33
KLOSE-VANASEK. 270 TONE & TECHNIQUE EXERCISES	C46
KNAUB, D. PROGRESSIVE TECHNIQUES	D71
KOPPRASCH, C.-SEYFFARTH. 60 ETUDES (2 VOL)	C75
KOPPRASCH, C. 60 ETUDES	D16
KOPPRASCH, C.-SEYFARTH. 60 ETUDES	C75
KOPPRASCH, C. 60 SELECTED STUDIES COMPLETE	D16
KUEHN. 28 ADVANCED STUDIES	F60
KUEHN. 60 MUSICAL STUDIES (2 VOL)	F60
LAAS, B. & F. WEBER. STUDIES AND MELODIOUS ETUDES FOR TUBA	G85
LACHMANN, H. 25 ETUDEN FUR BASSTUBA	C75
LACHMANN, H. 26 TUBA-ETUDEN	C75
MAENZ, O. 12 SPEZIALSTUDIEN	C75
MURPHY, B.-WELDON. ADVANCED ETUDES	B31
OSTRANDER, A. SHIFTING METER STUDIES	D16
RUSCH, H.W. 24 ARBAN-KLOSE-CONCONE STUDIES FOR TUBA	G85
RUSCH, H.W. 18 BARRET & JANCOURT STUDIES FOR TUBA	G85
RUSCH, H.W. 25 LAZARUS-CONCONE STUDIES FOR TUBA	G85
SEAR, W.E. ETUDES	B44
SEAR, W.E. ETUDES	D16
SIEBER, F.-KUEHN. 60 MUSICAL STUDIES	F60
SLAMA, A. 66 ETUDEN IN ALLEN TONARTEN	B50
SLAMA, A. 66 ETUDES IN ALL MAJOR & MINOR KEYS	C11
STONEBERG, A. (CMPL). ORCHESTERSTUDIEN (TRB & TUBA)(8 VOL)	C41
TEUCHERT, E. SCHULE	C75
TYRRELL, H.W. ADVANCED STUDIES FOR BB-FLAT BASS	A78
UBER, D.A. 30 ETUDES FOR THE BASS TUBA	B31
VANDERCOOK, H.A. ETUDES	F07
VASILIEV, S. 24 MELODIOUS ETUDES	D16

VIEULOU. ETUDES CARACTERISTIQUES   C49
WHISTLER, H.S. MODERN PARES   F07

0051   TUBA EXCERPTS

BERNARD, P. TRAITS DIFFICILES (4 VOL)   D36
BERNARD, P. (CMPL). DIFFICULT PASSAGES (2 VOL)   D36
BERTHOLD, G.(CMPL). STRAUSS ORCHESTRAL STUDIES FOR TRB & TUBA   E65
BROWN, K. ORCHESTRAL EXCERPTS (10 VOL) (MOSTLY FOR TRB)   C91
BRUCKNER, A.-SEYFFARTH. ORCHESTERSTUDIEN (2 VOL)   C75
FERRARI, B. DIFFICULT PASSAGES...ITALIAN OPERAS (TRB & TUBA)   E98
MORRIS. INTRODUCTION TO ORCH EXCERPTS   F43
SEAR, W.E. & WALDECK & LEWIS. EXCERPTS (5 VOL)   B44
SEYFFARTH, F. (CMPL). ORCHESTERSTUDIEN (2 VOL)   C75
STONEBERG, A. MODERN ORCH. STUDIES FOR TRB & TUBA (8 VOL)   F23
STRAUSS, R.-BERTHOLD. ORCHESTRA STUDIES (TRB & TUBA)   E65
TORCHINSKY, A. (ED). 20TH-CENTURY ORCHESTRA STUDIES   F23
WAGNER, R. ORCHESTRAL STUDIES (TRB & TUBA)   C91

0052   TUBA METHODS

ARBAN, J.J.B.L.-PRESCOTT. FIRST AND SECOND YEAR   C11
ARBAN, J.J.B.L.-BELL. THE ARBAN-BELL TUBA METHOD   B31
BEELER, W.R. METHOD (2 VOL)   E93
BEELER, W.R. METHOD FOR BB-FLAT, E-FLAT TUBAS   F23
BELL, W.J. FOUNDATION TO TUBA PLAYING   C11
BELL, W.J. WILLIAM BELL COMPLETE (2 VOL)   B31
BERGEIM, J. INSTRUMENTAL COURSE FOR E-FLAT & BB-FLAT TUBAS   A78
BERNARD, P. METHODE COMPLETE POUR ... TUBA...   D36
BIANCHINI, F. POPULAR METHOD   F16
BLEGER, M.-JOB. NEW COMPLETE METHOD   D36
BRASCH. EUPHONIUM & 4-VALVE BRASSES   N06
BUCHTEL, F.L. BUCK ELEMENTARY METHOD   D18
BUCK, L. ELEMENTARY METHOD FOR TUBA   D18
CARBONE, E. METODO TEORICO-PRATICO   B07
CARNAUD. METHODE COMPLETE (2 VOL)   C38
CIMERA, J. & J.M.KUHN. KUHN-CIMERA METHOD   A62
CLARKE, H.F. MILLS ELEMENTARY METHOD   D84
CLODOMIR, P.F.-JOB. COMPLETE METHOD FOR ALL SAXHORNS   D36
D'ERASMO. METHOD   F16
EBY, W.M. EBY'S SCIENTIFIC METHOD (2 VOL)   A70
EIDSON, A.D.-HOVEY. BRASS BASS METHOD (2 VOL)   A62
ENDRESEN, R.M. BB-FLAT OR E-FLAT TUBA METHOD (2 BK)   N27
GEIB, F. METHOD   C11
GORNSTON, D. VERY 1ST METHOD   A37
GOUSE. LEARN TO PLAY THE TUBA   A10
GOWER, W. & VOXMAN. RUBANK ADV. METHOD (2 VOL)   F07
HAWKES & SONS. SIMPLICITY TUTOR   A78
HERFURTH, C.P. & MILLER. A TUNE A DAY   A81
HERFURTH, C.P. & STUART. SOUNDS OF THE WINDS (2 VOL)   C11
HINDSLEY, M.H. CARL FISCHER BASIC METHOD   C11
HOVEY, N.W. RUBANK ELEMENTARY METHOD   F07
JOHNSON, H.M. AEOLIAN METHOD FOR TUBA   C13
KIETZER, R. SCHULE, OP. 84 (2 VOL) (F & E-FLAT)   G43

KIETZER, R. SCHULE, OP. 85 (2 VOL) (B-FLAT & C)		G43
KINYON, J. BASIC TRAINING COURSE FOR TUBA (2 VOL)		A10
KINYON, J.L. BREEZE-EASY METHOD		G31
KLIMENT, H. ANFANGERSCHULE		D20
KLIMENT, H. GRIFFTABELLE & ANFANGSBRUNDE		D20
KLIMENT, H. SCHULE FUR FORTGESCHRITTENE		D20
KLING. LEICHT FASSLICHE, PRAKTISCHE SCHULE		E43
KUHN, J.M. & CIMERA. KUHN-CIMERA METHCD		A62
LANGEY, O. NEW & REV. ED. OF CELEBRATED TUTORS		C11
LANGEY, O. PRACTICAL TUTOR (E-FLAT TUBA)		A78
LANGEY, O. TUTOR		C11
MARIANI, G.-ANDREONI. METODO POPOLARE		E98
MICHALEK, J. METHOD		A33
MOORE, E.C. & A.O. SIEG. PREPARATORY INSTRUCTOR FOR BASSES		C11
PARES, G.P. METHODE ELEMENTAIRE		D41
PEASE, D.J. E-FLAT OR BB-FLAT BASS METHOD		E80
PEASE, D.J. UNIVERSAL'S FUNDAMENTAL METHOD		F98
PEHL, A. & UJFALUSSY & PERLAKI. TUBA TUTOR		B84
PETERS, C. & M. BETTON. TAKE ONE		D18
PILAT, F. BASS TUBA SCHOOL		A33
PRO ART METHOD.		E80
REGER, W. TALKING TUBA		B31
ROLLINSON, T.H. MODERN SCHOOL		B72
SKORNICKA, J.E. MASTER METHOD		A78
SKORNICKA, J.E. & BOLTZ. RUBANK INTERMEDIATE METHOD		F07
STUART, H. & HERFURTH. SOUNDS OF THE WINDS		C11
TEUCHERT, E. LEHRGANG		C75
TEUCHERT, E.-SEYFFARTH. SCHULE		C75
TODOROV, G. SCHOOL		F36
UJFALUSI & PEHL & PERLAKI. TUBA TUTOR		B84
VOXMAN, H. & GOWER. RUBANK ADV. METHOD (2 VOL)		F07
WARD, N. ELEMENTARY SCHOOL		B41
WATELLE. GRAND METHOD (2 VOL)		F16
WEBER, F. & K. SWANSON. TUBA STUDENT		G85

0053   TUBA TECHNIQUES (Special Studies)

BELL, W.J.-COLIN. DAILY ROUTINE & BLAZEVICH INTERPRETATIONS		E31
BELL, W.J. TUBA WARM-UPS AND DAILY ROUTINE (2 VOL)		B31
BERNINGER, H. BLASERUBUNGEN ...TAGLICHE STUDIEN		C75
BLAZHEVICH, V.M.-OSTRANDER. ADV. DAILY DRILLS		B85
BLAZHEVICH, V.M.-BELL. TUBA INTERPRETATIONS		B31
BOWER, B.-COLIN. RHYTHMS (2 VOL)		B31
BOWER, B.-COLIN. RHYTHMS ADVANCED		B31
COLIN, C. 100 ORIGINAL WARM-UPS		B31
DAILY WARM-UPS WITH VITAL BRASS NOTES.		B31
DUFRESNE. DEVELOP SIGHT READING (2 VOL)		B31
GOLDMAN, E.F. DAILY EMBOUCHURE STUDIES		C11
GORNSTON, D. & MUSSER. TUBA DAILIES		D18
HOVEY, N.W. SUPPLEMENTARY DRILL BOOK		N27
KINYON, J. DAILY HALF DOZENS FOR TUBA		A10
LINDERMAN. MELODIOUS FUNDAMENTALS		B31
LITTLE, L. EMBOUCHURE BUILDER		E80
MUSSER, W.I. & GORNSTON. TUBA DAILIES		D18
PARES, G.P.C. DAILY EXERCISES AND SCALES		C11
PARES, G.P.C.-WHISTLER. SCALES		F07
PETERS, C. & P. YODER. MASTER DRILLS		D18
KONKA, E. STUDIES & LIP DRILLS		C11

SALVO. 240 DOUBLE & TRIPLE TONGUING EXERCISES   E80
SARGENT, W.A.B. LIP BUILDERS OR DAILY STIMULANTS   B53
WHITE, W.C. UNISONAL SCALES (3 VOL)   C11

SOLOS

0101   TRUMPET CONCERTOS AND CONCERTINOS

```
ADDISON, J.  CONCERTO (OP)                                      G26
AHLGRIMM, H.  KONZERT IN F MINOR (OP)                           D46
ALBINCNI, T.-THILDE.  CONCERTO IN A MINOR (OP)                  A71
ALBINCNI, T.-THILDE.  CONCERTO IN D MINOR                       A71
ALBINCNI, T.-THILDE.  CONCERTO IN F MAJOR (P)                   A71
ALBINCNI, T.-THILDE.  CONCERTO SAINT-MARC (P)                   F39
ALBRECHTSBERGER, J.G.  CONCERTINO IN E-FLAT (E-FLAT TPT) (OP)   M80
ANDRIEU, F.  CONCERTINO (P)                                     B85
ARUTUNIAN, A.  CONCERTO (P)                                     B17
ARUTUNIAN, A.  CONCERTO (P)                                     D81
ARUTUNIAN, A.-VOISIN.  CONCERTO (P)                             C91
ARUTUNIAN, A.  KONZERT (P)                                      C75
EACH, J.S.-WEAST.  BRANDENBURG CONCERTO #2 (1ST MOV'T) (P)      D55
BACH, J.S.-TILDE.  CONCERTO IN G MINOR                          A71
BACHNER, R.  TROMPETENKONZERT (O)                               A39
EAEYENS, A.L.  CONCERTO (OP)                                    B12
EAEYENS, A.L.  CONCERTO (P)                                     D80
BARRAUD, H.  SYMPHONIE CONCERTANTE (P)                          A78
EARTSCH, C.  CONCERT (OP)                                       D67
BELLINI, V.-THILDE.  CONCERTO                                   A71
BERTOUILLE, G.  CONCERTO (OP)                                   B12
EISCOGLI-TALBOT.  CONCERTO (O)                                  E14
BLAZHEVICH, V.M.-NAGEL.  CONCERTO NO.5 (P)                      C91
BOHME, O.  CONCERTO IN F MINOR, OP.18                           F52
BOHRNSTEDT, W.R.  CONCERTO (P)                                  E93
ECND, C.J.-FINZI.  TRUMPET CONCERTO (OP)                        A78
BONDON, J.  CONCERTO DE PRINTEMPS (OP)                          F87
BOUTRY, R.  CONCERTINO (P)                                      B92
BOUTRY, R.  CONCERTINO (P)                                      D36
BOZZA, E.  CONCERTINO (OP)                                      D36
BRENTA, G.  CONCERTINO (OP)                                     D36
BUCCI.  CONCERTO FOR A SINGING INSTRUMENT (P)                  C27
BULL.  CONCERTO #1 (P)                                          A71
BULL.  CONCERTO #2 (P)                                          A71
BUSH, G.  CONCERTO NO.1 (O)                                     C33
CASANCVA.  CONCERTO (P)                                         D36
CHAYNES, C.  CONCERTO (OP)                                      D36
CHEVREUILLE, R.J.  CONCERTO, OP. 58 (OP)                        B12
CLCSTRE.  CONCERT (P)                                           E36
COLIN, G.  CONCERTO (O)                                         D67
CONSTANT, F.  CONCERTO (P)                                      D80
CORBEEL, R.  CONCERTINO DE CANNERO (P)                          D67
CORELLI, A.-WERDIN.  CONCERTINO FUR 2 TROMPETEN (O)             F31
CUNNINGHAM, M.G.  CONCERTO (OP)                                 B35
DARCY, R.  CONCERTO (OP)                                        A96
IAVID, F.V.  CONCERTINO, OP.4 (O)                               B53
DE FRUMERIE, G.  TRUMPETKONSERT (OP)                            C39
DE JONG, M.  CONCERTO, OP.49 (P)                                D80
DEBAAE, M.  CONCERTINO (P)                                      A96
DEFOSSEZ, R.  CONCERTO (P)                                      B12
CELDEN, L. VAN.  CONCERTO (P)                                   B74
DELERUE, G.  CONCERTINO (OP)                                    D36
DEPELSENAIRE.  CONCERTINO BREF (P)                              E66
DEPELSENAIRE, J.M.  CONCERTO IN B-FLAT MAJOR (P)                F87
DESPORTES, Y.  CONCERTO (P)                                     F60
```

```
DESPREZ, F.  CONCERTINO (P)                                              A96
DINDALE, E.  CONCERTINO (P)                                              D67
DOULIEZ.  CONCERTO #1 (P)                                                J39
DUBOIS, P.M.  CONCERTINO (OP)                                            D36
ERICKSON, F.  CONCERTINO (B)                                             C11
FARBERMAN, H.  DOUBLE CONCERTO FOR SINGLE TRUMPET (O)                    A98
FASCH, J.F.-WINSCHERMANN.  KONZERT D-DUR FUR 2 TRUMPETE (O)              F50
FASCH, J.F.-WINSCHERMANN.  KONZERT IN D MAJOR (OP)                       F50
FIALA, J.  CONCERTINO IN G MINOR (P)                                     C91
FITZGERALD, R.B.  CONCERTO IN A-FLAT MINOR (P)                           C11
FITZGERALD, R.B.  CONCERTO IN A-FLAT MINOR, 1ST MOVEMENT (P)             C11
FITZGERALD, R.B.  CONCERTO IN A-FLAT MINOR, 2ND MOVEMENT (P)             C11
FOLLMAN-HULDEZANG.  PETIT CONCERTINO (P)                                 F21
FRANCESCHINI, P.  CONCERTO (OP)                                          E14
FRANCHESCHINI, P.  CONCERTO (2 TPT)                                      E14
FRUMERIE.  KONSERT (P)                                                   C39
FUGA, S.  CONCERTINO (OP)                                                E98
GIANNINI, V.  CONCERTO (P)                                               E11
GIANNINI, V.  CONCERTO (P)                                               H06
GLIERE, R.M.-VOISIN.  CONCERTO                                           C91
GLINDEMANN.  CONCERTO (P)                                                N16
GOEDICKE, A.  CONCERTO, OP.41 (P)                                        C75
GOEDICKE, A.  CONCERTO, OP.41 (P)                                        F50
GOEDICKE, A.F.-SATZ.  CONCERTO, OP. 41 (OP)                              D37
GOEDICKE, A.F.  CONCERTO, OP. 41 (P)                                     B17
GOEDICKE, A.F.-NAGEL.  CONCERTO, OP. 41 (P)                              C91
GOTKOVSKY, I.  CONCERTINO (P)                                            F16
GRAFE, F.  GRAND CONCERTO (P)                                            B53
GRAUPNER, C.-VOISIN.  CONCERTO NO.1 IN D MAJOR (P)                       C91
GRAUPNER, C.-WOJCIECHOWSKI.  KONZERT NO.1 IN D MAJOR (O)                 F50
GRIMM, C.H.  CONCERTINO, OP.49 (P)                                       F60
HAGERUP, B.  CONCERTO (P)                                                A71
HAMILTON, I.  CONCERTO FOR JAZZ TRUMPET, OP.37 (O)                       F31
HANDEL, G.F.-BENOY.  CONCERTINO (OP)                                     E51
HANDEL, G.F.-MUSSER.  CONCERTO (P)                                       C25
HANDEL, G.F.-THILDE.  CONCERTO IN D MINOR (P)                            A71
HANDEL, G.F.-VOISIN.  CONCERTO IN G MINOR (P)                            C91
HASQUENOPH, P.  CONCERTINO                                               C01
HAYDN, J.-HANNIKEN.  CONCERTO (B)                                        D92
HAYDN, J.  CONCERTO (O)                                                  F60
HAYDN, J.-GOEYENS.  CONCERTO (P)                                         C11
HAYDN, J.-GOEYENS.  CONCERTO (P)                                         F81
HAYDN, J.-HANDKE.  CONCERTO (P)                                          N56
HAYDN, J.  CONCERTO IN E-FLAT MAJOR                                      A89
HAYDN, J.-JOOSEN.  CONCERTO IN E-FLAT MAJOR (P)                          D64
HAYDN, J.-VOISIN.  CONCERTO IN E-FLAT MAJOR (P)                          C91
HAYDN, J.-WOLLHEIM.  TROMPETENKONZERT IN E-FLAT MAJOR (O)                A83
HAYDN, J.  TRUMPET CONCERTO (O)                                          D08
HAYDN, J.  TRUMPET CONCERTO (P)                                          A81
HAYDN, J.  TRUMPET CONCERTO (P)                                          D92
HAYDN, J.-BOWMAN.  TRUMPET CONCERTO (P)                                  F23
HAYDN, J.-HALL & PERRY.  TRUMPET CONCERTO (P)                            A78
HAYDN, M.-HASEKEL.  CONCERTO IN D MAJOR (P)                              F52
HAYDN, M.  CONCERTO NO.2 IN C (OP)                                       E14
HEIKING, W.  CONCERTINO A LA JAZZ                                        C75
HELDENBERG, A.  CONCERTINO NO.1 (P)                                      A96
HEMEL, O.V.  CONCERTINO (P)                                              D80
HENNEBERG, A.  TRUMPETKONSERT (P)                                        F69
HERFURTH, W.  CONCERTINO                                                 F52
HERING, S.  CONCERTINO (P)                                               C11
HERMANN, R.-SEVERINSEN.  CONCERTO (P)                                    N45
HERTEL-TARR.  CONCERTO #2 IN E-FLAT (P)                                  E14
```

HERTEL, J.W.-TARR. CONCERTO #1 IN E FLAT (E-FLAT TPT)	M80
HOROVITZ. CONCERTO (P)	E41
HOVHANESS, A.S. CONCERTO FOR TPT AND WINDS (B)	E65
HUMMEL, J.N. CONCERTO (OP)	E14
HUMMEL, J.N.-VOISIN. CONCERTO (OP)	C91
HUMMEL, J.N. CONCERTO (P)	E19
HUMMEL, J.N.-THILDE. CONCERTO IN E-FLAT (P)	A71
HUMMEL, J.N.-TESCHENDORFF. KONZERT IN E-FLAT (P)	C75
HUMMEL, J.N.-STEIN. KONZERT IN E-FLAT MAJOR (O)	C75
HUMMEL, J.N.-GHITALLA. TRUMPET CONCERTO (BP)	D15
HUMMEL, J.N. TRUMPET CONCERTO (E/E-FLAT TPT PART ONLY)	M92
JOLIVET, A. CONCERTINO(MORCEAU DE CONCOURS 1948) (OP)	B81
JOLIVET, A. CONCERTO NO.2 (OP)	C65
JONGEN, J.J. CONCERTINO, OP. 41 (O)	B12
JONGEN, J.J. CONCERTINO, OP. 41 (P)	A96
KAMINSKI, J. CONCERTINO (OP)	D71
KAZANDJIEV. CONCERTO (P)	E27
KETTING, O. CONCERTINO (2 TPT)(O)	B74
KLERK, J.DE. CONCERTINO (BP)	D92
KOPER, K.H. CONCERTINO FOR D TRUMPET (O)	A38
KOPER, K.H. CONCERTINO FOR D TRUMPET (O)	D44
KURZ, S. KONZERT, OP.23 (OP)	A89
LARSSON, L.E.V. CONCERTINO, OP.45,NO.6 (OP)	C39
LECAIL, C. CONCERTO ROMANTIQUE (P)	A62
LECLERCQ, E. CONCERTINO (P)	D67
LEWIS, A.C. CONCERTO (P)	D42
LIESERING, L. CONCERTINO (P)	F52
LOEILLET, J.B.-THILDE. CONCERTO IN D (OP)	A71
LOUCHEUR, R. CONCERTINO (P)	F16
LOUCHEUR, R. CONCERTINO (TPT + 6 CLAR)	F16
LOUTHE, R. CONCERTINO NO.1 (P)	B23
LOUTHE, R. CONCERTINO NO.1 (P)	D80
LOUTHE, R. CONCERTINO NO.2 (P)	D67
LOUTHE, R. CONCERTINO NO.3 (P)	D67
LOVELOCK, W. CONCERTO (OP)	F59
MAILMAN, M. CONCERTINO, OP.31 (BP)	D84
MANFREDINI, F.-JOOSEN. CONCERTO (2 TPT) (P)	D92
MANFREDINI, F.-VOISIN. CONCERTO (2 TPT) (P)	C91
MANIET, R. CONCERTINO NO.2 (P)	A96
MANIET, R. CONCERTO (O)	D67
MANIET, R. CONCERTO MINIATURE (P)	A96
MARTELLI, H. CONCERTINO, OP.99 (P)	C01
MATEJ, J. CONCERTO (P)	A33
MAURY, H. CONCERTINO #1	M80
MAURY, H. CONCERTINO #2	M80
MAURY, H. CONCERTINO #3	M80
MAURY, H. CONCERTINO #4	M80
MENDELSSOHN, F.-MENDEZ & KOFF. MENDELSSOHN CONCERTO (BP)	D22
MEULEMANS, A. CONCERTO (OP)	B12
MEULEMANS, A. CONCERTO (P)	A96
MOLTER, J.M.-GLOVER & SAWYER. CONCERTO #1 (P)	M80
MOLTER, J.M.-GLOVER & SAWYER. CONCERTO #2 (P)	M80
MOLTER, J.M.-GLOVER & SAWYER. CONCERTO #3 (P)	M80
MOULAERT, R. CONCERTINO (O)	B12
MOULAERT, R. CONCERTINO (P)	A96
MOZART, L.-LILLYA. CONCERTO (P)	C11
MOZART, L.-THILDE. CONCERTO IN D (P)	A71
MOZART, L.-KREINER. CONCERTO IN D MAJOR (O)	C60
MOZART, L.-KREINER. CONCERTO IN D MAJOR (O)	D17
MOZART, L.-THILDE. CONCERTO IN D MAJOR (O)	A71
MOZART, L.-SEIFFERT. KONZERT IN D MAJOR (O)	D17
MOZART, L. TROMPETENKONZERT IN D MAJOR (O)	D21

MOZART, W.A. CONCERTO, K.191 (P)	B85
MUDGE R. CONCERTO (OP)	E14
NAGEL, R. CONCERTO (P)	E68
NELHYBEL, V. GOLDEN CONCERTO ON A 12-TONE ROW (P)	B85
O'REILLY, J. CONCERTO (BP)	F43
OHANA, M. CONCERTINO (O)	E98
OSIECK, H.W. CONCERTO (O)	B74
PAKHMUTOVA, A.N. CONCERTO (BOP)	D71
PANUFNIK, A. CONCERTO IN MODO ANTICO (P)	A78
PATTERSON, P. CONCERTO (P)	G16
PELEMANS, W. CONCERTO (2 TPT)(O)	D67
PESKIN, V.A. CONCERTO NO.1 (P)	D81
PILSS, K. CONCERTO (P)	D16
PILSS, K. CONCERTO IN B-FLAT MAJOR (OP)	F97
PORRET, J. CONCERTINO NO.1 (P)	D64
PORRET, J. CONCERTINO NO.19 (P)	D64
PORRET, J. CONCERTINO NO.2 (P)	D64
PORRET, J. CONCERTINO NO.20 (P)	D64
PORRET, J. CONCERTINO NO.21 (P)	D64
PORRET, J. CONCERTINO NO.22 (P)	D64
PORRET, J. CONCERTINO NO.3 (P)	D64
PORRET, J. CONCERTINO NO.4 (P)	D64
PORRINO, E. CONCERTINO (OP)	E98
PAPHLING, S. CONCERTO (P)	A84
REITER, A. KONZERT (OP)	B73
RESZKE, R. CONCERTO (O)	A31
RICCIUS, R.A. CONCERTINO (2 TPT)(P)	D92
RIISAGER, K. CONCERTINO IN C, OP.29 (OP)	H30
RIMSKY-KORSAKOV, N.A. CONCERTO (P)	D71
RIVIER, J. CONCERTO (P)	A71
ROBERT. MINI CONCERTINO (P)	E66
ROLLE, F. CONCERTO AVEC VARIATIONS (P)	C38
ROSENBERG, V. CONCERTO BY WAL-BERG(PSEUD.) (OP)	D71
RULST & REMA. ALLEGRO DE CONCERTINO (P)	D67
RULST & REMA. BRAVURA (P)	D67
SANDAUER, H. TROMPETEN-KONZERT (O)	B73
SCARLATTI, D.-SCHONBACH. CONCERTO (OP)	E02
SCHIBLER, A. KONZERT, OP.68 (O)	F97
SCHRODER, W. CONCERTO, OP.45 (P)	A79
SCHUBERT, F.P. MOMENT MUSICAL (P)	B53
SENEE, H.-MAGER. CONCERTINO (P)	F60
SHAKHOV, I.E. CONCERTO (P)	D81
SHCHELOKOV, V. CONCERTO NO.1 (P)	D81
SIKORSKI, K. CONCERTO FOR TPT. (OP)	A31
SOUFFRIAU, A. CONCERTINO, OP. 17 (P)	A96
STANLEY, J.-VOISIN. CONCERTO (P)	C91
STEKKE, L. CONCERTO POUR TROMPETTE, OP.17 (P)	A96
STOELZEL-THILDE. CONCERTO IN D MAJOR (P)	A71
STOZEL, G.H. KONZERT FUR 2 TROMPETENCHORE (O)	A90
STRAUWEN, J. CONCERTINO (P)	F81
SZOKOLAY. CONCERTO (P)	D36
TARTINI, G.-THILDE. CONCERTO IN D MAJOR (P)	F39
TCHAIKOVSKY, P.I.-HUMMEL. CONCERTO IN B-FLAT MINOR (P)	F07
TELEMANN, G.P.-VOISIN. CONCERTO FOR 2 TPT(ORIG.FOR 2 HN)(P)	C91
TELEMANN, G.P.-THILDE. CONCERTO IN B-FLAT MAJOR (P)	A71
TELEMANN, G.P.-TOETTCHER. CONCERTO IN D MAJOR (P)	F52
TELEMANN, G.P.-VOISIN. CONCERTO IN D MAJOR (OP)	C91
TELEMANN, G.P.-GREBE. KONZERT IN D MAJOR FUR D-TPT (OP) (OP)	F50
THILMAN, J.P.-NEUBAUER. CONCERTINO FUR TROMPETE, OP. 66 (OP)	C75
TOMASI, H. CONCERTO POUR TROMPETTE (OP)	D36
TORELLI, G.-VOISIN. CONCERTINO IN C MAJOR (OP)	C91
TORELLI, G.-SEIBERT. CONCERTO #1 IN B-FLAT (P)	E02

```
TORELLI, G.-SEIBERT.  CONCERTO #2 IN B-FLAT (P)                      E02
TORELLI, G.-VOISIN.  CONCERTO IN C MAJOR (2 TPT)(OP)                 C91
TORELLI, G.  CONCERTO IN D FOR TPT. & STRS (OP)                      E14
TORELLI, G.-THILDE.  CONCERTO IN D MAJOR (P)                         A71
TORELLI, G.-NIELSEN.  CONCERTO IN D MAJOR (OP)                       C91
TORELLI, G.-OUBRADOUS.  CONCERTO IN D MAJOR (OP)                     F87
TORELLI, G.-PAILLARD.  KONZERT IN D FUR TROMPETE (OP)                A51
UYTTENHOVE, Y.  CONCERTINO NO.1 (P)                                  D67
VALLIER.  CONCERTINO (P)                                             F87
VAN DELDEN, L.  CONCERTO, OP.54 (OP)                                 B74
VAN DER VELDEN, R.  CONCERTO (O)                                     B12
VASSILENKO, S.N.-DOKSHITZER.  CONCERTO FOR TPT, OP. 113 (P)          E19
VERACINI-THILDE.  CONCERTO IN E MINOR (P)                            A71
VIDAL, P.  CONCERTINO (P)                                            A62
VIDAL, P.  CONCERTINO POUR CORNET A PISTONS (P)                      C38
VIVALDI, A.-THILDE.  CONCERTO IN A-FLAT (P)                          F39
VIVALDI, A.-THILDE.  CONCERTO IN B-FLAT MAJOR (OP)                   A71
VIVALDI, A.-CHEDINI.  CONCERTO IN C MAJOR FOR 2 TPT (OP)             C91
VIVALDI, A.-GHEDINI.  CONCERTO IN E-FLAT MAJOR (2 TPT)(OP)           C91
VIVALDI, A.-THILDE.  CONCERTO IN G MINOR (P)                         A71
VORLOVA, S.  CONCERTO FOR TPT, OP.31 (P)                             A33
VORLOVA, S.  KONZERT FUR TPT, OP.31 (OP)                             A51
WAIGNEIN, A.  CONCERTINO (P)                                         D67
WEISS, A.  CONCERTO FOR TPT (OP)(2 PIANOS)                           A13
WENS, F.  CONCERTINO DE CONCOURS (P)                                 D67
WHITNEY, M.C.  CONCERTINO (P)                                        A81
WHITNEY, M.C.  CONCERTINO FOR TPT & BAND (P)                         F23
WILDGANS, F.  KONZERT FUR TPT IN C (OP)                              B73
WILLIAMS, E.  CONCERTI NOS.1-6 (P)                                   B31
WISSMER, P.  CONCERTINO (O)                                          C61
ZBINDEN, J.F.  CONCERTINO, OP. 6 (OP)(PIANO & DRUM)                  F31
```

0102 TRUMPET SONATAS AND SONATINAS

```
ABEL-KINNEY.  SONATA I                                               N61
ALBERTI, G.M.  SONATA IN D (2 TPT) (O)                               E14
ALBINONI, T.  SONATA IN C (OP)                                       E14
ALBINONI, T.  SONATA NO.2 (OP)                                       E14
ALDROVANDINI, G.-VOISIN.  SONATA NO. 1                               C91
ALDROVANDINI, G.-VOISIN.  SONATA NO. 2                               C91
ALDROVANDINI, G.-VOISIN.  SONATA NO. 3                               C91
ANTHEIL, G.  SONATA IN C FOR TPT                                     G17
ASAFIEV, B.V.  SONATA                                                D71
ASHTON, J.H.  SONATA FOR TPT & PA                                    B35
AUBAIN.  SONATINE                                                    B24
BALDASSARE-BEER & BLOCK.  SONATA #1 IN F                             E14
BALDASSARE-BEER & BLOCK.  SONATA #2 IN F                             E14
BEETHOVEN, L.V.-GORNSTON.  BEETHOVEN SONATAS                         C46
BENDA, F.  SONATA IN F MAJOR                                         B85
BENTZON, N.V.  SONATA, OP. 73                                        H30
BEVERSDORF, T.  SONATA FOR TPT & PA                                  F60
BIBER, C.H.  TRE SONATA PER CLARINO                                  F97
BIBER, C.H.  TRE SONATA PER CLARINO                                  H05
BIBER, H.I.F.  SONATA A 6                                            F07
BIBER, H.I.F.  SONATA A 6 IN B-FLAT                                  E14
BODA, J.  SONATINA FOR TPT & PA                                      F60
BOTTJE, W.G.  SONATA                                                 E68
CASTEREDE, J.  SONATINE                                              D36
```

```
CAZZATI-BLOCK & TARR.   SONATA A 5, OP 35/10              E14
CAZZATI-BLOCK & TARR.   SONATA A 5, OP 35/11              E14
CAZZATI-BLOCK & TARR.   SONATA A 5, OP 35/12              E14
CHICHKOV. I.-VOLOTZKY.  SONATINA                          D81
COPE, D.  SONATA FOR TPT & PA                            B35
CORELLI, A.-NAGEL.  SONATA CON TROMBA                     D73
CORELLI, A.   SONATA IN D (TPT, 2 VLN) (C)               E14
CORELLI, A.   SONATA IN F                                B85
CORELLI, A.-SOLODOUIEW.  SONATA IN G MINOR               B85
CORELLI, A.-THILDE.  SONATE EN F                          A71
CUNNINGHAM, M.G.  SONATA IN F                            B35
DANDELOT, G.  SONATINA                                   C01
DARTER, T.  SONATINA                                     M92
DAVIES, P.M.  SONATA FOR TPT & PA                         F31
DE WOLF, J.E.  SONATINA IN OUDE STIJL                    D80
DEFAY, J.M.  SONATINE                                    D36
EMMANUEL, M.  SONATE                                     D36
FANTINI, G.-GLASEL & ROSENTHAL.  3 SONATAS               B15
FISCHER, J.K.F.  SONATINA                                D74
FRACKENPOHL, A.R.  SONATINA                              F23
FRANCAIX, J.  SONATINA                                   C01
GABAYE, P.  SONATINE                                     D36
GABRIELI, D.-VOISIN.  SONATA (2 TPT)                     C91
GABRIELI, D.-BLOCK & TARR.  SONATA #4 IN D               E14
GABRIELI, D.  SONATA NO.2 (OP)                           E14
GABRIELI, D.  2 SONATAS (OP)                             E14
GABRIELI, D.-VOISIN.  SONATAS (2 VOL)#6                  C91
GARLICK.  TRUMPET SONATA FOR TODAY, A                    G66
GENZMER.  SONATINE                                       E65
GOLUBEW, E.K.  SONATA, OP.36/2                           D81
GOSSEC, F.J.-KLERK.  SONATA                              D64
GOSSEC, F.J.  SONATE                                     D92
GRAAF, J.DE.  SONATINE                                   D64
GRAAF, J.DE.  SONATINE VOOR TROMPET                      D92
GROSSI-BLOCK.  SONATA A 5, OP. 3/11                      E14
GROSSI-BLOCK.  SONATA A 5, OP. 3/12                      E14
GROSSI-BLOCK.  SONATA DECIMA, OP. 3                      E14
HANDEL, G.F.-POWELL.  SONATA #3                          F60
HANDEL, G.F.-VOISIN.  SONATA NO.3                        C91
HANDEL, G.F.-MUSSER.  SONATA                             C25
HANDEL, G.F.-THILDE.  SONATE IN F                         A71
HARTLEY, W.S.  SONATINA FOR TPT (OP)                     E87
HAYDN, J.-MULLER.  SONATINE                              D67
HESS, W.  SONATINE, OP. 41                               C80
HINDEMITH, P.  SONATE                                     F31
HOLDHEIM, T.  SONATA FOR TPT & PA                        C93
HOLMES, P.  SONATA FOR TPT & PA                           F43
HOVHANESS, A.S.  SONATA, OP.200 (TPT,ORGAN)              E65
HUBEAU, J.  SONATE                                       B81
HUBSCHMANN, W.  SONATINA                                 C75
HUMMEL, B.  SONATINA                                     F52
JACCHINI-VOISIN.  SONATA                                 C91
KAUFMANN, A.  SONATINE, OP.53                            B73
KELLER, G.-SCHERCHEN.  SONATA FUR TPT (OP)               F31
KENNAN, K.W.  SONATA                                     E93
KOETSIER.  SONATINA                                      B74
KORDA, V.  SONATINA IN DREI SATZEN (OP)                  B73
KREISLER.  SONATINA                                      F60
LAURIDSEN.  SONATA                                       M98
LEGLEY, V.  SONATE, OP.40/6                              B12
LOEILLET, J.B.-MESSER & COMPBELL.  SONATA FOR TRUMPET & PIANO   A03
LOEILLET, J.B.-THILDE.  SONATE IN B-FLAT                  A71
```

```
LOEILLET, J.B.-THILDE.  SONATE IN G                                    A71
MARCELLO, B-GLOVER & BRAGE.  SONATA                                    M80
MARTELLI, H.  SONATINE                                                 A71
MARTELLI, H.  SONATINE                                                 D35
MARTINU, B.  SONATINE                                                  D36
MC KAY, G.F.  CONCERT SOLO SONATINE                                    A81
MEULEMANS, A.  SONATE                                                  B12
MILMAN, M.  SONATA FOR TPT & PA                                        E19
MOLINEUX.  SONATA IN 2 MVTS                                            F43
PEETERS, F.  SONATA, OP.51                                             E65
PERGOLESI, G.B.-SMIN.  TRIO-SONATA NO.12 IN E MAJOR                    B85
PERKOWSKI.  SONATINA                                                   E72
PEZEL, J.C.-TARR.  SONATA IN C (BSN & BC)                             M80
PEZEL, J.C.-TARR.  6 SONATINAS IN C (2 TPT)                           M80
PILSS, K.  SONATE                                                      F97
PURCELL, D.  2 SONATEN                                                 F31
PURCELL, H.-CORBIN.  SONATA FOR TPT & ORGAN                           B40
PURCELL, H.-GHITALLA.  SONATA FOR TPT & STRS                          D16
PURCELL, H.-LILLYA.  SONATA IN D MAJOR                                C11
PURCELL, H.  SONATA IN G MINOR                                        B85
PURCELL, H.-LUMSDEN.  SONATA IN G MINOR                               E14
PURCELL, H.  SONATA NO.1 (OP)                                         E14
PURCELL, H.  SONATA NO.2 (OP)                                         E14
PURCELL, H.-NAGY.  SONATA                                             F31
PURCELL, H.-VOISIN.  SONATA                                           C91
RUEFF, J.  SONATINE                                                   D36
RUNOLFSSON.  SONATA                                                   N26
RUSSELL, R.  SONATINA                                                 C40
SCARLATTI, D.-VOISIN.  SONATA NO.17                                   C91
SCHMUTZ, A.D.  SONATINE                                               D52
SCHNEIDER, W.  SONATINA FOR TPT & PA                                  D98
SEEBOTH, M.  SONATA                                                   E37
SHAPERO, H.  SONATA FOR TPT IN C                                      F59
SKOLNIK.  SONATA                                                      F80
SMITH, L.  SONATA                                                     E68
SOWERBY, L.  SONATA                                                   E11
SRAMEK.  SONATINA                                                     G81
STEIN, L.  SONATA (UNACC)                                            E36
STEVENS, H.  SONATA                                                   E65
STRADELLA, A.-OUBRADOUS.  SONATA DE CONCERT FOR TPT & STRS           F81
TAKACS, J.  SONATA BREVE, OP.67                                       B73
TELEMANN, G.P.-PUBRADOUS.  SONATE DE CONCERT                          F87
TELEMANN, G.P.-WINSCHERMANN & BUCK.  SONATE DE CONCERT                F50
TELEMANN, G.P.-THILDE.  SONATE EN C MINEUR                            A71
TESSARINI-THILDE.  SONATE IN D MAJOR                                  A71
TORELLI, G.-TARR & BLOCK.  SONATA                                     E14
TUTHILL, B.C.  SONATA FOR B-FLAT TPT & PA                             H06
TUTHILL, B.C.  SONATA, OP.29                                          E11
UBER.  SONATA                                                         F59
VACHEY, H.  SONATINE                                                  B66
VALEK, J.  SONATE EROICA                                             A33
VALENTINO-BOSWELL.  SONATA IN C                                       N62
VALENTINO-THILDE.  SONATE IN D MINOR                                  A71
VALENTINO-THILDE.  SONATE IN F MAJOR                                  A71
VEJVANOVSKY.  SONATA A 4                                              E54
VENTO, M.  SONATA IN 2 MOVEMENTS                                      B85
VIVIANI, G.B.  2 SONATAS (TPT, ORGAN)                                 E14
WEAST.  SONATA                                                        D14
WEBER, A.  SONATINE BREVE                                            D36
WHITE, D.  SONATA                                                     M98
WILDER, A.  TRUMPET SONATA                                            B14
WILLIAMS, E.  SONATA                                                  B31
```

WILLIS, R. SONATINA   F59
WOLF, J.E. DE. SONATINE   J39

0103   TRUMPET SOLOS WITH
BAND ACCOMPANIMENT

ABT, F. WALDANDACHT (B)   F10
ADAM, A.C.-BOUSQUET. CELEBRE NOEL (B)   D64
ADAMS, S. BABYLON (B)   A78
ADAMS, S.-DELAMATER. HOLY CITY (BP)   F07
ADAMS, S. HOLY CITY, THE (B)   A78
ADAMS, S. NIRVANA (B)   A78
AHLSTROM, D. SCHERZO FOR TPT (BOP)   E87
ALLITSEN, F. THERE'S A LAND (B)   A78
ANDRIEU. DIVERTISSEMENT POUR BUGLE OU CORNET (B)   D64
ANDRIEU. IMPRESSIONS NAPOLITAINES POUR PETIT BUGLE (B)   D64
ANDRIEU. J'AI DU BON TABAC, AIR VARIE (B)   D64
ANDRIEU. LA VIE EN ROSE, MAZURKA (B)   D64
ANDRIEU. NOUVELLE ETOILE, POLKA (B)   D64
ANDRIEU. PERLE ROSE (B)   D64
ANDRIEU, F. PRELUDE ET ALLEGRO (B)   D64
ANDROZZO, A.-WRIGHT. IF I CAN HELP SOMEBODY (B)   A78
ARBAN, J.J.B.L.-WANDERMEE. CAPRICE ETUDE POUR CL. OU TPT(B)   D36
ARDITI, L. IL BACIO, VALSE (B)   A78
ASCHER, J. ALICE WHERE ART THOU? (B)   A78
BALL, E. CONCHITA (B)   A78
BARBIER, R. BELLE SOISSONNAISE, MAZURKA (B)   D64
BAUST, C. TROMPETERSTUCKCHEN, EIN (B)   F10
BECHER, H. POSTILLION, DER (B)   C54
BECKER, E.A. ERNESTONIA (B)   G10
BELLSTEDT, H.-LEIDZEN. LA MANDOLINATA (B)   F60
BELLSTEDT, H.-SIMON. NAPOLI (B)   F60
BENNETT, D. TRUMPET ROYALE (BP)   D71
BIZET, G.-HARDING. FLOWER SONG FROM "CARMEN" (B)   D18
BLEMANT, L. ANDANTE ET RONDO (B)   D64
BOISSON. CANARI, LE (B)   D64
BOND, C.J. A PERFECT DAY (B)   A78
BOUCHEL. 2 COUSINS, LES (1 OR 2 TPT)   D64
BOULANGER, L. MY PRAYER (AVANT DE MOURIR)   E83
BOURGUIGNON, F.D. RECITATIF ET RONDE POUR TPT, OP.94 (BOP)   D80
BRAHMS, J.-KOFF. BRAHMS CZARDAS (BP)   D22
BRIEGEL, G.F. SOLOETTE (B)   A91
BUCHTEL, F.L. INTERMEZZO (B)   D18
BURKE, J.F. AMOURETTE (BP)   C11
BURKE, J.F. DANZA ALEGRE (BP)   C11
BURKE, J.F. MAGIC TRUMPET (BP)   C11
CADMAN, C.W. AT DAWNING (B)   A78
CHAVATTE. FOLLETTE (B)   D64
CHOPIN, F.-MARTIN. TRISTESSE (B)   D64
CHRISTEN, A. SONNTAG AUF DER HEIDE (B)   F10
CLARKE, H.L. CARNIVAL OF VENICE (BP)   G31
CLARKE, H.L. FLIRTATIONS (BP)   C09
CLARKE, J. TRUMPET VOLUNTARY (B)   A78
CLARKE, J.-TIEMERSMA. TRUMPET VOLUNTARY (B)   D92
CODE, P. 'NEATH AUSTRAL SKIES (B)   A78
CODE, P. LUCILLE (B)   A78
CODE, P. ZANETTE (B)   A78
CODE, P. ZELDA (B)   A78
COLLINS, J. BALLAD (B)   F21

```
MASTEN, I.J.  BONNIE ELOISE (BP)                                    D 52
MC FARLANE, A.  BLYTHE SPIRIT (B)                                   A 78
MC KAY, G.F.  RHUMBA SERENADE (BP)                                  B 72
MELLISH.  DRINK TO ME ONLY WITH THINE EYES (B)                      A 91
MELYAN, T.  DEBONAIR (BP)                                           F 43
MENDEZ, R.-KOFF.  FAREWELL MY GRANADA (BP)                          D 22
MENDEZ, R.-KOFF.  FLIGHT OF THE BUMBLE-BEE (BP)                     D 22
MENDEZ, R.-KOFF.  VIRGEN DE LA MACARENA, LA (BP)                    D 22
MONESTES.  BASSINETTE, LA (B)                                       D 64
MORRISSEY, J.J.  SOLILOQUY FOR TRUMPET (B)                          D 63
MOZART, W.A.  LARGHETTO DU QUINTETTE (B)                            D 64
MUSSORGSKY, M.P.-KOFF.  CHIT-CHAT (BP)                              D 22
NELHYBEL, V.  CONCERT PIECE (B)                                     G 68
NESSLER-MOLENAAR.  BEHUT DICH GOTT (B)                              D 92
NESTICO, S.  PORTRAIT OF A TPT (BP)                                 D 14
PALADHILE, E.-CHRISTOL.  MANDOLINATA (B)                            D 64
PARES, G.P.C.  PREMIER SOLO DE CONCERT (B)                          D 64
PETIT.  CYPRIS (B)                                                  D 64
PETIT.  GOUTTES D'EAU (B)                                           D 64
PRESSEL, G.A.-BREUER.  AN DER WESER (B)                             B 99
PURCELL, H.  TRUMPET VOLUNTARY (SEE CLARKE, J.)
REED, A.  ODE FOR TPT (B)                                           F 60
REINGARD.  LOCOMOTIVE, LA (B)                                       D 64
REYNOLDS.  TRIPLET, THE (B)                                         E 83
RICHARD.  DELICATESSE (B)                                           D 64
RIMSKY-KORSAKOV, N.A.-CHRISTOL.  CHANSON HINDOUE (SADKO)            D 64
RIMSKY-KORSAKOV, N.A.  FLIGHT OF THE BUMBLE BEE (B)                 A 91
ROSSINI, G.-LABOLE.  CAVATINE DU BARBIER DE SEVILLE (B)             D 64
ROSSINI, G.-TILLIARD.  CAVATINE DU BARBIER DE SEVILLE (B)           D 64
ROSSINI, G.-WANNEMACHER.  INFLAMMATUS (BP)                          C 11
ROSSO & EREZZA.  SILENCE, LE (B)                                    D 64
RUELLE, F.  ROSE OF SEPTEMBER (B)                                   D 92
SALT.  AIGRETTE (B)                                                 D 64
SCHAEFFER, H.-BREUER.  POST IM WALDE, DIE, OP. 12 (B)               B 99
SIEBERT, E.(PSEUD).  BOUNCING BALL (B)                              A 69
SIMEONE, H.  TPT IN THE NIGHT (BOP)                                 F 43
SIMON, F.  WILLOW ECHOES (BP)                                       C 11
SIMONS, G.  ATLANTIC ZEPHYRS (BP)                                   C 11
SMITH-HOLMES.  FRIENDS (B)                                          F 07
SMITH.  TRUMPETER'S FROLIC (B) (1 OR 2 TPT)                         A 91
STAIGERS, D.  CARNIVAL OF VENICE (BP)                               C 11
STORM.  ON THE SOUTHERN SEAS (3 TPT) (BP)                           D 33
STREET, A.  4 SOLOS (B)                                             E 59
STREET, A. (ARR).  OH CAN YE SEW CUSHIONS                           E 59
SULLIVAN, A.S.  LOST CHORD, THE (B)                                 A 78
SUPPE, F.V.  HIRTEN MORGENLIED, DES                                 A 20
THOMSON, V.  AT THE BEACH (BP)                                      C 11
TILLIARD.  CARNAVAL DE VENISE, LE (B)                               D 64
TILLIARD.  SEINE ET TAMISE                                          D 64
TIVOLLIER.  OH! MA CHERE! (B)                                       D 64
TROXELL-HENDERSON.  MISTY MORNING (B)                               D 14
VULGAR BOATMEN (B).                                                 F 54
WALTERS.  AD LIB (B)                                                A 91
WALTERS.  DARK EYES (B)                                             A 91
WALTERS, H.L.  3 JACKS (3 TPT) (BP)                                 D 52
WALTERS, H.L.  TRUMPET HOLIDAY (B)                                  F 07
WALTERS, H.L.  TRUMPTET FILIGREE (B)                                F 07
WHITE, M.V.  TO MARY (B)                                            A 78
WILLIAMS, C.  DRAMATIC ESSAY (B)                                    F 72
WINDSOR, B.  ALPINE ECHOES (B)                                      F 54
WINDSOR, B.  VALSE BRILLANTE (B)                                    A 78
WRIGHT, D.  MANTILLA, LA (B)                                        F 54
```

YODER, P. BOBBY'S BLUES (B)   D 18   27

0104 TRUMPET SOLOS WITH ORCHESTRAL ACCOMPANIMENT

AHLSTROM, D. SCHERZO FOR TPT (OBP)	E87
ALBERTI, G.M. SONATA IN D (OP)	E14
ALBINCNI, T. SONATA IN C (OP)	E14
ALPAERTS, F. KARAKTERSTUK POUR TPT (O)	B12
ARBAN, J.J.B.L.-BRINKMANN. FANTASIEN...KARNEVAL VON VENEDIG	A83
BACH, J.S.-THILDE. 3 BOUREES (O)	A71
BARBIER, R. PIECE SYMPHONIQUE, OP.17 (OP)	D36
BIBER, H.I.F. SONATA A 6 IN B-FLAT (OP)	E14
BLOCH, E. PROCLAMATION (OP)	A98
BORSCHEL, E.-BORMANN. KUBANISCHES LIEBESLIED (OP)	C30
BOURGUIGNON, F.D. RECITATIF ET RONDE, OP.94 (BOP)	D80
BRAHMS, J.-KOFF. CZARDAS (BOP)	D22
BREUER, K.G. ATONALYSES II (O)	F50
CLARKE, J. SUITE (OP)	E14
CLARKE, J.-JACQUES. TRUMPET VOLUNTARY (P)	E51
DEFOSSEZ, R. RECITATIVO E ALLEGRO POUR TPT (OP)	C42
DESENCLOS, A. INCANTATION, THRENE ET DANSE (OP)	D36
DEVREESE, G. ALLEGRO POUR TPT (OP)	B12
ENDLER, S-WOJCIECHOWSKI. SINFONIA CONCERTANTE (D TPT)	F50
FERRARI, G. DIVERTIMENTO CONCERTANTE (O)	E98
GABRIELI, D. SONATA NO.2 (OP)	E14
GABRIELI, D. 2 SONATAS (OP)	E14
GIBBONS, O.-CRUFT. SUITE FOR TPT (OP)	G26
GUILBERT, R. IMPROMPTU (OP)	D36
HANDEL, G.F. SUITE IN D (OP)	E14
HARTLEY, W.S. SONATINA (OP)	E87
HERTEL-TARR. DOPPELKONZERT (SAME AS CONCERTO A 6) (O)	F31
HOVHANESS, A.S. AVAK, THE HEALER	F59
HOVHANESS, A.S. HAROUTIUN.RESURRECTION,ARIA,& FUGUE	E65
HOVHANESS, A.S. HOLY CITY, THE (O)	E65
HOVHANESS, A.S. KHRIMIAN HAIRIG (O)	E65
HOVHANESS, A.S. PRAYER OF SAINT GREGORY (GOP)	F59
HOVHANESS, A.S. PROCESSIONAL AND FUGUE (O)	E65
KANITZ, E. CONCERT PIECE FOR TRUMPET (OP)	D84
KAUFMANN, A. MUSIK FUR TPT & STRS, OP.38 (OP)	F31
KELLER, G. SONATA FUR TPT, STRS & BC (OP)	F31
KLEIN-KOFF. QUIXOTE (BOP)	D22
KLEIN, G. TROMPETERLAUNEN (O)	C59
KOFF, C.-ARR. SPINNING SONG (BOP)	D22
KORDA, V. SONATINE IN DREI SATZEN (OP)	B73
KORDA, V. SONATINE IN 3 SATZEN (O)	B73
LAGENDOEN, J.C. PUPPET (O)	B91
LANTIER, P. CONCERT EN 3 PARTIES (OP)	D41
LAPARRA, R. SUITE ITALIENNE EN FORME DE BALLET (O)	E98
LE BOUCHER, M. SCHERZO APPASSIONATO (OP)	D36
MANCINI, F.-MINTER. SINFONIA TO "HYDASPES" (O)	E14
MEESTER, L.DE. PAVANE (O)	D67
MENDEZ, R. (ARR)-KOFF. FAREWELL MY GRENADA (BOP)	D22
MENDEZ, R. (ARR)-KOFF. FLIGHT OF THE BUMBLE BEE (BOP)	D22
MENDEZ, R. (ARR)-KOFF. LA VIRGEN DE LA MACARENA (BOP)	D22
MOULAERT, R. THEME ET VARIATIONS POUR TPT (OP)	B12
MUSSORGSKY, M.P.-KOFF. CHIT CHAT (BOP)	D22
NEUGEBAUER, F.W. DER ALTE DESSAUER	C30
OBOUSSIER, R. ENTRADA POUR TROMPETTE (O)	C61

0106   TRUMPET SOLOS WITH PIANO ACCOMPANIMENT

ALETTER, W.-PRICE. LITTLE STORY, A	C11
ALETTER, W. RENDEZVOUS (SOLO OR DUET)	A82
ALEXANDER. BURLESQUE (P)	C40
ALEXANDER. FUGUE (P)	C40
ALEXANDROV, J. 3 PIECES	D81
ALFORD, K.J.-WOOLDRIDGE. COLONEL BOGEY	A78
ALLAN, P.C. HARLEQUIN	G13
ALLAN, P.C. HIAWATHA	G13
ALLAN, P.C. REVELLER, THE	G13
ALLAN, P.C. ROYAL CADET	G13
ALLAN, P.C. SCOTSMAN	G13
ALLAN, P.C. VERNON	G13
ALLAN, W. ECLIPSE, THE	D64
ALPAERTS, F. KARAKTERSTUK (OP)	B12
AMBROSE-O'NEILL. ONE SWEETLY SOLEMN THOUGHT	G13
AMELLER, A.C. 3 RIVIERES FROM BELLE PROVINCE	D36
AMELLER, A.C. ROUYN FROM BELLE PROVINCE	D36
AMELLER, A.C. SHERBROOKE FROM BELLE PROVINCE	D36
AMELLER, A.C. TROMPETE FRANCAISE	D36
AMELLER, A.C. ZANNI (P)	E66
ANDERSEN, A.O. A GLAD TUNE	C11
ANDERSON, L. BELLE OF THE BALL	D84
ANDERSON, L.-EDWARDS. BLUE TANGO	D84
ANDERSON, L. BUGLER'S HOLIDAY	D84
ANDERSON, L. MUSIC OF LEROY ANDERSON, THE	D84
ANDERSON, L. TRUMPETER'S LULLABY, A	D84
ANDRE-BLOCH. MEOU-TAN YIN	C49
ANDRIEU, F. ANDANTE & RONDO	A10
ANDRIEU, F. ANDANTE & RONDO	A71
ANDRIEU, F. ANDANTE ET POLONAISE	A71
ANDRIEU, F. CONTEST SOLO #2	A10
ANDRIEU, F. 1ST CONTEST SOLO	A10
ANDRIEU, F. 3RD CONTEST SOLO	A10
ANDRIEU, F. 4TH CONTEST SOLO	A10
ANDRIEU, F. 5TH CONTEST SOLO	A10
ANDRIEU, F. DANS LA FORET	A71
ANDRIEU, F. DIVERTISSEMENT	A71
ANDRIEU, F. FANTAISIE MENUET	A71
ANDRIEU, F. PRELUDE ET ALLEGRO	A71
ANDRIEU, F. ROSSIGNOL D'AMOUR	A71
ANDRIEU, F. SOLO DE CONCOURS NO.1	A71
ANDRIEU, F. SOLO DE CONCOURS NO.3	A71
ANDRIEU, F. SOLO DE CONCOURS NO.4	A71
ANISIMOV, B.I. SCHERZO	D81
ANNIE LAURIE.	D92
ANTIUFEEV, B.I. VARIATIONS ON A BYELOROSSIAN THEME	D81
ANTIUFEEV, B.I.-NAGEL. VARIATIONS, OP.23	C91
ANTIUFEEV, B.I. & SHCHELOKOV. 2 PIECES	D81
ARBAN, J.J.B.L. AIDA	D36
ARBAN, J.J.B.L. CARNAVAL OF VENICE	D92
ARBAN, J.J.B.L. CARNAVAL OF VENISE	A78
ARBAN, J.J.B.L. CARNIVAL OF VENICE	B53
ARBAN, J.J.B.L.-GOLDMAN. CARNIVAL OF VENICE	C11
ARBAN, J.J.B.L.-PETIT. CARNIVAL OF VENICE	D36
ARBAN, J.J.B.L. CARVAVAL DE VENISE	D64
ARBAN, J.J.B.L. 12 CELEBRATED FANTAISIES & AIR VARIES (P)	C11
ARBAN, J.J.B.L.-GOLDMAN. 12 CELEBRATED FANTASIES & AIR VARIES	C11
ARBAN, J.J.B.L. DON PASQUALE (DONIZETTI)	D41
ARBAN, J.J.B.L. FAVORITE, NO. 2, LA	D41
ARBAN, J.J.B.L. FANTAISIE (VARIATIONS) ON NABUCO	M80
ARBAN, J.J.B.L. FANTASIA & VARIATIONS	B91
ARBAN, J.J.B.L. FANTASIA & VARIATIONS	D92

```
ARBAN, J.J.B.L.   FANTASIE BRILLANTE                              A71
ARBAN, J.J.B.L.   FANTASIE BRILLANTE                              B53
ARBAN, J.J.B.L.   FANTASIE BRILLANTE, SUR PIETRO IL GRANDE        D64
ARBAN, J.J.B.L.-PETIT.   2ND FANTASIE BRILLANTE                   B92
ARBAN, J.J.B.L.   FAVORITE NO. 1, LA                              D41
ARBAN, J.J.B.L.   GALATHEE (MASSE)                                D41
ARBAN, J.J.B.L.   GUILLAUME TELL (ROSSINI)                        D41
ARBAN, J.J.B.L.   HERNANI (VERDI)                                 D41
ARBAN, J.J.B.L.   MESSE DE REQUIEM (VERDI)                        D41
ARBAN, J.J.B.L.   NOCES DE JEANNETTE, LES   (MASSE)               D41
ARBAN, J.J.B.L.-JAKMA.   OBERTO AIR VARIE                         D92
ARBAN, J.J.B.L.-VANASEK.   PERPETUAL MOTION                       D71
ARBAN, J.J.B.L.   PRE AUX CLERCS, LE                              D41
ARBAN, J.J.B.L.   PREMIER GRAND SOLO                              D64
ARBAN, J.J.B.L.   RIGOLETTO (VERDI)                               D41
ARBAN, J.J.B.L.   SOUVENIR DE LA FORET NOIRE                      D64
ARBAN, J.J.B.L.-FRACKENPOHL.   TRUMPETUDE                         F23
ARBAN, J.J.B.L.   VARIATIONS ON ZAIRE                             M80
ARBAN, J.J.B.L.   VARIATIONS SUR LE THEME DE MERCANDANTE          D64
ARBAN, J.J.B.L.   VARIATIONS SUR LE THEME DE MERCANDANTE          D92
ARBAN, J.J.B.L.   VARIATIONS SUR MOLBROUGH                        D64
ARDITI, L.   BACIO, IL                                            B13
ARDITI, L.   BACIO, IL (2 TPT)                                    D92
ARDITI, L.-TYLER.   BACIO, IL                                     F07
ARENSKY, A.-GOLDSTEIN.   CONCERT WALTZ                            D81
ARLEN-SEARS.   BLUES IN THE NIGHT                                 E93
ARMSTRONG, L.   GOLDEN SERIES (ARMSTRONG DIXIELAND CLASSICS)      D96
ARNDT.   NOLA                                                     C25
ARNE, T.A.   DRINK TO ME ONLY                                     D92
ARNELL, R.   TRUMPET ALLEGRO, OP.58/2                             F31
ARNOLD, J.   EVERYBODY'S FAVORITE SERIES: #105 EASY TPT SOLOS     A18
ARNOLD, J.   EVERYBODY'S FAVORITE SERIES: #25 TRUMPET SOLOS       A18
ARNOLD, J.   EVERYBODY'S FAVORITE SERIES: #32 ELEM. TPT SOLOS     A18
ARNOLD, J.   EVERYBODY'S FAVORITE SERIES: #77EASY TPT SOLOS       A18
ARNOLD, J.   EVERYBODY'S FAVORITE SERIES:#42 TPT SOLOS            A18
ARNOLD, J.   MUSIC FOR MILLIONS SERIES: #15 EASY TPT SOLOS        B41
ARNOLD, J.   MUSIC FOR MILLIONS SERIES: #31 MORE EASY SOLOS       B41
ARRIEU, C.   PIECE BREVE                                          D41
ARUTUNIAN, A.   SONATINE, ARIA, TOCCATA                           B17
ASCHER, J.   ALICE, WHERE ARE YOU?                                D92
ASH GROVE, THE.                                                   D92
AUBAIN, J.E.   MARCHE ET SCHERZO                                  D36
AUBER, D.F.E.-HEKKER.   ANGELA ARIA FR. LE DOMINO NOIR            F81
AUBER, D.F.E.   PHILTRE, LE                                       A78
AUBERT.   GIGUE                                                   B85
AVIGNON.   GRAVE ET GIGUE                                         A71
BACH, J.S.-SINGERLING.   ADAGIO ET BADINERIE                      D92
BACH, J.S.-THILDE.   ARIA (G STRING) (P)                          A71
BACH, J.S.-KENT.   ARIOSO                                         C11
BACH, J.S.-VACHEY.   AUPRES DE TOI                                B66
BACH, J.S.-GOUNOD.   AVE MARIA                                    B13
BACH, J.S.-GOUNOD.   AVE MARIA                                    D92
BACH, J.S.-O'NEILL.   AVE MARIA                                   G13
BACH, J.S.-FITZGERALD.   BIST DU BEI MIR                          B32
BACH, J.S.-THILDE.   3 BOUREES (P)                                A71
BACH, J.S.-VACHEY.   CANTATE DE LA PENTECOTE NO.68               B66
BACH, J.S.-SMITH.   CHORALE MELODY # 19 (P)                       A62
BACH, J.S.-CLUWEN.   JESU, JOY OF MAN'S DESIRING                  D64
BACH, J.S.-O'NEILL.   MY HEART EVER TRUSTING                      G13
BACH, J.S.-PALANGE.   PRAELUDIUM (P)                              C25
BACH, J.S.-DEHERVE.   10 PRALUDIEN                                F30
BACH, J.S.-THILDE.   RONDEAU ET BADINERIE (P)                     A71
```

```
BACH, J.S.   SINGERLING<AIR                                       D92
BACH, J.S.   SPRING'S AWAKENING                                   B53
BACH, J.S.-THILDE.  SUITE IN B MINOR (P)                          A71
BACH, J.S.   THOU WHO SITS TO THE FATHER'S RIGHT                  B31
BACH, J.S.-DAVIDSON.  THOU WHO SITS TO THE FATHER'S RIGHT         B31
BACQUEVILLE.  PREMIERES MELODIES                                  C49
BADINGS, H.  CHACONNE FOR B-FLAT TPT & ELECTRONIC SOUND           B74
BAEYENS, A.L.  CANZONETTA                                         D80
BAINES, F.A.  PASTORALE                                           F31
BAKALEINIKOFF, V.R.  LEGEND                                       A62
BAKALEINIKOFF, V.R.  POLONAISE                                    A62
BAKALEINIKOFF, V.R.  SERENADE                                     A62
BALAY, G.-MAGER.  ANDANTE & ALLEGRETTO                            F60
BALAY, G.-NAGEL.  ANDANTE & ALLEGRETTO                            C91
BALAY, G.   ANDANTE ET ALLEGRO                                    D36
BALAY, G.   CONTEST PIECE                                         C91
BALAY, G.-VOISIN.  CONTEST PIECE (P)                              C91
BALAY, G.   PETITE PIECE                                          C38
BALAY, G.   PETITE PIECE CONCERTANTE                              D36
BALAY, G.   PETITE PIECE CONCERTANTE                              F60
BALAY, G.   PIECE DE CONCOURS                                     E11
BALAY, G.   PRELUDE ET BALLADE                                    A62
BALAY, G.   PRELUDE ET BALLADE                                    D36
BALFE, M.W.  KILLARNEY                                            D92
BALL, E.-GOSSETTE.  WHEN IRISH EYES ARE SMILING                  G31
BAR, E.  AIR VARIE                                                C38
BARAT, J.E.  ANDANTE ET SCHERZO                                   D36
BARAT, J.E.  FANTAISIE EN MI BEMOL                                D36
BARAT, J.E.  LENTO ET SCHERZO                                     D36
BARAT, J.E.  ORIENTALE                                            D36
BARATTO.  INTRADA GIOCOSA                                         N40
BARATTO.  O! SOLIS SPLENDOR (P)                                   N40
BARATTO.  POCULUM REGIS (E-FLAT TPT)                              N40
BARATTO.  STELLA MARIS (PIC TPT IN B-FLAT)                        N40
BARBE.  FANTASIE ORIGINALE, LE                                    D92
BARBIER, R.  PIECE SYMPHONIQUES, OP.18 (OP)                       B12
BARILLER, R.  CITOYEN MARDI-GRAS                                  D36
BARNARD, A.  PLAINS OF PEACE (1 OR 2 TPT)                         A82
BARNARD, G.D.  MOANA WALTZ                                        A55
BARNARD, G.D.  PUNCH & JUDY                                       A55
BARNES, C.P.  YOUNG ARTIST, THE                                  A78
BARNES, C.P.  YOUNG GENIUS, THE                                  A78
BARNES, C.P.  YOUNG MAESTRO, THE                                 A78
BARNES, C.P.  YOUNG VIRTUOSO                                     A78
BARNES, W.E.  MEADOW LARK POLKA                                  D52
BARNHOUSE, C.L.  ADESTE FIDELIS (2 TPT)                          A55
BARNHOUSE, C.L.  GOD BE WITH YOU                                 A55
BARNHOUSE, C.L.  I LOVE TO TELL THE STORY                       A55
BARNHOUSE, C.L.  LET THE LOWER LIGHTS BE BURNING               A55
BARNHOUSE, C.L.  MEDITATION REGIGIOSOS                           A55
BARNHOUSE, C.L.  ON THE MOUNTAIN TOP                             A55
BARNHOUSE, C.L.  REFUGE                                          A55
BARNHOUSE, C.L.  ROCK OF AGES                                    A55
BARNHOUSE, C.L.  SWEET BY AND BY                                 A55
BARNHOUSE, C.L.  TRAMP, TRAMP, TRAMP                             A55
BARON, M.  GRANDE VALSE VIENNOISE (P)                            A56
BARRAINE, E.  LAMENTO                                            C49
BARRAUD, H.  SYMPHONIE CONCERTANTE                               A56
BARSHAM.  SHORE'S TRUMPET                                        A78
BARSHAM.  10 TRUMPET TUNES                                       E51
BARTLETT, H.H.-HUMMEL.  DREAM, A                                 F07
BARTOK, B.-HARRIS.  EVENING IN THE COUNTRY                       D52
```

BAUDRIER. ANDANTE ET ALLEGRO COMMODO (P)	A71
BAUDRIER. SUITE	D36
BAUMGARTNER-BLAAUW. NACH SIND DIE TAGE DER ROSEN	D64
BAUMGARTNER. NOCH SIND DIE TAGE DER ROSEN	D92
BAZIN. MAITRE PATHELIN	D92
BEAUCAMP, A.M. ARLEQUINADE	D36
BECHER, H. CAPRICCIO	C54
BEDOUIN, P. FANTAISIE	D36
BEELER, W.R. CHRISTMAS FAVORITES	F23
BEELER, W.R. 29 CORNET SOLOS	F23
BEELER, W.R. SOLOS FOR THE TPT PLAYER	F23
BEETHOVEN, L.V. ADELAIDE	B53
BEETHOVEN, L.V. MINUET IN G (2 TPT)	B13
BEETHOVEN, L.V.-OSTRANDER. RONDO FR. SONATA IN F FOR HN & PA	B85
BEEZ. 4 OPTIMISMEN (P)	C75
BELLAMAH. CARREZONDO	F60
BELLINI, V. CASTA DIVA	B53
BELLSTEDT, H.-SIMON. AMERICAN BOY	F60
BELLSTEDT, H.-SIMON. CARMEN FANTASIE	F60
BELLSTEDT, H.-SIMON. CARNIVAL OF VENICE	F60
BELLSTEDT, H.-SIMON. COQUETTE, LA	F60
BELLSTEDT, H.-SIMON. ECHOES OF WILLOW GROVE	F60
BELLSTEDT, H.-SIMON. FANTASIA NO.1	F60
BELLSTEDT, H.-SIMON. INTRODUCTION & TARANTELLE	F60
BELLSTEDT, H.-SCHAEFFER. LITTLE PEACH POLKA, A	C09
BELLSTEDT, H.-SCHAEFFER. LITTLE PEACH POLKA, A	C11
BELLSTEDT, H.-SIMON. MANDOLINATA, LA	F60
BELLSTEDT, H.-SIMON. NAPOLI	F60
BELLSTEDT, H.-SIMON. PIECE DE CONCERTE (CHOPIN MELODY)	F60
BELLSTEDT, H.-SIMON. PRINCESS ALICE	F60
BELLSTEDT, H. SIMON<CAPRICCIO BRILLANTE	F60
BELLSTEDT, H.-SIMON. SKYROCKET	F60
BELLSTEDT, H.-SIMON. STUDENT'S SWEETHEART	F60
BELMANS, R. CONCERTSTUK	D67
BENNETT, D. MATADOR, EL	C11
BENNETT, D. TRUMPET ROYALE (BP)	D71
BENSON, W.F. PROLOGUE	E67
BENT, R. SWISS BOY	B53
BERGHMANS, J. CHENILLE, LA	D36
BERGSON, M. LUISA DI MONTFORT	B53
BERIOT, C.D. SCENE DE BALLET, OP.100	F60
BERLIOZ, H. AIR GAI	A71
BERLIOZ, H. PRELUDE ET RONDE	A71
BERLIOZ, H. 3 SONGS	B85
BERLIOZ, H.-OSTRANDER. UNKNOWN ISLE, THE	B85
BERNAUD, A. PAVANE ET SALTARELLE	E98
BERNSTEIN, L. RONDO FOR LIFEY	F23
BESANCON. SPOT (P)	A71
BESANCON, G. PETIT PAPA	C38
BIGOT, E.V. ELEGIE ET BOURREE	D36
BIGOT, P. COMPTINE (P)	A71
BISSELL, K. LITTLE SUITE	A93
BITSCH, M. CAPRICCIO	D36
BITSCH, M. FANTASIETTA	D36
BITSCH, M. 4 VARIATIONS SUR UN THEME DE D.SCARLATTI	D36
BIZET, G. AGNUS DEI	B85
BIZET, G. AGNUS DEI	D92
BIZET, G.-ARBAN. CARMEN	B24
BIZET, G.-LIGNER. CARMEN	B24
BIZET, G.-MENDEZ. CARMEN	D22
BIZET, G.-MENDEZ. DANSE BOHEME (CARMEN)	C11
BIZET, G.-LIGNER. FIRST FANTASIE	B24

```
BIZET, G.-HERMAN.  FIRST MENUET (L'ARLESIENNE)                      B24
BIZET, G.-O'NEILL.  GIVE ME NEWS OF MY MOTHER (CARMEN)             G13
BIZET, G.  HABANERA FROM CARMEN                                     B13
BIZET, G.-MARENGO.  HABANERA FROM CARMEN                            B24
BIZET, G.-MENDEZ.  HABANERA FROM CARMEN                             C11
BIZET, G.-O'NEILL.  INTERMEZO (L'ARLESSIENNE SUITE #2)             G13
BIZET, G.-LIGNER.  L'ARLESIENNE                                     B24
BIZET, G.-LIGNER.  SECOND FANTASIE                                  B24
BIZET, G.-HERMAN.  SECOND MENUET (L'ARLESIENNE)                     B24
BJELINSKI.  SERENADE (2 PIANOS)                                     F97
BLAAUW, L.  CANTILENE                                               F81
BLAAUW, L.  INTRODUCTIE EN VARIATIES                                D92
BLAAUW, L.  2 KARAKTERSTUKKEN                                       F81
BLACK EYES.                                                         A91
BLAKE-HARING.  MEMORIES OF YOU                                      F42
BLANCHETEAU.  DINARD                                                D64
BLATNY, J.  INTRODUCTION & HERO'S SONG, OP.21                       A33
BLAZHEVICH, V.M.-SHUMAN.  ETUDE NO.86                               F62
BLAZHEVICH, V.M.-SHUMAN.  ETUDE NO.92                               F62
BLEGER, M.  SOUVENIR DE VALENCE                                     D92
BLEMANT, L.  ANDANTE ET RONDO                                       D64
BLOCH, E.  PROCLAMATION (OP)                                        A98
BLOKKER, D.  CAPRICIO                                               F81
BLUM, R.  CAPRICCIO                                                 C61
BOHM, K.-VOXMAN.  CALM AS THE NIGHT                                 F07
BOHME, O.  AIR VARIE SUR UN AIR SUISSE                              A71
BOHME, O.  AIR VARIE SUR UN AIR TYROLIEN                            A71
BOHME, O.  LIEBESLIED                                               B53
BOHME, O.  NAPOLITAINE, LA, OP. 25                                  B53
BOHME, O.  RUSSIAN DANCE                                            F52
BOHME, O.  SERENADE, OP.22/1                                        B53
BOLOTIN, S.V.  12 EASY PIECES                                       D81
BOLOTIN, S.V.  FANTAZIIA TEMU IZ BALETA TARAS BUL'BA               E14
BOLOTIN, S.V.  14 PIECES BY RUSSIAN & WESTERN COMPOSERS            D81
BOLOTIN, S.V.  SCHERZO                                              D81
BOLOTIN, S.V.  VARIATIONS ON A RUSSIAN THEME                        D81
BOLOTIN, S.V. (CMPL).  YOUNG TRUMPET VIRTUOSO, THE                 E19
BOND, C.J.  PERFECT DAY                                             A81
BONNEAU, P.  FANTAISIE CONCERTANTE                                  D36
BONNEAU, P.  SUITE                                                  D36
BOOS, L.F.  CHARMER, THE                                            D18
BOOSEY'S SOLO ALBUM NO. 3.                                          A78
BORDES, C.  DIVERTISSEMENT POUR TPT                                 F05
BORDOGNI, G.M.-CLARK.  20 SOLO STUDIES (P)                          F60
BORODIN, A.P.-MENDEZ.  DANSE POLOVETSIENNE                          C11
BORSCHEL, E.-BORMANN.  KUBANISCHES LIEBESLIED (OP)                 C30
BORSCHEL, E.  SEET TRUMPET                                          C30
BOTTI, C.  ALLEGRO DA CONCERTO                                      B07
BOTTI, C.  ROMANZA                                                  B07
BOTTI, C.  SCHERZO                                                  B07
BOURGUIGNON, F.D.  MORCEAU DE CONCOURS, OP.85                       C42
BOURGUIGNON, F.D.  RECITATIF ET RONDE, OP.94 (BOP)                 D80
BOURNONVILLE, A.  PENDANT LA FETE                                   A71
BOUSQUET, N.  GAULE ET FRANCE                                       C38
BOUSQUET, N.  MARLBOROUGH (TPT IN A)                                C38
BOUTRY, R.  TROMPETUNIA                                             D36
BOUTRY, R.  TRUMPELDOR                                              D36
BOWER, M.  MELODIE MONTMARTE                                        F42
BOWMAN-HARING.  12TH STREET RAG                                     F42
BOZZA, E.  BADINAGE                                                 D36
BOZZA, E.  CAPRICE, OP.47                                           D36
BOZZA, E.  CORNETTINA                                               D36
```

```
BOZZA, E.  DIALOGUE                                  D36
BOZZA, E.  FRIGARIANA                                B92
BOZZA, E.  RHAPSODIE                                 D36
BOZZA, E.  RUSTIQUES                                 D36
BRAAL, A. DE.  CAPRICCIO                             B74
BRAGA, F.  ANGEL'S SERENADE                          B53
BRAHAM-STERLING.  LIMEHOUSE BLUES                    C58
BRAHE, M.H.-GLENN.  BLESS THIS HOUSE                 A78
BRAHMS, J.-SAWYER.  ANDANTE                          M80
BRAHMS, J.-KOFF.  BRAHMS CZARDAS (BP)               D22
BRAHMS, J.  CHANT POPULAIRE                          D92
BRAHMS, J.-BAUDRIER.  CHANT POPULAIRE               D64
BRAHMS, J.-MENDEZ.  HUNGARIAN DANCE NO.5            C11
BRAHMS, J.  LULLABY                                  B53
BRAHMS, J.-MORTIMER.  LULLABY                        A78
BRANDT, V.-VOISIN.  CONCERTPIECE #1, OP. 11         C91
BRANDT, V.-NAGEL.  CONCERTPIECE #2, OP. 12          C91
BRANDT, V.  FIRST CONCERT PIECE                      B53
BRATTON, J.W.-SEARS.  TEDDY BEARS' PICNIC           G31
BRENET, T.  INTER-SILENTIA                           D36
BRENET, T.  6 PIECES                                 B24
BRETON.  SOLO DE TROMPETA                            F95
BRETON Y HERNANDEZ, T.  SOLO DE TRCMPETA            F95
BRIEGEL, G.F.  CATHEDRAL ECHOES                      A91
BRIEGEL, G.F.  LITTLE SHEPHERD                       A91
BRIEGEL, G.F.  SOLOETTE                              A91
BROCKMAN.  LITTLE COLONEL                            C11
BROILES, M.  VERNAL EQUINOX                          B55
BROOKS, E.  MESSAGE, THE                             D18
BROWN, C.L.G.  ENTREE, AIR ET FINAL                 C01
BROWN, C.L.G.  PETITE MARCHE                         B66
BROWN, C.L.G.  PREMIER APPEL                         E66
BRUCKNER, A.  AVE MARIA                              B85
BRUN, F.J.  PROMENADE                                D36
BUCHHOLZ, H.  LAST FAREWELL, THE                     D84
BUCHTEL, F.L.  AT THE BALL                           D18
BUCHTEL, F.L.  BEAU BRUMMEL                          D18
BUCHTEL, F.L.  BOLERO                                D18
BUCHTEL, F.L.  CHANT D'AMOUR                         G10
BUCHTEL, F.L.  CHROMATICA WALTZ                      D18
BUCHTEL, F.L.  CIELITO LINTO                         D18
BUCHTEL, F.L.  DREAMER, THE                          D18
BUCHTEL, F.L.  DRUM MAJOR MARCH                      D18
BUCHTEL, F.L.  FANDANGO                              D18
BUCHTEL, F.L.  FLATTER, THE                          D84
BUCHTEL, F.L.  FORTUNE HUNTER                        D18
BUCHTEL, F.L.  GLADIATORS                            D18
BUCHTEL, F.L.  GOLDEN DREAMS                         D18
BUCHTEL, F.L.  GOLDEN GLOW WALTZ                     D84
BUCHTEL, F.L.  HARLEQUIN                             D18
BUCHTEL, F.L.  HIGH STEPPERS MARCH                   D84
BUCHTEL, F.L.  HOLY CITY                             D18
BUCHTEL, F.L.  IMPROMPTU                             D84
BUCHTEL, F.L.  INTERMEZZO                            D18
BUCHTEL, F.L.  INTRODUCTION & RONDO                  A55
BUCHTEL, F.L.  JEAN WALTZ                            D84
BUCHTEL, F.L.  JOVIAL MOOD                           D18
BUCHTEL, F.L.  LUCKY DAY                             D18
BUCHTEL, F.L.(ARR).  MARINES HYMN                    D18
BUCHTEL, F.L.  MEDITATION                            D18
BUCHTEL, F.L.  MORNING STAR                          D18
BUCHTEL, F.L.  MY BUDDY WALTZ                        D18
```

```
BUCHTEL, F.L.   NIN MIA                                              F07
BUCHTEL, F.L.   PIED PIPER                                           D18
BUCHTEL, F.L.   SPANISH GYPSY                                        D18
BUCHTEL, F.L.   VALSE ROMANTIQUE                                     G10
BUCHTEL, F.L.   WALTZ MEDLEY                                         D18
BUESSER.   12 ETUDES MELODIQUES                                      D36
BULLARD.   SOLILOQUY                                                 D14
BURGON.   TOCCATA                                                    F65
BURKE, J.F.   AMOURETTE                                              C11
BURKE, J.F.   DANZA ALEGRE (BP)                                      C11
BURKE, J.F.-SMITH.   HOCUS POLKA                                     D74
BURKE, J.F.-HUBBELL.   JOLENE                                        B31
BURKE, J.F.-HUBBEL.   JONETA                                         B31
BURKE, J.F.   MAGIC TRUMPET, THE                                     C11
BURKE, J.F.   PROM WALTZ                                             D74
BURKE, J.F.   RUNAWAY TPT, THE                                       D74
BURKE, J.F.   SERENADE IN 6/8                                        D74
BURKE, J.F.   SOUVENIRS                                              B31
BURKE, J.F.   STRICTLY G.I.                                          D74
BURKE, J.F.-SMITH.   TWILIGHT TUNE                                   D74
BURKE, J.F.-HUBBLE.   VOLUNTEER, THE                                 B31
BURKHARD-HARING.   OH MY PA-PA                                       F42
BUSCH, C.   CONCERT CAPRICE                                          E93
BUSSER, H.P.   ADESTE FIDELES                                        D36
BUSSER, H.P.   ANDANTE & SCHERZO, OP.44                              C04
BUSSER, H.P.-VOISIN.   ANDANTE & SCHERZO, OP.44                      C91
BUSSER, H.P.   APRES LA RETRAITE, OP.61                              C38
BUSSER, H.P.   APRES LA RETRAITE, OP.61                              F16
BUSSER, H.P.-VOISIN.   CONCERTPIECE                                  C91
BUSSER, H.P.   FANTAISIE SUR DES THEMES ECOSSAIS, OP.70              D36
BUSSER, H.P.   VARIATIONS IN D-FLAT, OP.53                           B53
BUSSER, H.P.   VARIATIONS, OP.53                                     D36
BUZZI¬PECCIA, A.-ANDREONI.   LOLITA                                  E98
CABUS, P.N.   LENTO E TEMPO DI MARCIA                                D67
CABUS, P.N.   RONDO OSTINATO                                         D67
CALS.   IMPROVISATION                                               D41
CAMPORI, A.F.   INTRODUCTION & ALLEGRO                               G38
CANIVEZ, L.   AIR VARIE                                             D64
CARDILLO-ANDREONI.   CORE'NGRATO                                     E98
CARISSIMI, G.G.-BARNES.   HEART VICTORIOUS                           F62
CARSTE.   TRUMPET SERENADE                                           D84
CASEY.   HONEYSUCKLE POLKA                                           D18
CASEY.   REMEMBERANCE OF LIBERATI                                    D18
CASTELLUCCI, L.S.   CORNET CAPERS                                    D84
CASTEREDE, J.   BREVES RENCONTRES                                    D36
CATELINET, P.B.   TRUMPET TUNE                                       C71
CATELINET, P.B.   TWINKLE, TWINKLE, LITTLE STAR (VARIATIONS)         C71
CATIZONE, J.   ALVERDO                                               G10
CATIZONE, J.   ANDANTE CON MOTO                                      G10
CATIZONE, J.   AU FAIT                                               G10
CATIZONE, J.   FOREST PINE                                           D37
CATIZONE, J.   ROD & REEL MARCH                                      D37
CATIZONE, J.   TUNE FOR PEPI                                         D37
CATIZONE, J.   VALSE JOYANCE                                         G10
CATIZONE, J.   VALSE SARDO                                           D37
CATIZONE, J.   WALTZING CADET                                        D84
CATIZONE, J.   WOW WOW POLKA                                         D37
CELLIER, A.   CHEVAUCHEE FANTASTIQUE                                 A71
CHAILLEUX, A.-VAILLANT.   MORCEAU DE CONCOURS                        D36
CHALLAN, H.   VARIATIONS                                             D36
CHAMBEARDJI, N.   PIONEERING                                         C11
CHAMBERS.   COMMODORE, THE                                           D18
```

```
CHANCE, J.B.   CREDO                                               A78
CHANDLER, WHITE & COHEN-STERLING.   CANADIAN CAPERS                E93
CHAPELLE, E.   UNE SERENADE                                        B53
CHAPLAEVSKY, P.-SATZ.   VALSE CAPRICE                              D37
CHAPUIS, A.   SOLO DE TPT EN FA                                    C04
CHAPUIS, A.   SOLO DE TPT EN FA                                    D36
CHARDON-SABARICH.   TROMPETTE ESPAGNOL, LA                         B24
CHARLIER, T.   SOLO DE CONCOURS                                    F30
CHARLIER, T.   2ME SOLO DE CONCOURS                                D41
CHATSCHATURIAN, A.-SCHOEBEL.   SABELTANZ AUS "GAYANEH"             F50
CHAVINEZ.   AIR VARIE                                              D92
CHEMBERDZHI, N.   PIONEER SUITE                                    D81
CHENETTE, M.E.   BETTY-JO POLKA                                    A62
CHENETTE, M.E.   GOLDEN TRUMPET                                    A62
CHENETTE, M.E.   HALAGUENO                                         A62
CHENETTE, M.E.   PALO DURO WALTZES                                 A62
CHENETTE, M.E.   STARLIGHT WALTZ                                   A62
CHERUBINI, L.   AVE MARIA                                          B85
CHOPIN, F.-EDWARDS.   CHOPIN'S POLONAISE                           D84
CHOPIN, F.-LIBERATI.   MAZURKA, OP.7/1                             D52
CHOPIN, F.-VACHEY.   POLONAISE EN LA                               B66
CHOPIN, F.-ANDREONI.   TRISTESSE, OP.10/3                          E98
CHOPIN, F.-MARTIN.   TRISTESSE                                     D64
CHOPIN, F.-VACHEY.   TRISTESSE                                     B66
CHRISTOL.   11E AIR VARIE                                          D92
CHRISTOL.   COEUR DE MA VIE, LE                                    D92
CIMERA, J.   CARNIVAL PETITE                                       A62
CIRRI, G.B.-FORST.   ARIOSO                                        B85
CLARIBEL-DE ROOY.   COME BACK TO ERWIN                             F81
CLARKE, H.L.   APOLLO POLKA                                        C09
CLARKE, H.L.   AUTUMN DAY, AN                                      C11
CLARKE, H.L.   BIRTH OF DAWN                                       C11
CLARKE, H.L.   BRIDE OF THE WAVES                                  C11
CLARKE, H.L.   BRIDE OF THE WAVES                                  G31
CLARKE, H.L.   CARNIVAL OF VENICE (BP)                             G31
CLARKE, H.L.   COLLECTION OF 10 SOLOS                              C11
CLARKE, H.L.   DEBUTANTE, THE                                      G31
CLARKE, H.L.   DU DU LIEGST MIR IM HERZEN                          G31
CLARKE, H.L.   FLIRTATIONS (BP)                                    C09
CLARKE, H.L.   FROM THE SHORES OF THE MIGHTY PACIFIC               G31
CLARKE, H.L.   HEBE LULLABY                                        C09
CLARKE, H.L.   KING NEPTUNE                                        B31
CLARKE, H.L.   LILLIAN                                             G31
CLARKE, H.L.   MAID OF THE MIST                                    G31
CLARKE, H.L.   MY LOVE TO YOU                                      G31
CLARKE, H.L.   NEPTUNE'S COURT                                     G31
CLARKE, H.L.   POLLY                                               C11
CLARKE, H.L.   SHOWERS OF GOLD                                     G31
CLARKE, H.L.   SIDE PARTNERS                                       G31
CLARKE, H.L.   SOUNDS FROM THE HUDSON                              C11
CLARKE, H.L.   SOUNDS FROM THE HUDSON                              G31
CLARKE, H.L.   SOUTHERN CROSS, THE                                 G31
CLARKE, H.L.   STARS IN A VELVETY SKY                             C11
CLARKE, H.L.   TWILIGHT DREAMS                                     G31
CLARKE, H.L.   VENUS WALTZ                                         C09
CLARKE, H.L.   VETA, LA                                            C11
CLARKE, H.L.   YOUTH DAUNTLESS, OP.240                             A62
CLARKE, J.   SUITE (OP)                                            E14
CLARKE, J.   TRUMPET VOLUNTARY (SEE ALSO H. PURCELL)
CLARKE, J.-CLUWEN.   TRUMPET VOLUNTARY                             D64
CLARKE, J.-LILLYA.   TRUMPET VOLUNTARY                             C11
CLARKE, J.-VOISIN.   TRUMPET VOLUNTARY                             C91
```

CLASSENS. CHANT DE JOIE	E66
CLASSENS. MARCHE BURLESQUE	E66
CLEMENT, F.W. EVENING ZEPHYR	A55
CLERGUE, J. SARABANDE ET RIGAUDON	D41
CLERISSE, R. ANDANTE ET ALLEGRO	A71
CLERISSE, R. CROISIERE, EN	E66
CLERISSE, R. INTRODUCTION ET DIVERTISSEMENT	A71
CLERISSE, R. NOCE VILLAGEOISE	B02
CLERISSE, R. NOCE VILLAGEOISE	D36
CLERISSE, R. RETOUR DU CENTURION	E66
CLERISSE, R. THEME VARIE	D36
CLERISSE, R. VACANCES JOYEUSES	E66
CLIMENT, C.W. MARCHING THRO' GEORGIA	B53
CLUWEN, P.(ARR). GO DOWN MOZES	D64
CLUWEN, P.(ARR). IT'S ME O LORD	F81
CLUWEN, P.(ARR). NOBODY KNOWS THE TROUBLE I'VE SEEN	D64
CLUWEN, P.(ARR). SWING LOW SWEET CHARIOT	D64
CLUWEN, P.(ARR). WERE YOU THERE?	D64
CODE, P. 'NEATH AUSTRAL SKIES	A11
CODE, P. AT DAWN	A11
CODE, P. AT SUNSET	A11
CODE, P. LUCILLE	A78
CODE, P. MIRANDA	A11
CODE, P. PRELUDE DE CONCERT	A11
CODE, P. VALSE CAPRICE	A11
CODE, P. WENDOUREE	A11
CODE, P. ZELDA	A11
CODE, P. ZELDA	A78
COHEN, S.E. GYPSY ROMANCE	F62
COLE, H. HAMMERSMITH GALOP, THE	F31
COMBELLE. SOLO DE CONCOURS NO.1	A71
CONCONE, G.-HAZELGROVE. 35 GRADED STUDIES & PIECES	E59
CONCONE, G. 4 SKETCHES	B53
CONRAD, C.E.-SCHOENFELD. CONTINENTAL, THE	C58
CONSTANT, F. ALLEGRO	D67
CONSTANT, F. MINUTE	D36
CONSTANT, M. 3 MOUVEMENTS	D36
CONTE, B. ALPEN POLKA	D80
CONTEMPORARY FRENCH RECITAL PIECES.	C91
CONTEST ALBUM.	B53
COOK, K. IMPROMPTU	C71
COOLIDGE, R. WEEPING DANCER	D14
COOLS, E. SOLO DE CONCOURS	D36
COOTS, J.F. YOU GO TO MY HEAD	E93
COPLAND, A. QUIET CITY	A78
CORDS, G. CONCERT FANTASIE	B53
CORDS, G. ROMANZE	B53
CORELLI, A. AIR & DANCE	B85
CORELLI, A. GIGUE	B85
CORELLI, A.-VACHEY. GRAVE	B66
CORELLI, A.-POWELL. PRELUDE & MENUET	F60
CORELLI, A. SUITE IN B-FLAT MAJOR	B85
CORELLI, A.-FITZGERALD. VIOLIN SONATA NO.8	B32
CORIOLIS, E. DE. FETE A SAONT CASSIEN, LA	D36
COUNTRY GARDENS.	B13
COUNTRY GARDENS. (2 TPT)	B13
COUPERIN, F. AIR DE DIABLE	B85
COUROUPOS. HIPPOS	N50
COWARD-STERLING. ZIGEUNER	C58
COWELL, H.D. TRIAD	E61
COWLES, E. FORGOTTEN	B72
CUSTER, A.R. RONDO	D33

```
DENMARK, M.F.  SCENE DE CONCERT                                    D52
DENZA, L.-ANDREONI.  FUNICULI-FUNICULA                            E98
DENZA, L.  FUNICULI, FUNICULA                                     B13
DEPELSENAIRE.  CONSEILS DE BACCHUS, LES                           D41
DEPELSENAIRE.  DINANDERIES                                        F87
DEPELSENAIRE.  HORIZONS                                           B24
DEPELSENAIRE.  MORMAL                                             F87
DEPELSENAIRE.  POUR LA SAINT-JEAN D'ETE                           B24
DEPELSENAIRE.  RONDO FANTASQUE                                    B24
DEPELSENAIRE.  VIVE LA CLIQUE                                     B24
DEPELSENAIRE, J.M.  DANSE WALLONNE                                F87
DEPELSENAIRE, J.M.  FUNAMBULES                                    F87
DEPELSENAIRE, J.M.  INTRODUCTION ET CORTEGE                       F30
DEPELSENAIRE, J.M.  RECITATIF ET AIR                              B66
DEPREZ, J.  ALLEGRETTO                                            D67
DEPREZ, J.  PREMIERE PIECE                                        D67
DESENCLOS, A.  INCANTATION, THRENE ET DANSE (OP)                  D36
DESPORTES, Y.  INTRODUCTION ET ALLEGRO                            D36
DESPREZ, F.  FANTAISIE CONCERTANTE                                D67
DESPREZ, F.  PETITE PIECE                                         D67
DESPREZ, F.  THEME ET VARIATIONS SUR "LA FOLIA"                   D67
DEVREESE, G.  ALLEGRO (OP)                                        B12
DEVREESE, G.  RECITATIF & ALLEGRO (OP)                            D80
DHOSSCHE, R.A.  INVOCATION                                        F60
DINDALE, E.  PEASANT DANCE                                        A96
DINICU, G.-HEIFETZ.  HORA STACCATO                                C11
DOKSHITZER, T. (CMPL).  SONGS FOR TRUMPET AND PIANO               E19
DONALDSON, W.-GOSSETTE.  MY BUDDY                                 E93
DONATO, A.  PRELUDE ET ALLEGRO                                    D36
DONAUDY, S.-FITZGERALD.  ARIA & ALLEGRO                           B32
DONAUDY, S.-FITZGERALD.  2 ARIAS                                  B32
DONAUDY, S.-FITZGERALD.  ARIOSO & CANZONE                         B32
DONIZETTI, G.-O'NEILL.  HERE AVENGING SHADES                      G13
DONIZETTI, G.  SOMNAMBULE, LA                                     D64
DONIZETTI, G.-RIMMER.  STILL SO GENTLY                            D92
DONIZETTI, G.  VARIATIONS ON CAVATINE D'ANNA BOLENA               N66
DOPPLER, A.  SOUVENIR DU RIGI                                     B53
DORSSELAER, W.VAN.  CHATEAU DE CHANTILLY, AUU                     A71
DOUANE, J.  DIPTYQUE                                              D36
DOUANE, J.  DIVERTISSEMENT                                        E66
DOULIEZ, V.  PIECE CONCERTANTE, OP.52                             A96
DRIGO, R.-DAMM.  SERENADE                                         B53
DRIGO, R.-SARTORIUS.  SERENADE                                    B13
DRIGO, R.-MENDEZ.  VALSE BLUETTE                                  C11
DUBOIS, F.C.T.  FANTAISIE                                         C65
DUBOIS, P.M.  BOUTADE                                             N50
DUBOIS, P.M.  CHORAL                                              D36
DUBOIS, P.M.  PETIT PISTON DEVIENDRA GRAND                        D36
DUBOIS, P.M.  PISTONNADE                                          N50
DUBOIS, P.M.  3 VALSES DE CONCERT                                 C01
DUBUIS.  CLE DES CHAMPS, LA                                       A71
DUBUIS.  6 PIECES (2 VOL)                                         A71
DUCK, L.  TONE SKETCHES                                           C71
DUHEM, H.-GOEYENS.  SOUVENIR D'ANGLETERRE                         F81
DUIJCK.  DIALOG                                                   D67
DUIJCK.  PETITE PIECE                                             D67
DUMORTIER, G.  3 MUSIC POUR TPT ET PA.                            D67
DUQUESNE, A.  ELEGIE                                              A96
DVORAK, A.  HUMORESKE                                             B13
DVORAK, A.-GOLDMAN.  HUMORESKE, OP.101/7                          C11
DVORAK, A.  LARGO FROM "NEW WORLD SYMPHONY"                       B53
DVORAK, A.  SONGS MY MOTHER TAUGHT ME                            A91
```

```
FIRST DIV BAND COURSE.   GOLDEN GLOW                              A62
FIRST DIV BAND COURSE.   HAPPY GO LUCKY                           A62
FIRST DIV BAND COURSE.   NEOPHYTE                                 A62
FIRST DIV BAND COURSE.   PASO DOBLE NUEVO                         A62
FIRST DIV BAND COURSE.   PICNIC TIME                              A62
FIRST DIV BAND COURSE.   TALL MEN                                 A62
FIRST DIV BAND COURSE.   VALIANT                                  A62
FIRST DIV BAND COURSE.   VENTURE                                  A62
FIRST SOLO ALBUM.                                                 E77
FISCHER, C.A.  NELLIE GRAY                                        B53
FISCHER, C.A. (ARR).  MY OLD KENTUCKY HOME                        B53
FITZGERALD, R.B.   ARIA & ALLEGRO                                 E77
FITZGERALD, R.B.   ENGLISH SUITE                                  E77
FITZGERALD, R.B.   INTRODUCTION & FANTASY                         A62
FITZGERALD, R.B.   MODERN SUITE                                   C11
FITZGERALD, R.B.   RONDO CAPRICCIO                                C11
FLETCHER.  LITTLE SUITE                                           N27
FLIARKOVSKY, A.   2 PIECES                                        D81
FLOORE.  9 SIMPLE PIECES                                          F81
FLOTHUIS, M.  ARIA, OP.18                                         B74
FLOTHUIS, M.  KLEINE SUITE, OP.47                                 B74
FLOTOW, F.V.-ARBAN.  MARTHA                                       B24
FLOTOW, F.V.-BLAAUW.  MARTHA                                      D64
FOLLMAN-HULDEZANG.  CHANT D'HOMMAGE                               F21
FORESTIER, J.J.-BLAAUW.  BELLONA                                  D64
FORESTIER, J.J.-LEEUWEN.  SOLO POUR CORNET                        D64
FORET, F.  2 PIECES                                               D36
FOSTER, S.C.  BEAUTIFUL DREAMER                                   D92
FOSTER, S.C.  JEANIE WITH THE LIGHT BROWN HAIR                    D92
FOSTER, S.C.-BRIEGEL.  2 STEPHEN FOSTER MELODIES                  A91
FOVEAU, E. & KARTZEV, A.   2 PIECES                               D81
FOX ALBUM OF CORNET SOLOS (4 VOL).                                C25
FRACKENPOHL, A.R.   SUITE                                         F23
FRACKENPOHL, A.R.   TRUMPETUDE (ARBAN)                            F43
FRANCK, C.   PANIS ANGELICUS                                      A91
FRANCK, C.   PANIS ANGELICUS                                      D92
FRANCO, J.  BOOK OF JOB, THE (G)                                  A13
FRANGKISER, C.   ABOVE THE CLOUDS                                 A62
FRANGKISER, C.   MORNING                                          A62
FRANGKISER, C.   STAR MAGIC                                       A62
FRANGKISER, C.   TWIN STARS                                       A62
FRANK, C.-O'NEILL.  O LORD MOST HOLY                              G13
FREED, I.  GENERAL BURGOYNE'S MINUET                              A62
FRIBOULET, G.  GAMINERIE                                          D36
FRIML, R.  DONKEY SERENADE                                        A81
FRIML, R.-GOSSETTE.  INDIAN LOVE CALL                             C58
FRIML, R.-GOSSETTE.  L'AMOUR-TOUJOURS L'AMOUR                     C58
FRIML, R. & STOTHART, H.-BEELER.  DONKEY SERENADE, THE           F23
FRISON, C.  SUITE DE CONCERT                                      D80
FURMAN, S.H.-EDWARDS.  LAZY SUSAN                                 D84
FUSTE-LAMBEZAT.  SOLO                                             E66
GABAYE, P.  BOUTADE                                               D36
GABAYE, P.  FEU D'ARTIFICE                                        B92
GABRIELI.  MARCH FOR ST. MARKS                                    F64
GALAJIKIAN, F.G.  ALLEGRO MARZIALE                                A62
GALLAY, J.F.  AUX ETOILES                                         D41
GALLAY, J.F.  BATELIERE DU RHIN, LA                               D41
GALLAY, J.F.  3 CAPRICES, OP.60                                   D41
GALLAY, J.F.  COR, LA                                             D41
GALLAY, J.F.  FANTAISIE SUR DES OPERAS                            D41
GALLAY, J.F.  FANTASIE                                            D41
GALLAY, J.F.  HARMONIES DU SOIR                                   D41
```

```
GALLAY, J.F.  NOCTURNE SUR L'ECLAIR                                  D41
GALLAY, J.F.  NOSTALGIE, LA                                          D41
GALLAY, J.F.  REGRETS                                               D41
GALLAY, J.F.  9E SOLO, OP.39                                        D41
GALLAY, J.F.  TE DIRE ADIEU                                         D41
GALLAY, J.F.  ZEPHIR, LE                                            D41
GALLET.  COMPLAINTE ET CORTEGE                                      A71
GALLOIS-MONTBRUN, R.  LIED                                          D36
GALLOIS-MONTBRUN, R.  MARCHE                                        D36
GALLOIS-MONTBRUN, R.  SARABAND ET FINALE                           D36
GALLOIS-MONTBRUN, R.  SCHERZO                                       D36
GANNE, L.G.  CZARINE, LA                                            B95
GARLAND, J.C.-HARING.  IN THE MOOD                                  F42
GARTENLAUB, O.  3 PIECES BREVES                                     C01
GAUBERT, P.  CANTABILE ET SCHERZETTO                                B53
GAUBERT, P.  CANTABILE ET SCHERZETTO                                D36
GAUDERFROY.  FEUILLES LEGERES                                       C49
GAUDRON.  ANDANTE ET ALLEGRO MODERATO                              A71
GAUDRON.  SOUVENIRS D'ASIE                                          A71
GAUTIER-DAVIS.  SECRET, LE                                          F07
GAUTIER-HAZEL.  SECRET, LE                                          C11
GEDALGE, A.-VOISIN.  CONTEST PIECE                                  C91
GEDALGE, A.  PIECE POUR TPT UT OU SI-BEMOL ET PA                   D36
GEEHL, H.E.  CONCERTSTUCK                                           A78
GEEHL, H.E.  FOR YOU ALONE                                          D92
GEORGES, A.  LEGENDE DE LARMOR                                      B95
GERSCHEFSKI, E.  "AMERICA" VARIATIONS, OP. 44, NOS. 9, 11, 12      A13
GERSCHEFSKI, E.  SONG WITHOUT WORDS                                 A13
GERSHWIN, G.-SEARS.  AMERICAN IN PARIS, AN                          E34
GERSHWIN, G.-STONE.  ANDANTE & FINALE FR. RHAPSOLY IN BLUE          E34
GERSHWIN, G.-STERLING.  EMBRACEABLE YOU                             E34
GERSHWIN, G.-STERLING.  I GOT RHYTHM                                E34
GERSHWIN, G.-SEARS.  LIZA                                           E34
GERSHWIN, G.-SEARS.  MAN I LOVE, THE                                E34
GERSHWIN, G.-SEARS.  OH, LADY BE GOOD                               E34
GERSHWIN, G.-STONE.  2ND PRELUDE                                    E34
GEVERS, E.  KLEINE FANTASIE                                         D67
GIASSON.  PORTRAIT OF A CITY                                        N49
GIAZOTTO-ORSOMANDO.  ADAGIO ON 2 THEMES OF ALBINONI                 E98
GIBBONS, O.-CRUFT.  SUITE FOR TPT & STRINGS (OP)                    G26
GIBBONS, O.-CRUFT.  SUITE FOR TRUMPET (OP)                          C33
GIORDANI, T.  CARO MIO BEN                                          D92
GIORDANI, T.-FELIX.  18TH CENTURY AIR, AN                           B85
GIRLAMO-VINCENT.  BALLAD IN BLUE                                    AE2
GLANTZ, H.  SOLOS                                                   B31
GLASENAPP, F. & E.WOLF.  ROSTOCKER SUITE...18. JAHRHUNDERTS         C75
GLIERE, R.M.-MOGILEVESKY.  2 PIECES                                 D81
GLINKA, M.I.  ROMANCE MELODY                                        F62
GLOVER, C.W.  ROSE OF TRALEE                                        D92
GLUCK, C.W.  ACH ICH HAB SIE VERLOREN                              D92
GLUCK, C.W.  2 CLASSIC AIRS                                         B85
GLUCK, C.W.-MEIJNS.  J'AI PERDU MON EURYDICE                        D64
GLUCK, C.W.  LARGO                                                  C19
GO DOWN MOZES.                                                      D92
GODARD, B.-ROBERTS.  BERCEUSE FROM JOCELYN                          C11
GODARD, E.  BERCEUSE OF JOCELYN                                     D92
GOEB, R.  LYRIC PIECE                                               D74
GOEDICKE, A.F.  CONCERT ETUDE , OP.49                               F50
GOEDICKE, A.F.-SATZ.  CONCERT ETUDE, OP.49                          D37
GOEDICKE, A.F.-NAGEL.  CONCERT STUDY, OP.49                         C91
GOEDICKE, A.F.  ETUDE DE CONCERT, OP.49                             B17
GOEYENS, A.  ALL ANTICA                                             F60
```

```
GOEYENS, A.   ANDANTE ET ACHERZANDO                                      A96
GOEYENS, A.   CONTEST PIECE                                              A96
GOEYENS, A.   ENGLISH MELODY                                             A96
GOEYENS, A.   FANTASIA DRAMATIC                                          F81
GOEYENS, A.   FANTASIE DRAMATIQUE                                        A96
GOEYENS, A.   IMPROVISATA                                                D80
GOEYENS, A.   INTRODUCTION ET SCHERZO                                    C11
GOEYENS, A.   INTRODUCTION ET SCHERZO                                    F81
GOEYENS, A.   MORCEAU DE CONCOURS                                        A96
GOEYENS, A.   MORCEAU DE CONCOURS NO.2                                   A96
GOEYENS, A.   SOLO IN ANCIENT STYLE                                      F81
GOEYENS, F.   HYMNE                                                      A96
GOEYENS, F.   SUITE ROMANTIQUE                                           F30
GOLDMAN, E.F.   A PRAYER                                                 C11
GOLDMAN, E.F.   AMONG THE STARS                                          C11
GOLDMAN, E.F.-LEIDZEN.  BUGLER, THE                                      D84
GOLDMAN, E.F.   CONCERT WALTZ                                            E77
GOLDMAN, E.F.   COUNTRY DANCE                                            C11
GOLDMAN, E.F.   ESPANITA TANGO                                           C11
GOLDMAN, E.F.   EVENING SONG                                             C11
GOLDMAN, E.F.   IN THE CLOUDS                                            C11
GOLDMAN, E.F.-LEIDZEN.  INTRODUCTION & TARANTELLA                        D74
GOLDMAN, E.F.   JOYOUS YOUTH                                             C11
GOLDMAN, E.F.   JUPITER                                                  C11
GOLDMAN, E.F.   LOVE THOUGHTS                                            C11
GOLDMAN, E.F.   MARS                                                     C11
GOLDMAN, E.F.   MERCURY POLKA                                            C11
GOLDMAN, E.F.-TOBANI.  MY OLD KENTUCKY HOME                              C11
GOLDMAN, E.F.   RAINBOW                                                  C11
GOLDMAN, E.F.   SANS SOUCI                                               C11
GOLDMAN, E.F.   SCHERZO (BOP)                                            A44
GOLDMAN, E.F.   SUNSET                                                   C11
GOLDMAN, E.F.-TOBANI.  TRAMP, TRAMP,TRAMP                                C11
GOMEZ-MENDEZ.  AIRES ANDALUCES                                           C11
GOSSIAUX, A.   CHORAL ET VARIATIONS                                      D67
GOSSIAUX, A.   PETIT CAPRICE                                             D67
GOTTWALD, H.   FANTASIE HEROIQUE                                         B53
GOUGNON.  PRIERE                                                         C49
GOULD, E.  ANDANTE                                                       B92
GOULD, M.-EDWARDS.  PAVANNE                                              D84
GOUNOD, C.F.   AVE MARIA                                                 E03
GOUNOD, C.F.-BLAAUW.  AVE MARIA                                          D64
GOUNOD, C.F.-VACHEY.  AVE MARIA                                          B66
GOUNOD, C.F.   CAVATINE                                                  D92
GOUNOD, C.F.   DIO POSSENTE                                              B53
GOUNOD, C.F.-O'NEILL.  EVEN BRAVEST HEART MAY SWELL (FAUST)              G13
GOUNOD, C.F.-ARBAN.  FAUST                                               B24
GOUNOD, C.F.-HERMAN & CLODOMIR.  FAUST                                   B24
GOUNOD, C.F.-O'NEILL.  INSPIREZ MOI FROM LA REINE DE SABA                G13
GOUNOD, C.F.-HERMAN & CLODOMIR.  MIREILLE                                B24
GOUNOD, C.F.-HERMAN & CLODOMIR.  RCMEO ET JULIETTE FANTASIE              B24
GOUNOD, C.F.-MORTIMER.  WALTZ SONG FR. "ROMEO & JULIET"                  A78
GOVAERT-BLAAUW.  AIR VARIE                                               D64
GOVAERT-BLAAUW.  AIR VARIE                                               D92
GRAAF, J.DE.  3 LICHTE STUKJES                                           D64
GRAAF, J.DE.  3 LICHTE STUKJES                                           D92
GRANADOS-MENDEZ.  ANDALUZA                                               C11
GREEN-HUFFINE.  BODY & SOUL                                              C58
GREEN, H.  FANFARE & PROCESSIONAL                                        E83
GREEN, H.B.  SOFT-EYED DRAGONS                                           E83
GREENE, M. & BOYCE.  SUITE OF TPT VOLUNTARIES (D TPT)                    M80
GRIEG, E.H.  ALBUM                                                       C71
```

```
GRIEG, E.H.-BLAAUW.  CHANSON DE SOLVEJG                        D 64
GRIEG, E.H.-BLAAUW.  DERNIER PRINTEMPS                         D 64
GRIEG, E.H.  I LOVE THEE, OP.41/3                              E 65
GRIEG, E.H.  ICH LIEBE DICH                                    D 92
GRIEG, E.H.-BLAAUW.  JE T'AIME                                 D 64
GRIEG, E.H.  LETZTER FRUHLING                                  D 92
GRIEG, E.H.  POEME EROTIQUE                                    D 92
GRIEG, E.H.-BLAAUW.  POEME EROTIQUE                            D 64
GRIEG, E.H.  SOLVEJGS LIED                                     D 92
GRIEG, E.H.  TO SPRING                                         B 13
GRILLARD, O.  SERENADE                                         D 80
GROOMS.  DARK EYES                                             B 13
GROOMS.  2 GUITARS                                             B 13
GRUDZINSKI, C.  MINIATURY                                      E 72
GUBBY.  BAROQUE SUITE                                          A 84
GUILBERT, R.  IMPROMPTU (OP)                                   D 36
GUILLAUME, E.  ANDANTE ET ALLEGRO                              A 96
GUILLAUME, E.  THEME ET VARIATIONS                             F 81
GUILLEMENT.  BLAISE ET BABET                                   C 49
HADJIEV, P.  BURLESQUE                                         F 36
HAEYER, F. D'.  ALLEGRO                                        A 96
HAEYER, F. D'.  MORCEAU DE CONCERT                             A 96
HAGEN-HARING.  HARLEM NOCTURNE                                 F 42
HAGER.  POST VON APPENZELL, DIE                                E 03
HAMILTON, I.  CAPRICCIO                                        F 31
HAMILTON, I.  5 SCENES                                         E 77
HANDEL, G.F.-FITZGERALD.  ADAGIO & ALLEGRO MARZIALE            E 77
HANDEL, G.F.-FITZGERALD.  ADAGIO & ALLEGRO                     E 77
HANDEL, G.F.-BLAAUW.  AIR FR. THE WATER MUSIC                  D 92
HANDEL, G.F.-FITZGERALD.  ALLEGRO                              E 77
HANDEL, G.F.-O'NEILL.  ANGELS EVER BRIGHT & FAIR              G 13
HANDEL, G.F.-WRIGHT.  ANGLES, EVER BRIGHT & FAIR               A 78
HANDEL, G.F.-FITZGERALD.  ARIA & BOURREE                       E 77
HANDEL, G.F.-FITZGERALD.  ARIA CON VARIAZIONI                  B 32
HANDEL, G.F.  ART THOU TROUBLED                                D 92
HANDEL, G.F.  CANTILENA                                        D 18
HANDEL, G.F.  CELEBRE "LARGO"                                  B 66
HANDEL, G.F.  I KNOW THAT MY REDEEMER LIVETH                   D 92
HANDEL, G.F.  LARGO                                            B 53
HANDEL, G.F.  LARGO                                            D 92
HANDEL, G.F.-FITZGERALD.  LARGO AND ALLEGRO                    E 77
HANDEL, G.F.-O'NEILL.  OH HAD I JUBEL'S LYRE                   G 13
HANDEL, G.F.-SHEPPARD.  OH LIGHT DEVINE                        G 13
HANDEL, G.F.-MORRIS.  REVENGE TIMOTHEUS CRIES!                 D 52
HANDEL, G.F.-LETHBRIDGE.  SOLO ALBUM                           E 51
HANDEL, G.F.-BARNES.  SOUND AN ALARM                          F 62
HANDEL, G.F.  SUITE IN D (OP)                                  E 14
HANDEL, G.F.-OSTRANDER.  THUNDER, LIGHTNING & WHISTLING WIND   D 14
HANDEL, G.F.-OSTRANDER.  TOTAL ECLIPSE FROM SAMSON             F 60
HANDEL, G.F.-O'NEILL.  WHERE'ER YOU WALK                       G 13
HANMER.  3 SKETCHES                                            N 75
HANSEN, T.  ROMANCE                                            H 30
HANSEN, T.  SCHERZO                                            H 30
HANUS, J.  IMPROMPTUS, OP.45                                   A 33
HARDT.  DUSK                                                   F 79
HARRIS, F.O.  BRASS BANGLES                                    D 52
HARRIS, F.O.  CHARMING BALLERINA                               A 55
HARRIS, F.O.  FAIRY PRINCESS                                   D 52
HARRIS, F.O.  GAY LIEUTENANT, THE                             A 55
HARRIS, F.O.  LITTLE COMMANDER                                 D 52
HARRIS, F.O.  2 LITTLE STARS                                   D 52
HARRIS, F.O.  MARILEE                                          A 55
```

```
HARRIS, F.O.   OCEAN BEACH                                    D52
HARRIS, F.O.   2 REVERIES                                     A55
HARRIS, F.O.   SCOUT PATROL                                   D52
HARRIS, F.O.   SHERILEE WALTZES NO.1 & 2                      D52
HARRIS, F.O.   SPARKLES                                       D52
HARRIS, F.O.   2 YOUNG BRAVADO'S                              A55
HARRIS, F.O.   YOUNG PRINCE, THE                              D52
HARTLEY, W.S.   CAPRICE FOR TPT & PA                          B98
HARTMANN, J.   ALEXIS                                         D92
HARTMANN, J.-ROCHON.   ALEXIS                                 D64
HARTMANN, J.   ARBUCKLENIAN POLKA (BP)                        A78
HARTMANN, J.   AULD LANG SIJNE                                D92
HARTMANN, J.   BEAUTIFUL AMERICAN, THE                        D92
HARTMANN, J.   BLUE BELLS OF SCOTLAND (TPT IN A)              B53
HARTMANN, J.   FACILITA (BP)                                  A78
HARTMANN, J.   FANTASIE BRILLANTE                             D92
HARTMANN, J.   FATHERLAND                                     D92
HARTMANN, J.   GIPSY'S WARNING                                D92
HARTMANN, J.   IN MY OLD KENTUCKY HOME                        D92
HARTMANN, J.   LE CARNAVAL DE VENISE                          D64
HARTMANN, J.   LIZZIE POLKA (BP)                              A78
HARTMANN, J.   OLD FOLKS                                      D92
HARTMANN, J.   ON THE BANKS OF ALLAN WATER                    D92
HARTMANN, J.   RETURN, THE                                    D92
HARTMANN, J.   ROBIN ADAIR                                    D92
HARTMANN, J.   SEHNSUCHT NACH DER HEIMAT                      D92
HARTMANN, J.   VARATIE'S ON CARNAVAL DE VENISE                D92
HARTMANN, J.   WEVER'S LAST WALTZ                             B53
HARTZELL, D.   BALLAD FOR YOUNG CATS                          F43
HASSELMAN, E.   BRAVOUR-ARIE, OP. 70                          F52
HASSELMAN, E.   CAVATINA NO.1, OP.70                          F52
HAWTHORNE-JOHNSON.   MOCKING BIRD                             F07
HAWTHORNE.   WHISPERING HOPE                                  A91
HAYDN, J.-VOXMAN.   ANDANTE FR. CONCERTO IN E-FLAT            F07
HAYDN, J.   ANDANTE FROM CONCERTO                             F62
HAYDN, J.-VOXMAN.   ARIA & ALLEGRO                            F07
HAYDN, J.-BRAHMS.   CHORALE: ST. ANTONI                       F64
HAYDN, J.-SPEETS.   GRTIAS                                    F81
HAYDN, J.   OXEN MINUET                                       B53
HAYDN, J.-MILLARS.   REVE D'AMOUR, LE                         D64
HAYDN, J.-WOOD.   ROSES OF PICARDY                            D92
HAYDN, J.-LAWRENCE.   SOLO ALBUM                              E51
HAYES.   CORNUCOPIA                                           D14
HEINDORF, R.J.-SEARS.   MELANCHOLY RHAPSODY                   G31
HEKHUIS, J.   3 BAGATELLEN                                    F81
HELDENBERG, A.   INTRODUCTION & SCHERZO                       A96
HENDERSON, K.   ROCKET SHIP TO THE MOON                       D14
HENDERSON, K.   TRUMPETERS SERENADE, A                        D14
HENDERSON, R.J.-SEARS.   BIRTH OF THE BLUES, THE              C58
HENDERSON, R.J.-SCHOENFELD.   DEEP NIGHT                      A04
HERBERT, V.-GOSSETTE.   AH! SWEET MYSTERY OF LIFE             G31
HERBERT, V.-GOSSETTE.   BECAUSE YOU'RE YOU                    G31
HERBERT, V.   CZARDAS                                         D18
HERBERT, V.   GYPSY LOVE SONG                                 D18
HERBERT, V.-HARRIS.   GYPSY LOVE SONG                         D52
HERBERT, V.-GOSSETTE.   I'M FALLING IN LOVE WITH SOMEONE      G31
HERBERT, V.-GOSSETTE.   INDIAN SUMMER                         C58
HERBERT, V.-GOSSETTE.   KISS IN THE DARK                      G31
HERBERT, V.-GOSSETTE.   ROSE OF THE WORLD                     G31
HERBERT, V.-GOSSETTE.   THINE ALONE                           G31
HERBERT, V.-GOSSETTE.   TOYLAND                               G31
```

```
HERBERT, V.-SEARS.  TRAMP! TRAMP! TRAMP!                         G31
HERBERT, V.-GOSSETTE.  WHEN YOU'RE AWAY                          G31
HERFURTH, R.  ALPINE ECHOES                                      A78
HERING, S.  CLASSIC PIECES FOR THE ADVANCING TRUMPETER          C11
HERVE, A. DE.  MORCEAU DE CONCERT                               F30
HEUBERGER, R.-LEIDZEN.  MIDNIGHT BELLS                           C18
HIGUET, N.  PIECE POUR CONCOURS NO.1                             D67
HILGEMAN, P.  BAROQUE IS BACK                                    B31
HILL.  MY PRAYER                                                 G13
HILL.  ORCHIDS                                                   G13
HILLEMACHER, P.  PREMIERE SOLO DE TPT                            B53
HIRT, A.  ON BOURBON STREET                                      A70
HIRT, A.  PLAY TRUMPET LIKE AL HIRT                             A70
HITTLER, L.  COUNTRY GARDENS                                     F62
HLOBIL, E.  INTERMEZZO                                           A33
HOCH, T.  FANTASIE CONCERTANTE                                   D64
HOCH, T.  FANTASIE CONCERTANTE                                   D92
HOCH, T.  LOVE'S DREAM                                           D92
HOCH, T.  NORTHERN FANTASIA                                      B53
HOCH, T.  SINGVOGELCHEN AUS DEM THURINGERWALD                    D92
HOCH, T.  UNE PERLE DE L'OCEAN                                   D92
HODDINOTT, A.  RONDO SCHERZOSO, OP.12/1                          E51
HOFMANN, R.-HERBST.  38 MELODISCHE STUDIEN (2 VOL)              C75
HOLMES, G.E.  COSETTE                                            A55
HOLMES, G.E.  ZAYDA                                              A55
HOLMES, G.E. (ARR).  CARNIVAL OF VENICE                          F07
HONEGGER, A.  INTRADA FOR TPT IN C AND PIANO                     F16
HONEGGER, ENESCO & BOZZA.  INTRADA, LEGEND & RURAL SKETCHES      E19
HOOGHE.  FANTAISIE-CAPRICE                                       F21
HORLICK, H.-STONE.  DARK EYES                                    C11
HOUDY, P.  SARABANDE                                             D36
HOVHANESS, A.S.  HAROUTIUN                                       E65
HOVHANESS, A.S.  PRAYER OF SAINT GREGORY (OP)                    F59
HOWELL.  RUSTIC DANCE                                            B13
HUBAY, J.-MENDEZ.  HEJRE KATI                                    C11
HUBER, B.E.-GABRIEL.  VORLAUTE TROMPETE, DIE                     C30
HUBERT.  AU PARC                                                 D64
HUBERT.  DANS LES PINS                                           D64
HUDADOFF.  MARCHES, MARCHES, MARCHES                             E80
HUDADOFF, I.  15 INTERMEDIATE SOLO SERIES                        E80
HUDADOFF, I.  50 STANDARD SOLO SERIES                            E80
HUE, G.A.-VOISIN.  CONCERTPIECE                                  C91
HUE, G.A.  PREMIER SOLO DE CORNET A PISTONS                      D36
HUE, G.A.-MAGER.  SOLO DE CONCERT                                F60
HUGHES, D.-PELZ.  ENTRANCE OF THE NOBLEMEN                       C25
HUGHES, D.-PELZ.  MOODS & CONTRASTS                              C25
HUGON, G.  INTRODUCTION & ALLEGRO                                F87
HUME, J.O.  HARMONIOUS BLACKSMITH, THE                           D92
HUNDZIAK, A.  VARIATIONS                                         E72
HURRELL, C.E.  GYPSY DREAMS                                      A91
HURRELL, C.E.  SILVER SHADOWS                                    A91
HURRELL, C.E.  SUMMER NIGHT                                      A91
HURRELL, C.E.  SUMMER SERENADE                                   F07
IBERT, J.  IMPROMPTU                                             D36
IDEAL COLLECTION OF FAMOUS CORNET SOLOS.                         C11
INTERMEDIATE PIECES FOR CORNET.                                  A37
IRONS, E.D.  ECHOES FROM THE PAINTED DESERT                      C09
IRONS, E.D.  EMERALD ISLE                                        C09
IRONS, E.D.  GRAND CANYON                                        F60
IRONS, E.D.  RECITAL REPERTOIRE                                  F07
IRONS, E.D.  SONG OF THE PINES                                   F60
IVANOVICI-EDWARDS.  WAVES OF THE DANUBE                          D84
```

JACOB. 4 LITTLE PIECES		N75
JAEGGI. CARINTHIA-MELODIE		F10
JAHRL. FROLIC OF THE KEYS		A91
JAKMA, F. CAVATINE		F81
JAKMA, F. CHARMEUSE, LA		F81
JAKMA, F. HERFSTBLOEMEN		F81
JAKMA, F. SANCTA LUCIA		D92
JAMES, W. ELEGY (BP)		D52
JEANJEAN, P. CAPRICCIOSO		A10
JEANJEAN, P. CAPRICCIOSO		A71
JEANJEAN, P. CAPRICCIOSO		C91
JEANJEAN, P. DOUCE QUIETUDE		A71
JEANJEAN, P. SERENADE		C38
JESSEL-KLICKMAN. PARADE OF THE WOODEN SOLDIERS		D63
JOHNSON. SACRED SOLOS		F07
JOHNSON, C.W. HACIENDA REVELS		A62
JOHNSON, C.W. LAND OF ENCHANTMENT		A62
JOHNSON, C.W. SCHOOL DAYS		A62
JOHNSON, H. PRELUDE		A62
JOHNSON, R. QUETZALCOATL		F43
JOHNSTON. ESSAY		H06
JOHNSTON, H. ANNA KARENINA		A11
JOHNSTON, H. LEONIE		A11
JOLIVET, A. AIR DE BRAVOURE		C91
JONES & BOUSTED (CMPL). ESSENTIAL REPERTOIRE FOR TPT		F97
JONGEN, L. AIR ET DANSE		D41
JONGEN, L. CADENCE ET RIGODON		A96
JUERISALU. SIGNALS		G83
KALIMOWSKI(ED). OLD MUSIC FOR TPT		E72
KANITZ, E. CONCERT PIECE FOR TPT & PA. (OP)		D84
KAPLAN, D. ANCIENT STORY		A62
KAPPEY. INTRODUCTION & VARIATIONS ON A WELSH SONG		D92
KARTZEV, A.A. 2 PIECES, OP.9		D81
KARTZEV, A.A.-FOVEAU. 2 PIECES		C91
KATSCHER, R.-GOSSETTE. WHEN DAY IS DONE		C58
KAUFMANN, A. MUSIK FUR TROMPETE, OP.38		F31
KELIBES-MENDEZ. LAKME		D22
KELLY, R. TUNE OF THE TOY TPT		E68
KENDALL, B.(ARR). WONDERFUL MUSIC OF CHRISTMAS, THE		D84
KENNEDY, A.-HUMMEL. STARS OF THE EAST		F07
KEPNER, F. TEMPESTO, EL		D71
KERS, R. DE. TRUMPET WALTZ		J39
KETELBEY, A.W.-TEAGUE. IN A MONASTERY GARDEN		C58
KETELBEY, A.W. IN A PERSIAN MARKET		A82
KETELBEY, A.W. SANCTUARY OF THE HEART		A82
KETTING, O. INTRADA		B74
KHACHATURIAN, A.-BOLOTIN. 3 DANCES FROM THE BALLET "GAYANE"		D81
KHACHATURIAN, A.-VOISIN. DANCES FROM THE BALLET "GAYNE"		C91
KHACHATURIAN, A.-FITELBERG. SABER DANCE FROM "GAYANNE" BALLET		A38
KHACHATURIAN, A.-SCHUEBEL. SABRE DANCE		D71
KIEFER-HOLMES. ELENA POLKA		A55
KILLMAYER, W. 3 PIECES		F31
KILPATRICK, J.F. HORNPIPE		E68
KING, K.L. NIGHT IN JUNE		A55
KINYON, J.L. (ARR). BREEZE-EASY RECITAL PIECES		G31
KINYON, J.L. (ARR). PROGRAM PIECES FOR TRUMPET		G31
KLEIN & KOFF. QUIXOTE		D22
KLEIN, G. TROMPETERLAUNEN		C59
KLERK, J.DE. CONCERTINO (BP)		D92
KLOSE. AIR VARIE, OP.21		A71
KNAPP, F.-HENNEMAN. OPEN THE GATES OF THE TEMPLE		C11

```
KNIGHT-CLEMENT.  ROCKED IN THE CRADLE OF THE DEEP        G10
KNIGHT, M.  INTRODUCTION & ALLEGRO                       F80
KNIPFEL, G.-BELDON.  CANDELERO, EL                       A62
KNIPFEL, G.-BELDON.  CASA, LA                            A62
KNIPFEL, G.-BELDON.  MEXICANA                            A62
KNIPFEL, G.-BELDON.  MIRANDA, LA                         A62
KNIPFEL, G.-BELDON.  VERANO, EL                          A62
KNOX, C.  SOLO FOR TPT WITH BRASS TRIO (OR PIANO)        G83
KOCH.  5 "POPS"                                          C40
KOENIG, A.  POSTHOORNGALOP (BP)                          D92
KOFF-KLEIN.  LAUREL CANYON SERENADE                      D22
KOFF-KLEIN.  VOICES OF THE MID-EAST                      D22
KOFF, C.(ARR).  BRAHMS CZARDAS                           D22
KOFF, C.(ARR).  CHIT CHAT                                D22
KOFF, C.  SPINNING SONG (BP)                             D22
KOGAN, L.  BULGARIAN RHAPSOCY                            D81
KOLAR, V.  CANZONE DELLA SERA                            D84
KOPELENT, M.  KLEINE SUITE FUR TPT & KLAV                A51
KOPELENT, M.  LITTLE SUITE FOR TPT & PA                  A33
KOPKE, H.-LAUBE.  SILVER PEARLS                          B53
KOTT.  VIRTUOSENSTUCKCHEN, EIN,OP.100                    E43
KOUGELL, A.  INTERMEZZO                                  C25
KREBS, J.L.  8 CHORALE PRELUDES                          D74
KREISLER, F.-LEIDZEN.  LIEBESLIED                        C18
KREISLER, F.-LEIDZEN.  MIDNIGHT BELLS                    C18
KREISLER, F.-LEIDZEN.  MINIATURE VIENNESE MARCH          C18
KREISLER, F.-LEIDZEN.  RONDINO ON A THEME OF BEETHOVEN   C18
KREISLER, F.-VAN HOESEN.  SCHON ROSMARIN                 C18
KRIEGER-FITZGERALD.  ALLEGRO (WITH TENAGLIA: ARIA)       E77
KRIUKOV, V.N.  CONCERT-POEM, OP.59                       D81
KROL, B.  MAGNIFICAT-VARIATIONS, OP.40                   F52
KRUMPFER, H.J.  6 COMPOSITIONS                           B69
KULIEV, T.  LESGINKA                                     D81
KUPFERMAN.  3 IDEAS                                      C40
KUPFERMAN.  INFINITIES 22                                C40
KURKA, R.F.  BALLAD                                      G17
KURPAROV, P.  ETUDES FOR TPT AND PIANO                   F36
KURPAROV, P. (CMPL).  PIECES FOR TRUMPET & PIANO (3 VOL) F36
KURPINSKI, K.-BUTKIEWICZ.  CAVATINA                      E72
KUTSCH, B.(ARR).  BLASERS LIEBLINGE                      G43
LAAS, W.  SKYLINE SILHOUETTES                            A62
LABITZKY.  DREAM OF THE SHEPHERDESS                      B13
LAKE, M.L.  NAIDA (BP)                                   D52
LALA, J.  CERBERUS                                       D92
LAMPERTI-WEATHERLY.  BRAVURA STUDIES                     F23
LANCEN.  PILE OU FACE                                    D64
LANCEN.  SOLDATS D'OPERETTE                              A71
LANCIEN, N.  VOCALISES                                   B24
LANGENDOEN, J.C.  PUPPET (BOP)                           B91
LANGLAIS.  7 CHORALS                                     E66
LANGLOIS, L.  AIR VARIE                                  F81
LANGLOIS, L.  GRAND AIR VARIE                            D64
LANGLOIS, T.  INTERMEZZO                                 D67
LANTIER, P.  CONCERT EN 3 PARTIES (OP)                   D41
LARA, A.  GRANADA                                        F59
LASSEN, E.  AT DEVOTIONS                                 B85
LATHAM, W.P.  SUITE (BP)                                 B26
LATY, C.  FANTAISIE, OP.49                               D41
LAUBE (CMPL).  CONTEST ALBUM                             B53
LAUDEN, G.-FARLEY.  SON OF THE GOLDEN TPT, THE           D84
LAVALLE-TARTO.  TRUMPET POLKA                            C25
```

LAWTON, S.M.   OLD ENGLISH TRUMPET TUNES   E51
LAWTON, S.M.(ARR).   YOUNG TRUMPET PLAYER, THE (3 VOL)   E51
LAX, F.   BONNIE SCOTLAND   B53
LE BOUCHER, M.   SCHERZO APPASSIONATO (OP)   D36
LE THIERE, C.   REVERIE, A SONG OF JOY, MELODIE RELIGIOSO   B53
LECLERCQ, E.   INTIMATE   A96
LECUONA-KLICKMAN.   ANDALUCIA   D93
LECUONA-KLICKMAN.   MALAGUENA   D63
LEDUC, J.   ALLEGRO RITMICO, OP.2   D67
LEDUC, J.   FANTAISIE   D67
LEE, W.   MINI SUITE   N74
LEFEBVRE, R.   INITIUM   D67
LEGLEY, V.   RHAPSODIE   D36
LEHAR, F.-SEARS.   YOURS IS MY HEART ALONE   E11
LEIDIG.   TRUMPET TODAY   N10
LEIDZEN.   ECHOES FROM OLD VIENNA   C25
LEMARE, E.H.-LONG.   ANDANTINO   G10
LENGSFELDER-LEIDZEN.   TROPICAL TRUMPETS   C25
LENZ, L.   CICERO   B53
LEONCAVALLO. R.   MATTINATA (BP)   D52
LESTER.   CRIMSON BLUSHES   B13
LEVADE, C.   CAPRICE   D36
LEVINE, M.   SCHERZO   D81
LEVINE, M.-NAGEL.   SCHERZO   C91
LEVY, J.   GRAND RUSSIAN FANTASIA   D18
LEVY, J.-SMITH.   GRAND RUSSIAN FANTASIA   C11
LEYBACH.   5TH NOCTURNE   B13
LIBERATI, A.   COLIMA POLKA   B53
LIBERATI, A.   VALSE CAPRICE   D52
LICHTENDAHL, A.   QUICK & SLOW   F81
LIEBE, H.   FREUT EUCH DES LIEBENS   C30
LIEBE, H.   PURZELBAUME   C30
LIEBE, W.   BRAVOUR POLKA   C30
LIEBE, W.   LIEBESGESCHICHTEN   C30
LINCKE, P.   GLOW WORM   D18
LINCKE, P.-WALTERS.   GLOW WORM, THE   F07
LINCKE, P.-KLICKMAN.   GLOW-WORM   D63
LINK, J.D.   BURLESKE   C75
LIPKIN(ARR).   3 PIECES   D81
LISZT, F.   LIEBESTRAUM   D92
LISZT, F.-SMITH.   LIEBESTRAUM   A55
LISZT, F.   LIEBESTRAUME   B53
LISZT, F.-BLAAUW.   REVE D'AMOUR   D64
LISZT, F.-VACHEY.   REVE D'AMOUR   B66
LITTLE, L.   VALSE LYNNETTE   A62
LLEWELLYN, E.   MY REGARDS   C11
LLEWELLYN, E.   MY REGARDS   E11
LLOYD, G.   L'EVENEMENT   B35
LOCKWOOD, N.   L'HOMME ARME   E68
LOHMANN, G.-PERL.   BAYRISCHE POLKA   C30
LONDONDERRY AIR.   A91
LONDONDERRY AIR.   D92
LONG.   HOME SWEET HOME   G10
LONG, LONG AGO.   D92
LONQUE, A.   ALLA HANACCA   D67
LONQUE, A.   IMPROMPTU   A96
LOSEY, F.H.   AT THE DAWN   A55
LOTTI.   ARIETTA   B85
LOTZENHISER, G.W.   PETITE VALSE   A62
LOUIGUY-SEARS.   VIE EN ROSE, LA   C58
LOUMEY.   SHADOWS ON THE WATER   B13
LUENING.   INTRO & ALLEGRO   E65

```
LUIGINI, A.  CAPRICE                                        A71
LUREMAN.  GROOTVADER'S KLOK                                 D92
LYNES, W.  JUNIOR SOLOIST, THE                             A55
MACDONALD.  APRIL BUDS                                     G13
MACDOWELL, E.A.  TO A WILD ROSE                            D92
MACDOWELL, E.A.-ISAAC.  TO A WILD ROSE                     C11
MACMURROUGH, D.  MACUSHLA                                  A78
MAES, J.  CONCERTSTUK                                      A96
MAGANINI, Q.  ANCIENT GREEK MELODY, AN                    B85
MAGANINI, Q.  ARIA                                        B85
MAGANINI, Q.  I'LL BE GOING HOME                          B85
MAGANINI, Q.  SONG OF THE CHINESE FISHERMAN               B85
MAGANINI, Q.  TUOLUMNE                                    B85
MAGER.  9 GRAND SOLOS DE CONCERT                          F60
MAHLER-MAGANINI.  PRIMEVAL LIGHT                          B85
MAHLER, G.  POSTHORN SOLO (FR SYM. #3)                    B85
MALEZIEUX, G.  MELODY RELIGIEUSE                          C38
MALEZIEUX, G.  ROMANCE SANS PAROLES, OP.20               C38
MALIPIERO, G.F.  FANFARON DE LA FANFARE, LE              D36
MALOTTE, A.H.  LORD'S PRAYER, THE                        A81
MALOTTE, A.H.-LAKE.  LORD'S PRAYER, THE                  F23
MALTBY, R.  CEREMONIAL MARCH                              D14
MALTBY, R.  TRUMPET NOCTURNE                             D84
MALTER, L.  CANZONA                                      D81
MANCINI, F.-MINTER.  SINFONIA TO "HYDASPES"             E14
MANIET, R.  ALLA MARCIA                                  A96
MANIET, R.  CHANTECLER                                   D67
MANIET, R.  DEUXIEME SOLO                                A96
MANIET, R.  FIRST PIECE                                  A96
MANIET, R.  PETIT MORCEAU DE CONCOURS                   A96
MANIET, R.  PRELUDE ET SCHERZO                           D67
MANIET, R.-VOXMAN.  PREMIER SOLO DE CONCOURSE           F07
MANIET, R.  RITMICO                                     D67
MANIET, R.  SOLO #1                                      C42
MARCHETTI-HURRELL.  FASCINATION                          F07
MARI.  JASERIE                                           E66
MARITANA.                                                D92
MARTEAU, H.-BARNES.  MORCEAU VIVANT                      F62
MARTERIE, R.-ALAGNA.  TRUMPET & A PRAYER, A              D84
MARTIN, V.  CHORAL                                       E66
MARTIN, V.  CORTEGE                                      E66
MARTINI, J.P.E.  PLAISIR D'AMOUR                         B85
MARTINI, J.P.E.-OVERVELD.  PLAISIR D'AMOUR              F81
MARTY, G.E.  CHORAL FOR TPT IN C                        F05
MARTY, G.E.-VOISIN.  CHORALE                            C91
MASCAGNI, P.  INTERMEZZO FROM CAVALLERIA RUSTICANA      B13
MASCAGNI, P.  SICILIANA                                  E93
MASCOGNI, P.  INTERMEZZO FROM CAVALLERIA RUSTICANA      B53
MASSENET, J.  2 OPERATIC SCENES                         B85
MASSIAS.  CHORAL ET MENUET OBSTINE                      A71
MASSO, G.  DANCE FOR LISA                               E83
MASSO, G.  MARHORIE'S HOLIDAY                           E83
MASSO, G.  PAULA JEANNE POLKA                           D14
MASSO, G.  SONG FOR DAVID                               E83
MASTEN, I.J.  BONNIE ELOISE  (BP)                       D52
MASTEN, I.J. (ARR).  BELIEVE ME IF ALL THOSE ENDEARING... D52
MATYS, K.  SUITE                                         G81
MAUGUE, J.M.  LIED ET MOTIF HEROIQUE                    A71
MAUGUE, J.M.  LIED ET MOTIF HEROIQUE                    B46
MAUPIN, W.C.  CHARMING ANNABEL                          A55
MAURAT, E.  PETITES INVENTIONS, OP.21/3                C01
MAURY, H.  CONTEST SOLO NO.5                            A10
```

```
MAURY, H.    DEUXIEME SOLO DE CONCOURS                           D64
MAURY, H.    PREMIER SOLO DE CONCOURS                            D64
MAURY, H.    QUATRIEME SOLO DE CONCOURS                          D64
MAURY, H.    SOLO DE CONCOURS NO.5                               A71
MAURY, H.    TROISEME SOLO DE CONCOURS                           D64
MAYER, W.R.  CONCERT PIECE                                       A78
MAZELLIER, J.    LEGENDE DRAMATIQUE                              B02
MC CALL, H.E.    CANDLE-LIGHT                                    A81
MC CALL, H.E.    CANDLE-LIGNT                                    C11
MC CALL, H.E.    CATHEDRAL ECHOES                                C11
MC CALL, H.E.    CHANGING SHADOWS                                C11
MC CALL, H.E.    REFLECTIONS                                     F07
MC CALL, H.E.    STARLIGHT                                       C11
MC KAY, F.H.    BUCKBOARD BLUES                                  A55
MC KAY, F.H.    DREAM WALTZ                                      A55
MC KAY, F.H.    HERNANDO'S HOLIDAY                               A55
MC KAY, F.H.    JIG FOR JEANINE                                  A55
MC KAY, F.H.    POWDERED WIG                                     A55
MC KAY, F.H.    YE TRAVELING TROUBADOR                           A55
MC KAY, G.F.    ARRIETTA & CAPRICCIO                             A81
MC KAY, G.F.    CONCERT SOLO SUITE FOR YOUNG PLAYERS             C11
MC KAY, G.F.    RHUMBA SERENADE (BP)                             B72
MC KAY, G.F.    4 RHYTHMIC PIECES                                C11
MEACHAM-HUMMEL.    AMERICAN PATROL                               F07
MEESTER, L.DE.    PAVANE                                         D67
MEIER, A.-BOHME.    TROMPETERLEIN                                C30
MEIER, A.-BOHME.    VERLIEBTES PARCHEN                           C30
MELYAN, T.    DEBONAIR FOR TRUMPET (BP)                          F43
MEN OF HARLACH.                                                  D92
MENDELSSOHN, F.-HARRIES.    ALLEGRO (VLN CONCERTO IN E MINOR)    E59
MENDELSSOHN, F.-HARRIES.    ANDANTE (VLN CONCERTO IN E MINOR)    E59
MENDELSSOHN, F.    AUF FLUGELN DES GESANGES                      D92
MENDELSSOHN, F.    FRUHLINGSLIED                                 D92
MENDELSSOHN, F.    HOCHZEITMARS VOOR TROMPET                     D92
MENDELSSOHN, F.-OSTRANDER.    IF WITH ALL YOUR HEARTS            F60
MENDELSSOHN, F.-CLUWEN.    MON CHANT TE BERCE MON ANGE           D64
MENDELSSOHN, F.    ON WINGS OF SONG                              D18
MENDELSSOHN, F.    SPRING SONG                                   B53
MENDEZ, R.(ARR).    BAMBUCO                                      C11
MENDEZ, R.(ARR).    CANTO MORIO                                  C11
MENDEZ, R.(ARR).    DANCE OF THE COMEDIANS (SMETENA)            C11
MENDEZ, R.(ARR).    DARK EYES                                    C11
MENDEZ, R.   FANDANGO (JOTA #3)                                  C11
MENDEZ, R.-KOFF.    FAREWELL MY GRANADA (BP)                     D22
MENDEZ, R.-KOFF.    FLIGHT OF THE BUMBLE-BEE (BP)                D22
MENDEZ, R.   GEMS FOR TPT & PA                                   C11
MENDEZ, R.(ARR).    HEJRE KATI                                   C11
MENDEZ, R.(ARR).    HUNGARIAN CHANT                              C11
MENDEZ, R.(ARR).    HUNGARIAN DANCE NO.5 (BRAHMS)                C11
MENDEZ, R.(ARR).    INTERMEZZO                                   C11
MENDEZ, R.(ARR).    JOTA NO.2                                    C11
MENDEZ, R.(ARR).    JOTA                                         C11
MENDEZ, R.   LITTLE RUSSIAN DONKEY                               C11
MENDEZ, R.(ARR).    MEXICAN HAT DANCE                            C11
MENDEZ, R.(ARR).    OVER THE WAVES                               C11
MENDEZ, R.   PLEGARIA TAURINA                                    C11
MENDEZ, R.(ARR).    SAMBA                                        C11
MENDEZ, R.(ARR).    SCHERZO IN D MINOR                           C11
MENDEZ, R.(ARR).    VALSE BLUETTE                                C11
MENDEZ, R.(ARR).    VALSE SURIANO                                C11
MENDEZ, R.-KOFF.    VIRGEN DE LA MACARENA (BP)                   D22
MENDEZ, R.(ARR).    ZIGEUNERWEISEN                               C11
```

```
MENDEZ, R. (ARR).  BELL SONG (LAKME, DELIBES)              C11
MENDEZ, R. (ARR).  CARO NOME (RIGOLETTO, VERDI)           C11
MENDEZ, R. (ARR).  CHIAPANECAS                            C11
MENDEZ, R. (ARR).  CZARDAS (MONTI)                        C11
MENDEZ, R. (ARR).  DANCE BOHEME (CARMEN)                  C11
MENDEZ, R. (ARR).  DANSE POLOVETSIENNE (BORODIN)          C11
MERETTA, L.  HIBRITEN                                     D84
MERLET.  MONDE S'SOUVRE, LE                               D36
MESSNER, E.O.  DVA ETIUDA DLIA TRUBY I FORTEP'IANO        D97
METEHEN, E.  ANDANTE ET POLONAISE                         C38
METRA, O.  GAMBRINUS                                      C65
METRA, O.  ROSES, LES                                     C65
METRA, O.  SERENADE                                       C65
METRA, O.  VAGUE, LA                                      C65
METRA, O.  VOLUNTAIRES, LES                               C65
MEVER, P.V.  3 PIECES                                     D92
MEYER, J.  MOUSAILLON-MARCHE                              D36
MEYER, J.H. & KAHN-STERLING.  CRAZY RHYTHM               C58
MEYER, L.J.  15 FOLK TUNES FOR TPT                        F43
MEYERBEER, G.  CAVATINA FR. "ROBERT THE DEVIL"           B53
MIELENZ, H.  STERNENHIMMEL                                C30
MIGNION.  2 MOUVEMENTS                                    D92
MIHALOVICI, M.  MEDITATION                                D36
MIHALOVICI, M.  SCHERZO-VALSE                             D36
MILLER, R.M.  MEMORIES                                    A62
MOLLEY.  LOVE'S OLD SWEET SONG                            D92
MOLLEY-BLAAUW.  LOVE'S OLD SWEET SONG                     D64
MONTBRUN, R.G.  LIED                                      D36
MONTBRUN, R.G.  MARCHE                                    D36
MONTBRUN, R.G.  SARABANDE ET FINALE                       D36
MONTBRUN, R.G.  SCHERZO                                   D36
MONTERDE, B.B.-BEELER.  VIRGEN DE LA MACARENA, LA         F59
MONTI-ANDREONI.  AUBADE D'AMOUR                           E98
MOREE, L.D.  SERENADE                                     F81
MOREL, F.  SOLO FOR C TPT                                 C49
MORGAN, R.O.  LEGENDE, OP.35                              A42
MORRISSEY, J.J.-APPLEBAUM.  SOLILOQUY                     E67
MORTIMER, H.  8 IRISH SONGS                               E59
MORTIMER, H.  8 SACRED SONGS                              E59
MORTIMER, H. (ARR).  VARIATIONS ON A THEME BY MOZART      E59
MOULAERT, R.  THEME ET VARIATIONS (OP)                    E43
MOUQUET, J.  IMPROMPTU, OP.40                             D36
MOUQUET, J.  LEGENDE HEROIQUE, OP.27                      B53
MOUQUET, J.  LEGENDE HEROIQUE, OP.27                      D36
MOZART, W.A.-STOUFFER.  ALLEGRETTO                        D14
MOZART, W.A.-O'NEILL.  ALLELUIA FR EXCULTATE JUBILATE     G13
MOZART, W.A.-POWELL.  ARIETTA & ALLEGRO                   F60
MOZART, W.A.  AVE VERUM                                   D92
MOZART, W.A.-CLUWEN.  AVE VERUM CORPUS                    D64
MOZART, W.A.-VOXMAN.  CONCERT ARIA, K.382H                F07
MOZART, W.A.-LETHBRIDGE.  MOZART SOLO ALBUM, A            E51
MOZART, W.A.-BARNES.  PER QUESTA BELLA MONA, K.612        F62
MOZART, W.A.-THILDE.  RONDO                               A71
MOZART, W.A.-O'NEILL.  VOI CHE SAPETE FR FIGARO           G13
MURPHY, J.  ARCOLA (EASY JAZZ)                            F74
MUSSER-CAMPBELL.  COURANTE                                A03
MUSSER-CAMPBELL.  POEME FOR TRUMPET                       D14
MUSSORGSKY, M.P.-KOFF.  CHIT-CHAT (BP)                    D22
NAGEL, R.(ED).  BAROQUE MUSIC FOR TPT                     D63
NAGEL, R.  REGAL TRUMPET                                  D63
NAGEL, R.  TRUMPET PROCESSIONAL                           C25
NAGEL, R. & TRUCHET.  PRELUDE ET DANSE                    E66
```

NAPRAVNIK, E.F. ROMANZETTA   B85
NAUBER-GAUDIN. FANTAISIE   D92
NEHR, E. FANTAISIA   B53
NELHYBEL, V. CONCERT PIECE   G68
NELHYBEL, V. SUITE FOR TPT & PA   C40
NESSLER. TROMPETER VON SACKINGEN, DER   D92
NESTICO, S. PORTRAIT OF A TRUMPET (BP)   D14
NEUBERT. 3 RECITAL PIECES   C75
NEUBERT, H.E. BRASS REEF   D71
NEUBERT, H.E. CHORAL REEF   D71
NEUGEBAUER, F.W. ALTE DESSAUER, DER (OP)   C30
NEUKOMM, S.R.-KAPLAN. ARIA   F62
NEVIN, E.W.-HUMMEL. MIGHT LAK' A ROSE   F07
NEVIN, E.W. MIGHTY LIKE A ROSE   D92
NEVIN, E.W. NARCISSUS   A81
NEVIN, E.W.-EDWARDS. NARCISSUS   D84
NEVIN, E.W.-HARRIS. ROSARY, THE   D52
NEWMANN-LEVINE. SENTIMENTAL RHAPSODY   A70
NIEUWENHOVE, E.V. SEE AGREVES, E.D.(PSEUD)
NIVERD, R. ARIA ET TOCCATA   D36
NOBODY KNOWS.   D92
NOWKA. INTERMEZZO AL OBEREK   D48
NUSSIO, O. IMPROMPTU   F52
NYQUIST, M.A. GOLDEN ECHOES   A62
O, LOVELY NIGHT.   D92
O'NEILL, C. CLOVER LEAF POLKA   G13
O'NEILL, C. EVENING THOUGHTS   A62
O'NEILL, C. EVENING THOUGHTS   G13
C'NEILL, C. PALS   G13
O'NEILL, C. PIONEER, THE   G13
C'NEILL, C. VALLEY OF THE ROSES   G13
O'NEILL, C. YOUNG SOLOIST, THE   G13
CBOUSSIER, R. ENTRADA   C16
OFFENBACH, J. WALTZ, "LA PERICHOLE"   D18
OLCOTT, C. MY WILD IRISH ROSE   D18
OLCOTT, C.-GOSSETTE. MY WILD IRISH ROSE   G31
OLDFIELD. COOL HARBOR, A   C11
CLLONE, M.D. SOLO DE TROMPETTE EN FA (TPT IN F)   D36
ORVID-TABAKOV. 15 PIECES BY WESTERN & RUSSIAN COMPOSERS   D81
OSTRANDER, A. ANTIQUE AIRS   B85
OSTRANDER, A. CONCERT PIECE IN FUGAL STYLE   B85
CSTRANDER, A. ON THE FAIR GROUNDS   B85
OSTRANDER, A. 3 PIECES OF BRASS   C11
PADILLA-MENDEZ. PRINCESITA   C11
PADILLA-STONE. RELICARIO, EL   C45
PADILLA-SCHOENFELD. VALENCIA   C58
PALA, J. CONCERT PIECE   D92
PALA, J. GREEN HILLS   D92
PALADILHE, E. MANDOLINATA   C65
PALANGE, L.S.(ARR). DANZA, LA   C45
PALANGE, L.S.(ARR). FLIGHT OF THE BUMBLE BEE   C45
PALANGE, L.S.(ARR). PRAELUDIUM   C45
PALANGE, L.S.(ARR). SCENE DE BALLET, OP.100   C45
PALANGE, L.S.(ARR). ZIGEUNERWEISEN   C45
PANELLA. 2 BACHELORS   G10
PANELLA. 2 GNOMES   G10
PANELLA. JOLLY TWO   G10
PANELLA. 2 LOVERS   G10
PANELLA. TOM & JERRY   G10
PARES, G.P.C. CREPUSCULE   A71
PARES, G.P.C. FANTAISIE-CAPRICE   A71
PARES, G.P.C. SOLO #1   A71

```
PASCAL, A.  ELEGIE ET PASTORALE                              F87
PASFIELD.  3 CONTRASTS                                       A36
PATUSSET, A.  CAPRICE A LA HONGROISE                         C38
PEASLEE.  NIGHTSONGS                                         G68
PELEMANS, W.  SUITE                                          D67
PELZ, W.  COUNTRY DANCE                                      A62
PELZ, W.  DEDICATION                                         A62
PELZ, W.  ENCHANTED SWING, THE                               A62
PELZ, W.  ROMANTIC INTERLUDE                                 A62
PELZ, W.  VALIANT, THE                                       A62
PELZ, W.  VALSE                                              A62
PELZ, W. & D. HUGHES.  MOODS & CONTRASTS                     C25
PENNEQUIN, J.G.  MORCEAU DE CONCERT                          D36
PERCK, W. VAN.  BEAU JOUR, UN                                F81
PERGOLESI, G.B.-BARNES.  CANZONA                             F62
PERRIER.  PRELUDE ET ALLEGRO                                 A71
PERRIN, C.  BAGATELLE                                        E66
PERRIN, C.  COMPLAINTE                                       E66
PERSICHETTI, V.  HOLLOW MEN, THE                             B92
PERTI, G.-VOISIN.  SERENADE                                  C91
PESKIN, V.A.  PRELUDE                                        D81
PESSARD, E.  PREMIER SOLO, OP.105                            D36
PETER, GO RING THEM BELLS, SWING LOW.                        D92
PETERS-LEIDZEN.  TRUMPET SERENADE                            C25
PETIT, A.S.  ETUDE DE CONCOURS                               A10
PETIT, A.S.  ETUDE DE CONCOURS NO.1                          A71
PETIT, A.S.  GOUTTES D'EAU                                   A71
PETIT, A.S.  O BELLES MONTAGNES                              C38
PETIT, A.S.  PREMIERE ETUDE DE CONCOURS                      B53
PETIT, A.S.-LAUBE.  PREMIERE ETUDE DE CONCOURS               C11
PFEIFFER, G.J.  MOMENTS OF HAPPINESS                         A91
PHILLIPS, D.  TRUMPET FIESTA                                 D84
PHILLIPS, H.  8 BEL CANTO SONGS                              F43
PHILLIPS, I.C.(CMPL).  CLASSICAL & ROMANTIC ALBUM            E51
PICAVAIS.  PIECE POUR CONCOURS                               A71
PICAVAIS.  PREMIER SUCCESS                                   A71
PICAVAIS.  VERS L'AVENIR                                     A71
PICHAUREAU, C.  ARISTOLOCHOS                                 D36
PIGALLO, F.-GURSCH.  KANSAS CITY RAMBLE                      C30
PINARD, A.  AUTUMN                                           C11
PINKHAM, D.  TRUMPET VOLUNTARY                               A13
PLAY-ALONG SING (3 VOL).                                     E77
POLLIN & CLASSENS.  TROMPETTE CLASSIQUE (2 BKS)              E66
POLONSKIJ, A.  ROMANZE & IMPROVISATION                       D97
POOT, M.  ETUDE DE CONCERT                                   C01
POOT, M.  HUMORESQUE                                         D36
PORRET, J.  DIALOGUE                                         D64
PORRET, J.  11E SOLO DE CONCOURS                             D92
PORRET, J.  12E SOLO DE CONCOURS                             D92
PORRET, J.  13E SOLO DE CONCOURS                             D92
PORRET, J.  14E SOLO DE CONCOURS                             D92
PORRET, J.  27E SOLO DE CONCOURS                             D92
PORRET, J.  28E SOLO DE CONCOURS                             D92
PORRINO, E.  PRELUDE, ARIA & SCHERZO                         G41
PORTER, C.-GOSSETTE.  BEGIN THE BEGUINE                      C58
PORTER, C.-HUFFINE.  NIGHT & DAY                             C58
POSKIN, P.  PROLOOG EN ALLEGRO                               D67
POULAIN, S.  MELODIE                                         A96
PRESSEL, G.A.  AN DER WESER                                  D92
PRESSER, W.H.  SUITE FOR TRUMPET                             D14
PRICE.  LET US HAVE MUSIC                                    C11
PROKOFIEV, S.-OSTRANDER.  KIJE'S WEDDING                     B85
```

PROKOFIEV, S. 3 STUCKE	D97
PUCCINI, G.-MENDEZ. MUSETTA FR. LA BOHEME	C11
PUCCINI, G.-ANDREONI. VISSI D'ARTE, VISSI D'AMORE (TOSCA)	B32
PURCELL, H.-GOLDMAN. 2 AIRS FROM BONDUCA	D74
PURCELL, H. ARISE YE SUBTERRANEAN WINDS	B85
PURCELL, H. DANCE SUITE	B85
PURCELL, H.-LONGINOTTI. INTRADA ET RIGAUDON	A71
PURCELL, H.-FITZGERALD. PURCELL SUITE	E77
PURCELL, H.-THILDE. QUEEN'S DOLOUR	A71
PURCELL, H.-MAGANINI. SUITE IN F	B85
PURCELL, H.-GARDNER. TRUMPET FANTARE & TUNE	F64
PURCELL, H.-CLUWEN. TRUMPET TUNE & AIR	D92
PURCELL, H.-SLUIVEN. TRUMPET TUNE & AIR	B91
PURCELL, H.-SLUIVEN. TRUMPET TUNE & AIR	D92
PURCELL, H.-NORDEN. TRUMPET TUNE	A81
PURCELL, H. TRUMPET VOLUNTARY	D92
PURCELL, H. TRUMPET VOLUNTARY (SEE ALSO CLARKE, J.)	
PURCELL, H.-CLUWEN. TRUMPET VOLUNTARY	D64
PURCELL, H.-GARDNER. TRUMPET VOLUNTARY	F64
PURCELL, H.-THILDE. TRUMPET VOLUNTARY	A71
RAFF, J.J. CAVATINA	B53
RAFF, J.J. CAVATINA	D92
RAITCHEV, A. 3 PIECES FOR TPT	F36
RAKOV, N.P. MELODY	D81
RAKOV, N.P. SUITE	D81
RAMIREZ-MENDEZ. MALAGUENA SALEROSA	C11
RANGER. CARNIVAL OF VENICE	C11
RAPHAEL, G. MARCHE	D36
RAPHLING, S. SQUARE DANCE	B85
RASBACH, O.-CLARK. TREES	F23
RASCH. UITNEMENT KABINET, BK 6	N84
RASSE, F. IMPROVISATA (OP)	E43
RATEAU. SONNANT	D36
RATEZ, E.P. GIGUE	C49
RATEZ, E.P. REVEIL	C55
RAUKHVERGER, M.R. JOKE, A	D81
RAUKHVERGER, M.R. 3 PIECES	D81
RAVEL, M. PAVANE	B85
RAVEL, M.-NAGEL. PAVANE	C91
RAVEL, M.-WALTERS. PAVANE	F07
RAYMOND, L. DESIGN	G21
REED, A. ODE FOR TRUMPET	F60
REGER, M.-PIGUET. ROMANZE IN G MAJOR	A89
REGER, W. TALKING TRUMPET	B31
REINHARDT, B. MUSIC FOR TRUMPET SOLO	C94
RELMES. PRELUDE ET FINAL	A71
REMA. TRUMPET BOY	D67
REUTTER, H. FANFARES	D36
REUTTER, H. SCHERZO	D36
REYNAUD, J. AH! VOUS DIRAI-HE, MAMAN	C38
REYNAUD, J. DEESSE	C38
REYNAUD, J. HYLDA	C38
REYNAUD, J. IL PLEUT BERGERE	C38
REYNAUD, J. L'ETOILE DU MIDI	C38
REYNAUD, J. MERLE ET PINSON	C38
REYNAUD, J. SUR LE PONT D'AVIGNON	C38
RICHARD, C. TOUR DE FRANCE, LE	C38
RICHARDS, J.J. SUNBEAMS	A55
RICHARDS, J.J. VILLETTA	A55
RICHARDSON, N. 6 MORE TRUMPET TUNES	A78
RICHARDSON, N.(ARR). 6 TRUMPET TUNES	A78

```
RIMSKY-KORSAKOV, N.A.   CHANSON HINDOE                             D92
RIMSKY-KORSAKOV, N.A.-VACHEY.   CHANSON HINDOE (SADKO)             B66
RIMSKY-KORSAKOV, N.A.   FLIGHT OF THE BUMBLE BEE                   A91
RIMSKY-KORSAKOV, N.A.   FLIGHT OF THE BUMBLE BEE                   B53
RIMSKY-KORSAKOV, N.A.-DAVIS.   FLIGHT OF THE BUMBLE BEE            F07
RIMSKY-KORSAKOV, N.A.-DOKSHITZER.   FLIGHT OF THE BUMBLE BEE       D81
RIMSKY-KORSAKOV, N.A.-JAMES.   FLIGHT OF THE BUMBLE BEE            A78
RIMSKY-KORSAKOV, N.A.-SWIFT.   FLIGHT OF THE BUMBLE BEE            A78
RIMSKY-KORSAKOV, N.A.-JAMES.   HUMMELFLUG                          A90
RIMSKY-KORSAKOV, N.A.-VACHEY.   HYMNE AU SOLEIL                    B66
RIMSKY-KORSAKOV, N.A.-VACHEY.   ROSE ET LE ROSSIGNOL, LA           B66
RIMSKY-KORSAKOV, N.A.   SONG OF INDIA                              B53
RIMSKY-KORSAKOV, N.A.   SONG OF INDIA                              D18
RIMSKY-KORSAKOV, N.A.-DAVIS.   SONG OF INDIA                       F07
RIMSKY-KORSAKOV, N.A.-JAMES.   TALE OF TSAR SALTAN, THE            A78
RIVIERE.   CAVATINE DU BABIER DE SEVILLE                          C38
ROBBINS, G.   MONT SAINT-MICHEL                                    D36
ROBERTS.   SERENADE                                                B44
ROBYN, A.G.-O'NEILL.   ANSWER                                      G13
RODGERS-SEARS.   BLUE ROOM, THE                                    C58
RODOLPHE.   MODERATO                                               J39
ROGERS, W.   AULD LANG SYNE                                        B31
ROGERS, W.   HARP OF TARA                                          B31
ROGERS, W.B.   IN DIXIE                                            B31
ROGERS, W.B.   LAND OF THE FREE                                    B31
ROGERS, W.B.   LULLE                                               B31
ROGERS, W.B.   MENNEHA-HA                                          B31
ROGERS, W.B.   SOLDIER'S DREAM, A                                  C11
ROGERS, W.B.   VOLUNTEER POLKA, THE                                C11
ROGERS, W.B.   WAR SONG                                            B31
ROLLINSON, T.H.   BRUNNETTE & BLONDE                               B72
ROLLINSON, T.H.   COLUMBIA                                         D18
ROLLINSON, T.H.   COLUMBIA FANTASIA POLKA                          B72
ROLLINSON, T.H.   PRISMATIC POLKA                                  B72
ROLLINSON, T.H.   16 STANDARD SOLOS                                E77
ROLLINSON, T.H.   VACANT CHAIR                                     B53
ROMBERG, S.-BEELER.   AUF WIEDERSEHN!                              A81
ROMBERG, S.-SCHOENFELD.   LOVER, COME BACK TO ME                   C58
ROMBERG, S.-SEARS.   ONE ALONE                                     C58
ROMBERG, S.-GOSSETTE.   SERENADE (FR STUDENT PRINCE                C58
ROPARTZ, J.G.   ANDANTE ET ALLEGRO                                 B53
ROPARTZ, J.G.   ANDANTE ET ALLEGRO                                 B85
ROPARTZ, J.G.   ANDANTE ET ALLEGRO                                 C91
ROPARTZ, J.G.   ANDANTE ET ALLEGRO                                 F05
ROPARTZ, J.G.-MAGER.   ANDANTE ET ALLEGRO                          F60
ROSAS-MENDEZ.   SOBRE LAS OLAS                                     C11
ROSS, B.   MAGIC HORN, THE                                         D37
ROSSINI, G.-LUREMAN.   ADAGIO, ANDANTINO...FR WILLIAM TELL         F81
ROSSINI, G.-LEMARC.   CAVATINE FROM SEMIRAMIDE                     F81
ROSSINI, G.-ARMSTRONG.   CUJUS ANIMAM                              C11
ROSSINI, G.-PALANGE.   DANZA, LA                                   C45
ROSSINI, G.   INFLAMMATUS                                          B53
ROSSINI, G.-WANNEMACHER.   INFLAMMATUS (BP)                        C11
ROSSINI, G.   LORD PRESERVE ME                                     B85
ROSSINI, G.-MENDEZ.   VOCE POCO FA, UNA                            C11
ROSSUM.   PRELUDIO, LARGHETTO & RONDO                              D67
ROSY MORN, THE.                                                    D92
ROUBANIS-EDWARDS.   MISIRLOU                                       D84
ROUGNON, P.-MAGER.   CONCERT POLONAISE                             F60
ROUGNON, P.   1ST CONTEST FANTASIE                                 A10
ROUGNON, P.   PREMIER SOLO DE CONCERT                              D36
ROUGNON, P.   SOLO DE CONCERT NO.2                                 A71
```

```
ROUGNON, P.  SOLO DE CONCERT NO.8                                    A71
ROUND, H.-BLAAUW.  ASH GROVE, THE                                   D64
ROUND, H.-BLAAUW.  ASH GROVE, THE                                   D92
ROUND, H.  MARITANA                                                  D64
ROUND, H.  ZENOBIA                                                   D92
ROWLEY, A.  TRUMPET MARCH                                            C33
RUBANK CONCERT & CONTEST COLLECTION.                                 F07
RUBINSTEIN, A.G.  MELODIE                                            D92
RUBINSTEIN, A.G.  ROMANCE                                            C25
RUBINSTEIN, A.G.-LONG.  ROMANCE                                      G10
RUEFF, J.  FANTAISIE CONCERTANTE                                     D36
RUEFF, J.  MOBILES                                                   D36
RUELLE, F.-MANIET.  ALLEGRO IN BLUE                                  D-57
RULST & REMA.  ALLA POLACCA                                          D67
RULST & REMA.  FIERAMENTE                                            D67
RUYSSEN, P.C.  ALLEGRO                                               B66
SAER, W.  MORCEAU DE CONCERT                                         A96
SAEYS, E.  DIVERTISSEMENT                                            D67
SAINT¬SAENS, C.-BUSSER.  FANTAISIE EN MI BEMOL                       D36
SAINT¬SAENS, C.  MY HEART AT THY SWEET VOICE                        B13
SAINT¬SAENS, C.  ROMANCE, OP.36                                      B85
SAINT¬SAENS, C.  SWAN, THE                                           B13
SAMBIN, V.  MAMAN LES P'TITS BATEAUX                                 C38
SANCAN.  RAPSODIE                                                    N50
SANDERS, R.L.  SQUARE DANCE                                          C33
SARASATE-MENDEZ.  ZAPATEADO                                          C11
SARASATE, P.D.-MENDEZ & KOFF.  ZIGEUNERWEISEN                        D22
SATTERFIELD.  2 MINIATURES                                           A94
SAVARD, A.  CONTEST PIECE                                            B53
SAVARD, A.  MORCEAU DE CONCOURS                                      D36
SAVARD, A.-MAGER.  MORCEAU DE CONCOURS                               F60
SAVERIO-HARRIS.  FLOWER OF THE ORIENT                                D52
SCARLATTI-TALBOT.  GIARDINO DI AMORE, IL                             E14
SCARLATTI, A.-BARNES.  ARIA FROM "TIGRAINE"                          F62
SCHAD.  56 MASTERPIECES                                              F62
SCHAEFER.  SOLOIST, THE                                              C11
SCHAEFFER, H.  POST IM WALDE, DIE                                    D92
SCHAEFFER, H.  POST IM WALDE, DIE                                    E03
SCHAMPAERT, J.  MELODIANA                                            D80
SCHAMPERT.  CAPRICCIO                                                J39
SCHARF, R.-DRABEK.  TROMPETEN SERENADE                               C30
SCHARRES, C.  3 DANSES                                               D67
SCHMEISSER, E.  BERCEUSE                                             F52
SCHMEISSER, E.  VALSE CAPRICE NO.1                                   F52
SCHMIDT, H.  CAPRICCIO                                               D62
SCHMIDT, H.  DEVIL'S TONGUE                                          C11
SCHMIDT, H.  TEUFELSZUNGE, DIE                                       E43
SCHMIDT, W.  TURKISH LADY                                            A43
SCHMITT, F.  ANDANTINO, OP.30B                                       D36
SCHMITT, F.  SUITE, OP.133 (OP)                                      B81
SCHNEIDER, W.(ARR).  KLEINE VORTRAGSSTUCKE ALTER MEISTER             F31
SCHOEMAKER, M.  MORCEAU DE CONCERT                                   A96
SCHOLLUM, R.  SUITE FUR TPT & KLAV                                   A51
SCHUBERT, F.P.-SHEPPARD.  ADIEU                                      G13
SCHUBERT, F.P.-MOLENAAR.  AIR DE ROSAMUNDE                           D64
SCHUBERT, F.P.  AVE MARIA                                            A78
SCHUBERT, F.P.-VACHEY.  AVE MARIA                                    B66
SCHUBERT, F.P.  BERCEUSE                                             D92
SCHUBERT, F.P.-ANDREONI.  MOMENT MUSICALE, OP.94/3                   E98
SCHUBERT, F.P.  POST, OP.89/13                                       B53
SCHUBERT, F.P.  ROSAMUNDE                                            D92
SCHUBERT, F.P.  SERENADE                                             B13
```

```
SCHUBERT, F.P.  SERENADE                                    B53
SCHUBERT, F.P.  SERENADE                                    D92
SCHUBERT, F.P.-MAIJNS.  SERENADE                            D64
SCHUBERT, F.P.-O'NEILL.  SERENADE                           G13
SCHUBERT, F.P.-VACHEY.  SERENADE                            B66
SCHUBERT, F.P.-ANDREONI.  SERENATA                          E98
SCHUMANN, R.-VACHEY.  REVERIE                               B66
SCHUMANN, R.-ANDREONI.  SOGNO, OP.15/7                      E98
SCHUMANN, R.  TRAEUMEREI                                    C19
SCHUMANN, R.-TOBANI.  VOICE OF LOVE                         C11
SCHWAEN.  6 BAGATELLEN                                      B69
SCHWARTZ, A.-SEARS.  DANCING IN THE DARK                    C58
SCHWARTZ, L.  BLUES                                         D81
SCHWARZ, S.  ROMANZE FUR TPT & KLAV                         G03
SCOTT, R.H.W.-TEAGUE.  TOY TRUMPET, THE                     A04
SCOTT, R.H.W.-TEAGUE.  TOY TRUMPET, THE                     E11
SCULL.  BENEATH THY WINDOW                                  G10
SELECTED COMPOSITIONS.                                      A33
SELLENICK.  BAVARDE, LA (TPT IN A)                          D64
SEMLER-COLLERY, A.  AIR ET FINAL                            E66
SEMLER-COLLERY, J.  ETUDES MELODIQUES                       C01
SEMLER-COLLERY, J.  EVOCATION ET SCHERZETTO                 C01
SEMLER-COLLERY, J.  ROMANCE ET TARENTELLE                   C01
SERLY, T.  MIDNIGHT MADRIGAL                                D84
SERRADELL.  GOLONDRINA, LA                                  D92
SHCHELCKOV, V.-GOWER.  BALLADE                              F07
SHCHELOKOV, V.-GOWER.  CAVALIER, THE                        F07
SHCHELOKOV, V.-SATZ.  CONCERT ETUDE NO.1                    D37
SHCHELOKOV, V.-NAGEL.  CONCERT STUDY                        C91
SHCHELOKOV, V.  2 ETUDES                                    D81
SHCHELCKOV, V.-GOWER.  FANFARE MARCH                        F07
SHCHELOKOV, V.-GOWER.  LEGEND                               F07
SHCHELOKOV, V.-GOWER.  SCHERZO                              F07
SHCHELOKOV, V. & ANTIUFEEF.  POEM                           D81
SHEPPARD.  PRIMROSE POLKA                                   G13
SHEPPARD.  WHITE VELVET                                     G13
SHIKHOV, I.  RHUMBA-SCHERZO                                 D81
SHINN.  SOLILOQUY & DIALOGUE                                N91
SHINOHARA, M.  3 PIECES CONCERTANTES                        D36
SHORT.  GLEN ISLAND WALTZ                                   C11
SHORT-BARNES.  ORIOLE                                       D52
SHORT, D.  LITURGICAL SUITE                                 H27
SHOSTAKOVICH, D.  DANSES FANTASTIQUES                       B85
SHOSTAKOVICH, D.  POLKA (THE GOLDEN AGE)                    B85
SHOSTAKOVICH, D.  SATIRICAL DANCE (THE BOLT)               B85
SHOSTAKOVICH, D.-HOLLAND.  SENTIMENTAL ROMANCE              D71
SIEBERT.  LATIN AMERICAN ALBUM                              A78
SIGNARD.  VARIATIONS ON ANNA BOLENA                         M80
SILVER, C.  SCHERZO                                         D36
SILVERMAN(ARR).  HITS FROM BROADWAY                         C27
SILVERMAN(ARR).  PLAY AWAY                                  D63
SILVERTONE FOLIO.                                           F07
SIMEONE, H.  TRUMPET IN THE NIGHT (BOP)                     F43
SIMON.  MISS BLUE BONNET                                    F60
SIMON, F.  WILLOW ECHOES (BP)                               C11
SIMONS, G.  ATLANTIC ZEPHYRS (BP)                           C11
SINGER, L.(ARR).  TENDERLY                                  D96
SINGERLING.  24 TRUMPET TUNES                               D92
SLATER, K.B.-EDWARDS.  MOHAWK VIEW                          A62
SLUYS, L.  ALLEGRO                                          D67
SMETANA-MENDEZ.  DANCE OF THE COMEDIANS                     C11
SMIDVIG, E.  FANFARE & LAMENT                               F43
```

```
SMITH-BARNES.  ENCORE POLKA                               D52
SMITH.  FRIENDS                                           F07
SMITH.  LITTLE MONARCH, THE                               D18
SMITH.  TRUMPETER'S FROLIC                                A91
SMITH, C.  AMONG THE SYCAMORES                            A55
SMITH, C.  ANNIE LAURIE                                   A55
SMITH, C.  CLAY SMITH SOLOS                               A55
SMITH, C.  FANCY FREE                                     A55
SMITH, C.  HARBOR LIGHTS                                  A55
SMITH, C.  IMOGENE                                        A55
SMITH, C.  ITALIANA                                       A55
SMITH, C.  LIFE'S LIGHTER HOURS                           A55
SMITH, C.  MEMORIES OF THE PAST                           A55
SMITH, C.  MILADY'S PLEASURE                              A55
SMITH, C.  MIRAFLORES                                     A55
SMITH, C.  OLD FOLKS AT HOME                              A55
SMITH, C.  OLD KENTUCKY HOME                              A55
SMITH, C.  PHILISTINE                                     A55
SMITH, C.  PIPES O' PAN                                   A55
SMITH, C.  RAINBOW HUES                                   A55
SMITH, C.  SATELLITE                                      A55
SMITH, C.  SMITHSONIAN                                    A55
SMITH, C.  SOUL OF THE SURF                               A55
SMITH, C.  TRUMPETER, THE                                 A55
SMITH, C.  WATER WITCH                                    A55
SMITH, C.  WINGS OF THE MORNING                           A55
SMITH, C. & HOLMES.  CALL OF THE SEA                      A55
SMITH, C. & HOLMES.  MASSA'S IN THE COLD, COLD GROUND     A55
SMITH, C. & HOLMES.  SILVER THREADS AMONG THE GOLD        A55
SMITH, C. & HOLMES.  SMITH & HOLMES FAVORITES             A55
SMITH, C. & HOLMES.  THROUGH SHADOWED VALES               A55
SMITH, C. & HOLMES.  WAYFARER                             A55
SMITH, J.(ARR).  CONCERT ALBUM                            B85
SMITH, J.(ARR).  SUITE CLASSIQUE                          B85
SMITH, L.B.  BLUE DANUBE WALTZ                            G13
SMITH, L.B.  ECSTASY WALTZ                                C11
SMITH, L.B.  FIREFLY                                      A62
SMITH, L.B.  GOLDEN GLOW                                  A62
SMITH, L.B.  NEOPHYTE                                     A62
SMITH, L.B.  PACIFICA                                     F07
SMITH, L.B.  PICNIC TIME                                  A62
SMITH, L.B.  SCOTTISCH FANTASIE                           G13
SMITH, L.E.  SPANISH CAPRICE                              B31
SMITH, L.B.  VENTURE                                      A62
SMITH, L.B.  VIGNETTE                                     C11
SMITH, L.B.  WATERLOO ECHOES                              G13
SMITH, L.B.  WEARIN' O' THE GREEN                         G13
SMITH, R.  CAPRICE CANADIENNE                             G13
SMITH, R.  WATERLOO WALTZ                                 G13
SMITH, W.M.  CAVALIER                                     C11
SMITH, W.M.  DON QUIXOTE                                  C11
SMOLANOFF.  CANTO FOR TPT & STRINGS, OP.18                D84
SODOMKA, K.  PARTITA SEMPLICE (AD LIB CLAR)               A33
SOLLBERGER, H.  IRON MOUNTAIN SONG                        A13
SOUSA, J.P.  STARS & STRIPES FOREVER                      B26
SOUSA, J.P.  STARS & STRIPES FOREVER                      D18
SOUSA, J.P.-WALTERS.  STARS & STRIPES FOREVER            F07
SPARGO.  AIR & MARCH                                      E83
SPEAKS, O.-CLARK.  SYLVIA                                 F23
SPILER, M.  PRELUDE                                       D11
ST. CLAIR.  ADMIRATION                                    G10
ST. CLAIR.  DREAM TIME                                    G10
```

```
ST. CLAIR.  GOLDEN DAY                                          G10
STACHE, H.  CREPUSCULE                                          D67
STAIGERS, D.  CARNIVAL OF VENICE (BP)                           C11
STALMEIER, P.  REVERIE EN ALLEGRO                               D92
STALMEIER, P.  REVERIE ET ALLEGRO SCHERZANDO                    D64
STALMEIER, P.  SOLO DE CONCOURS                                 D92
STANLEY, J.-TARR.  SUITE #1 OF TPT VOLUNTARIES (1 OR 2 D TPT)   M80
STANLEY, J.-COLEMAN.  TRUMPET TUNE "IN C" (OP)                  E51
STARER, R.  INVOCATION                                          D84
STEGMANN.  HUSSASSA                                             N63
STEGMANN.  TROMPETER-KAPRIOLEN                                  F11
STEINEACHER, E.-MIELENZ.  TROMPETISMEN                          C30
STEINER-SCHOENFELD.  TARA THEME                                 E93
STEWART, H.M.(ARR).  BOSTON MUSIC CO. TPT FAVORITES             A81
STOKER, R.  FESTIVAL SUITE                                      B20
STONE, G.  RELICARIO, EL (BULL FIGHTER'S MARCH)                 C45
STONE, G.(ARR).  SHEPHERD'S SONG                                C45
STORM.  ON THE SOUTHERN SEAS (BP)                               D33
STORM.  ROYAL PRINCE                                            D33
STORM.  TEAM WORK                                               D33
STORM, C.W.  GLEN EDEN                                          F07
STORM, C.W.  KENDRICKIS                                         A55
STORM, C.W.  NEW FRIENDSHIP                                     F07
STOUTAMIRE, A.L.  PRELUDE & FUGUE                               D52
STRADELLA, A.  PIETA, SIGNORE                                   B85
STRADELLA, A.-BLOCK.  SINFONIA TO IL BARCHEGGIO, PT 2           E14
STRADELLA, A.-OUBRADOUS.  SONATE DE CONCERT                     F87
STRAUSS-TEAGUE.  MY HERO                                        G31
STRAUSS, R.-WALTERS.  ALLERSEELEN                               F07
STRAUSS, R.  TOMORROW                                           B85
STRAUSS, R.  ZUEIGNUNG                                          B85
STRAUWEN, J.  PETIT CAPRICE                                     A96
STRAVINSKY, I.  DANCE OF THE BALLERINA                          B85
STRAVINSKY, I.  DANCE OF THE PRINCESSES                         B85
STRAVINSKY, I.-GLOVER.  MARCH & CHORALE FR L'HISTOIRE ...       M80
STRAVINSKY, I.-GLOVER.  ROYAL MARCH & CHORALE FR L'HISTOIRE...  M80
STREET.  RONDINO                                                A78
STUARI, H.  FAMOUS TRUMPET FAVORITES                            A81
STULTZ, R.M.-HUMMEL.  SWEETEST STORY EVER TOLD, THE             F07
SUCCESS MODERNES (2 VOL).                                       B24
SULLIVAN, A.S.-O'NEILL.  AH! LEAVE ME NOT TO PINE ALONE         G13
SULLIVAN, A.S.  LOST CHORD, THE                                 D92
SULLIVAN, A.S.-CHAPMAN.  LOST CHORD, THE                        A78
SULLIVAN, A.S.-LEEUWEN.  LOST CHORD, THE                        D64
SULPIZI.  SUITE TROVADORICA                                     M76
SUPPE, F.V.-LONG.  ANDANTE MAESTOSO FR POET & PEASANT           G10
SUPPE, F.V.  BOCCACIO                                           D92
SUPPE, F.V.  HIRTEN MORGENLIED, DES,OP.10                       E03
SUPPE, F.V.  POET & PEASANT OVERTURE                            B13
SUTERMEISTER, H.  GAVOTTE DE CONCERT                            F21
SWINSON, L.  SOLILOQUY (JAZZ-BALLAD STYLE)                      F74
SYDEMAN, W.  AFFECTIONS, THE                                    A38
TABAKOV & ORVID (CMPL).  15 PIECES                              D81
TAILLEFERRE.  GAILLARDE                                         D41
TANENBAUM, E.  ANDANTE & ALLEGRO                                E68
TANNER, P.  BALLAD                                              D71
TANNER, P.  HOEDOWN POLKA                                       D71
TANNER, P.  MINIATURE SUITE OF THE AMERICAS                     D71
TANNER, P.  WALTZ                                               D71
TARTINI, G.-MAGANINI.  INTRODUCTION AND ALLEGRO ASSAI           B85
TARTINI, G.-ORVID & NAGEL.  LARGO & ALLEGRO                     C91
```

TATE-KLICKMAN. SOMEWHERE A VOICE IS CALLING   C58
TAYLOR. 3 SHORT PIECES   C71
TCHAIKOVSKY, P.I. MIGNON'S LAMENT   B53
TCHAIKOVSKY, P.I. NUN WER DIE SEHNSUCHT KENNT   F81
TCHAIKOVSKY, P.I.-BALASANIAN. 12 PIECES FR. CHILDREN'S ALBUM   D81
TCHAIKOVSKY, P.I.-NAGEL. VALSE SENTIMENTALE, OP.51/6   C91
TCHAIKOVSKY, P.I.-HARRIS. WALTZ FR. ALBUM FOR THE YOUNG   D52
TCHEMBERDJY, N.-HOHSTADT. PIONEER SUITE   E87
TELEMANN, G.P.-RUBARDT. AIR   E65
TELEMANN, G.P.-CHIDESTER. ANDANTE AND PRESTO   F60
TELEMANN, G.P.-BARNES. ARIE FROM PIMPINONE   F62
TELEMANN, G.P.-LYMAN. HEROIC MUSIC   C91
TELEMANN, G.P.-CHIDESTER. PRESTO (FR SONATA IN B-FLAT MAJOR)   F60
TEMPLETON, A. TRUMPET TUNE   D37
TENAGLIA, A.F.-FITZGERALD. ARIA (WITH KRIEGER: ALLEGRO)   E77
TENAGLIA, A.F. ARIA ANTICA   B85
THIELE, S. BRILLANTE POLKA   G13
THILMAN. 5 KLEINE STUCKE   D48
THIRY. CAPRICE   D92
THOMAS, A. ARIA UIT MIGNON   D92
THOMAS, S.F. JESTER   F27
THOMAS, S.F. TORERO, EL   F27
THOMAS, S.F. TRUMPET OF DAIRWOOD   F27
THOMAS, S.F. WALTZ PASTEL   F27
THOME, F. FANTAISIE   B53
THOME, F. FANTAISIE   D36
THOME, F.-MAGER. FANTASIE   F60
THOME, F. FANTASY   C91
THOME, F. SIMPLE AVEU   D92
THOMSON, V. AT THE BEACH (BP)   C11
TOLLOT, J. AIR VARIE   C38
TOMASI, H. SEMAINE SAINTE A CUZCO (TPT & PICC. TPT)(OP)   B92
TOMASI, H. SEMAINE SAINTE A CUZCO (TPT & PICC. TPT)(OP)   D36
TOMASI, H. TRIPTYQUE   D36
TOMASI, H. VARIATIONS GREGORIENNES   D36
TORELLI, G.-TARR. SINFONIA IN D G4   E14
TORELLI, G.-SIEDEL. SINFONIA IN D MAJOR   F50
TORELLI, G.-TARR. SINFONIA IN D   E14
TORELLI, G.-TARR. SONATA IN D G5   E14
TOSELLI, E.-VACHEY. CELEBRE "SERENATA"   B66
TOSTI-ANDREONI. IDEALE   E98
TOURNIER. ARIA ET THEME VARIE   N50
TROJE-MILLER, N. HEROIC EPISODE   A62
TROMPETTE, LA.   A71
TROTERE. IN OLD MADRID   B13
TROWBRIDGE, L. ALLA MARCIA   B38
TROWBRIDGE, L. ALLA MARCIA   F60
TROXELL-HENDERSON. MISTY MORNING   D14
TRUMPET TUNES.   F07
TULOU, J.L.-ARBAN. VARIATIONS BRILLANTES   B85
TULST-REMA. ABEA   D67
TULST-REMA. ALLA POLACCA   D67
TULST-REMA. ALLEGRO DE CONCERTINO   D67
TULST-REMA. BRAVURA   D67
TULST-REMA. FIERAMENTE   D67
TULST-REMA. MARCH ANTIQUE   D67
TULST-REMA. MILITARMENTE   D67
TULST-REMA. PETIT MENUET   D67
TULST-REMA. PETIT PIECE CONCERTANTE   D67
TUTHILL, B.C. SCHERZO, OP.10   E11
TYLER, G.H. MIRAGE, THE   F07
TYLER, G.H. PACIFIC ECHOES   F07

ULTAN, L. POET & THE HARLEQUIN, THE   A 13
USOV, G.(ARR). SONGS BY SOVIET COMPOSERS   E 19
UYTTENHOVE, Y. PIECE TRISTE   D 67
VACHEY. RECITATIF ET CARILLON   D 36
VACHEY, H. ARIA & MARCATO   D 36
VACHEY, H. OSTINATI   D 36
VACHEY, H.(ARR). TROMPETTE SELECTION (3 VOL)   B 66
VALLIER. SUITE, OP. 75   D 71
VALVERDE-MENDEZ. CLAVELITAS   C 11
VAN DE MOORTEL, L. ALLEGRO MARZIALE   D 67
VAN DOREN, T. FANTASIE CONCERTANTE   D 80
VAN NERYNEN, J. INTRADA   D 92
VANDERCOOK, H.A. ALBATROSS   F 07
VANDERCOOK, H.A. ALTAIR   F 07
VANDERCOOK, H.A. ANTARES   F 07
VANDERCOOK, H.A. ARBUTUS   C 11
VANDERCOOK, H.A. ARCTURUS   F 07
VANDERCOOK, H.A. BONITA   F 07
VANDERCOOK, H.A. CARNATIONS   C 11
VANDERCOOK, H.A. CHRYSANTHEMUM   C 11
VANDERCOOK, H.A. COLUMBINE   C 11
VANDERCOOK, H.A. COMMANDER, THE   F 07
VANDERCOOK, H.A. DAISIES   C 11
VANDERCOOK, H.A. DEBONNAIRE   F 07
VANDERCOOK, H.A.-BUCHTEL. DEWDROPS   C 11
VANDERCOOK, H.A. FALCON, THE   F 07
VANDERCOOK, H.A. HAWTHORNE   C 11
VANDERCOOK, H.A. HELIOTROPE   C 11
VANDERCOOK, H.A. HYACINTHE   D 18
VANDERCOOK, H.A. IVY   C 11
VANDERCOOK, H.A. JESSAMINE   C 11
VANDERCOOK, H.A. KINGLET   F 07
VANDERCOOK, H.A. LILACS   C 11
VANDERCOOK, H.A. LILY   C 11
VANDERCOOK, H.A. LYRA   F 07
VANDERCOOK, H.A. MAGNOLIA   D 18
VANDERCOOK, H.A. MARIGOLD   C 11
VANDERCOOK, H.A. MEADOWLARK   F 07
VANDERCOOK, H.A. MIGNONETTE   C 11
VANDERCOOK, H.A. MIRA   F 07
VANDERCOOK, H.A. MORNING GLORY   C 11
VANDERCOOK, H.A. MOSS ROSE   C 11
VANDERCOOK, H.A. MYRTLE   C 11
VANDERCOOK, H.A. ORIOLE   F 07
VANDERCOOK, H.A. ORION   F 07
VANDERCOOK, H.A. PANSIES   C 11
VANDERCOOK, H.A. PEONY   C 11
VANDERCOOK, H.A. PRIMROSE   C 11
VANDERCOOK, H.A. PUNCHINELLO   F 07
VANDERCOOK, H.A. RIGEL   F 07
VANDERCOOK, H.A. ROSEBUDS   C 11
VANDERCOOK, H.A. SIRUS   F 07
VANDERCOOK, H.A. SPICA   F 07
VANDERCOOK, H.A. STARLING   F 07
VANDERCOOK, H.A. TULIP   C 11
VANDERCOOK, H.A. VEGA   F 07
VANDERCOOK, H.A. WILD ROSE   C 11
VARDI. MODERN SENSATIONS   D 84
VASSILENKO, S.N.-BLAZHEVICH. 2 PIECES   D 81
VELLERE, L. ARLEQUINADE   D 67
VERACINI. 2 CLASSIC DANCES   B 85
VERDI, G.-ANDREONI. ADDIO, DEL PASSATO (LA TRAVIATA)   E 98

VERDI, G.-O'NEILL. AH! WAS IT HIM MY HEART FORETOLD(TRAVIATA)	G13
VERDI, G.-ANDREONI. AH, FORSE E LUI CHE L'ANIMA (TRAVIATA)	E98
VERDI, G. ATILLA GRAND AIR	D92
VERDI, G.-MENDEZ. CARO NOME (RIGOLETTO)	C11
VERDI, G.-ANDREONI. CARO NOME CHE IL MIO COR (RIGOLETTO)	E98
VERDI, G.-ARBAN. FANTAISIE ON NABUCCO	N66
VERDI, G.-ANDREONI. LIBIAM NE'LIETI CALIMI (TRAVIATA)	E98
VERDI, G. RIGOLETTO FANTASIE	D92
VERDI, G.-ANDREONI. STRIDE LA VAMPA (TROVATORE)	E98
VERDI, G.-ANDREONI. TACEA LA NOTTE PLACIDA (TROVATORE)	E98
VERDI, G.-ANDREONI. TUTTE LE FESTE (RIGOLETTO)	E98
VERDI, G.-ANDREONI. VA, PENSIERO	E98
VICTORY. TRIPTYQUE	D36
VIDAL, P. AIR ET FANFARE	D36
VILLE, P.D. BLUE BELLS OF SCOTLAND (BP)	C11
VINCENT. GALAXY	A62
VITTORIA, M. CHANSON ET DANSE	D36
VIVALDI, A.-FITZGERALD. ALLEGRO	B32
VIVALDI, A.-MAGANINI. SUITE IN C MINOR	B85
VLASOV, V.A. ARIA	D81
VOISIN, R.L.(CMPL). ALBUM OF 12 CLASSICAL PIECES	C91
VOXMAN, H.(ED). CONCERT & CONTEST COLLECTION	F07
VREULS, V. MORCEAU DE CONCERT	A82
WAGNER, R.-BUCHTEL. EVENING STAR	D18
WAGNER, R.-ROBERTS. SONG TO THE EVENING STAR	C11
WAGNER, R. WALTER'S PREISLIED	D92
WAGNER, R.-TRINKHAUS. WALTER'S PRIZE SONG	C09
WAIGNEIN, A. DIVERTIMENTO	D67
WAIGNEIN, A. FANFAREN, LE	D67
WAIGNEIN, A. HUMORESQUE	D67
WAIGNEIN, A. 3 MOVEMENTS	D36
WAIGNEIN, A. TRUMPETINA	D67
WALDTEUFEL, E. ESPANA	B95
WALDTEUFEL, E. ESTUDIANTINA	B95
WALKER. VALSE CASUEL	A81
WALLACE-O'NEILL. EXCERPTS FROM MARTANA	G13
WALTERS. AD LIB	A91
WALTERS. AMAZING GRACE	F07
WALTERS, D. EPISODE	F60
WALTERS, D. FANTASY	E80
WALTERS, H.L. BEGUINE & BOP IN B-FLAT	F07
WALTERS, H.L. DARK EYES	A91
WALTERS, H.L. FAT BOY POLKA	F07
WALTERS, H.L. ONE-FINGER POLKA (BP)	F07
WALTERS, H.L. SHINDIG	F07
WALTERS, H.L. TRUMPET HOLIDAY	F07
WALTERS, H.L. WHEN THE SAINTS GO MARCHING IN	F07
WARD. SIERRA MORENA	F62
WARD, N. FANTASY	D14
WARNER & SHUMAN. BILLY & I	D84
WARNIZEK. THEMA MET VARIATIES	D92
WARREN, D. SHAKOS ON PARADE	D52
WARRINGTON, J.(ARR). MAME, & HELLO DOLLY	D92
WASSILJEW, S. SCHERZINO	D97
WATTERS, C.(ARR). 5 GREAT TUNES	A78
WATTERS, C.(ARR). RHYTHM ROUNDABOUT	A78
WEBBER, L. CASTLE HEDINGHAM	A35
WEBBER, L. SUITE IN F MAJOR	D84
WEBER, A. STROPHES (OP)	D36
WEBER, C.M.V.-O'NEILL. LEISSE, LEISSE FROMME WEISE	G13
WEBER, C.M.V.-LAUBE. ROMANZA APPASSIONATA	B53
WEBER, F.(ARR). CARNIVAL OF VENICE	A62

WURMSER. FANTASIA	F87
WURMSER. PETIT SOLO DE CONCOURS	A71
WURMSER. POCHADE	A71
YADIER. PALOMA, LA	D92
YEREMIN, S.(CMPL). 40 SELECTED ETUDES (2 VOL)	D81
YORKE, P. GOLD DUST	E59
YUSTE, M. ANDRANZAS MEMORIAS, OP. 96	A38
YUSTE, M. ANORANZAS MEMORIAS, OP.96	F95
ZANINELLI. AUTUMN MUSIC	F79
ZBINDEN, J.F. PRAELUDIUM, FUGUE AND POSTLUDIUM	A78
ZBINDEN, J.F. PRALUDIUM, FUGE UND POSTLUDIUM,OP.39	A90
ZEHM, F. CANTO E RONDO	F31
ZELLER. OBERSTEIGER, DER	D92
ZELLER. SCHENKT MAN SICH ROSEN	D92
ZELLER-JAKMA. SCHENKT MAN SICH ROSEN	D64
ZIMMERMAN. AUTUMN DREAMS	H06
ZOBEL. AFTERGLOW	D18
ZOBEL. DESERT DREAMS	D18
ZOBEL. FOREST MOODS	D18
ZOBEL. MIDNIGHT SERENADE	D18
ZOBEL. SPRUCE SHADOWS	D18
ZVEREV, V.I. 3 PIECES	D81

0107   TRUMPET SOLOS, UNACCOMPANIED

ADLER, S.H. CANTO I	E51
ARMENIAN, G. 4 IMPROVISATIONS	D81
ARNOLD, M. FANTASY	C05
BARTLES. SONATINA	M80
BLANK, A. 3 PIECES	N37
BON. PETITE TRILOGOE	B74
BROADWAY SHOWCASE.	H06
BRONS. MONOLOGUE V	B74
CAMPO. TIMES, OP. 39	N43
CHANSONS DE FRANCE, LES.	A71
CHILDS, B. INTERBALANCES IV (TPT OPT. NARRATOR)	F88
COPE, D. ETRB (THEATRE PIECE)	M80
CROLEY, R. VARIAZIONI	F80
DARTER. SONATINA	M92
DUFOUR, O. PETITE PIECE D'EXAMEN, SIMPLEX	C49
ENDSLEY, G. CHANT	M80
ENDSLEY, G. CHANT	N66
FERNAND. 1ST PIECE D'EXAMEN	C49
GALLAY, J.F. 20 MELODIES, OP.33 (2 VOL)	D41
GALLAY, J.F. 18 MELODIES, OP.53 (2 VOL)	D41
GAMMES DE LARUE.	A71
GAUDERFROY. PETITE PIECE D'EXAMEN	C49
GOLDSTEIN, A.E. FIRST BOOK OF SOLOS FOR TPT, A	B44
GREAT THEMES MADE EASY.	H06
GREEN, G. TRIPTYCH	D50
GREEN, G. TRIPTYCH	G83
HACOUT, E. PIECE D'EXAMEN, 1ST DIVISION	C49
HACOUT, E. PIECE D'EXAMEN, 2ND DIVISION	C49
HENDERSON. VARIATION MOVEMENTS	A43
HOFFMAN. 4 MINIATURES	N66
HOUSIAUX. IMPROMPTU	C49
HOUSTON-COLIN. TIJUANA TRUMPETS	B31
JAEGGI. CARINTHIA-MELODIE	F10

```
JOB, M. (CMPL).  SCHOOL FOR CANTABILE AND STYLE            D36
JOLIVET, A.  AIR DE BRAVOURE                               C91
KARG-ELERT.  25 CAPRICEN & SONATE (2 BKS)                  G43
KETTING, O.  INTRADA                                       B74
KLAUSS, K.  SONATA FOR SOLO TRUMPET                        B35
KOBETZ.  VARIANTS                                          N42
LAMB, J.D.  WILDERNESS SKETCHES                            G89
LEDUC, P.  ECHOS ALPESTRES, LES (2 VOL)                    D41
MANCINI, A.  DIVERTISSEMENTS FOR TPT (2 VOL)               G85
METRA, O.  50 CELEBRATED DANCES                            C65
MOREL.  5TH ETUDE                                          C49
MORYL.  SALVOS                                             C40
NATRA.  SONATINA                                           A78
PETIT, A.S.(& OTHERS).  POPULAR REPERTOIRE FOR THE CORNETIST  C38
POWELL.  ALONE                                             N79
POWELL, M.  ALONE                                          M80
PRESSER, W.H.  SUITE                                       B98
RAHN.  COUNTERPOINTS                                       G83
RASCH.  'T UITNEMENT KABINET, BK 1                         N84
RENWICK, W.  ENCORE PIECE                                  M80
ROBINSON, K.  VISIONS-ELOQUENT & TRIUMPHANT                N07
SACCO.  3 SONGS                                            N38
SAMBATARO, D.  STUDI                                       G41
SCHNEIDER, W.  FIRST TROMPETENSPIEL, LIEDER (1-3 TPT)      F31
SCHNEIDER, W.  SUITE                                       D98
SCHROTER, H.  FANFARETTE                                   D36
SCHUBERT, F.P.-MUSSER.  SCHUBERT UNACCOMPANIED SONG STUDIES  A03
SHADWELL.  THEME & VARIATIONS                              N66
STEIN, L.  SONATA                                          B36
TOUR DU MONDE, LE.                                         A71
VACKER.  PARTITA                                           C03
VACKER.  4 POEMS                                           C03
WEINER.  5 PIECES                                          A71
WHITTENBERG, C.  POLYPHONY FOR SOLO C TRUMPET              E68
WINICK.  EQUINOCTIAL POINTS                                G83
WOLPE.  SOLO PIECE                                         D55
```

0111 HORN CONCERTOS AND CONCERTINOS

ALBRECHTSBERGER. CONCERTO IN B-FLAT MAJOR (P)	C91
AMRAM. CONCERTO (P)	E65
ARNOLD, M. CONCERTO (P)	D42
ARNOLD, M. CONCERTO #2, OP. 58 (O)	E58
ASCHENERENNER, J. KONZERT (O)	F50
ATTERBERG, K. CONCERTO, OP. 28 (OP)	A89
ATTERBERG, K. KONSERT, OP. 28 (P)	B90
BANKS. CONCERTO (O)	F31
BARBIER, R. CONCERTO, OP. 106 (OP)	B12
BARTSCH, C. CONCERTINO (O)	D67
BECKER, J.J. CONCERTO (O)	E30
BENNETT, R.R. KONZERT (O)	F97
BERTINI-PELLEG. CONCERTO (P)	C94
BJELINSKI. CONCERTINO (P)	C41
BLUME, H. KONZERT (P)	C54
BORRIS, S. KONZERT, OP. 89 (O)	F53
BRESGEN, C. KONZERT (P)	C41
CORRETTE-LELOIR. CONCERTO "LA CHOISY" (P)	C60
DAETWYLER, J. CONCERTO POUR 4 CORS	H03
DANZI, F. CONCERTO (O)	D61
DEBAAR, M. CONCERTO (O)	D67
DEVIENNE-LELOIR. CONCERTO IN C (P)	D11
DRIESSLER, J. KONZERT, OP. 16 (O)	A51
DUBOIS, P.M. CONCERTO (OP)	D36
DUVERNOY, F.-LELOIR. CONCERTO #3	D11
DUVERNOY, F.-LELOIR. CONCERTO #5 (OP)	D11
FLOTHUIS, M. CONCERTO, OP. 24 (OP)	B74
FOERSTER-JANETZKY. KONZERT (O)	C75
FORSTER, C.-JANETZKY & SCHLENKER. CONCERT, E-FLAT (P)	C75
FREHSE, A. STUDIENKONZERT FUR TIEFES HORN (P)	C75
GALLAY, J.F.-LELOIR. CONCERTO (OP)	D11
GERSTER, O. KONZERT (P)	E65
GLIERE, R.M.-POLEKH. CONCERTO IN B-FLAT, OP. 91	C91
GLIERE, R.M.-SEROSTANOV. CONCERTO, OP 82 (1ST MOV'T) (P)	D81
GLIERE, R.M.-SINGER. CONCERTO, OP. 91 (OP)	D37
GLIERE, R.M.-SINGER. CONCERTO, OP. 91 (P)	E98
GLIERE, R.M. KCNZERT, OP. 91 (P)	F50
GOEDICKE, A.F. ADAGIO FROM "CONCERTO" (P)	B53
GOEDICKE, A.F. ALLEGRO FROM "CONCERTO" (P)	B53
GOEDICKE, A.F. CONCERTO (OP)	D71
GOEDICKE, A.F. CONCERTO, OP. 40 (P)	D81
GOEDICKE, A.F. KONZERT, OP. 40 (P)	F50
GOLTERMANN, G.E. ANDANTE FROM CELLO CCNCERTO, OP.14 (P)	B53
HANDEL, G.F.-BARR. SARABANDE PR CONCERTO IN F MINOR (P)	D52
HASQUENOPH, P. CONCERTINO (O)	F31
HASQUENOPH, P. CONCERTINO (OP)	C01
HAUGLAND, A.O. CONCERTINO (P)	B30
HAYDN, J.-SHERMAN. CONCERTINO (O)	F97
HAYDN, J. CONCERTINO (OP)	H05
HAYDN, J. CONCERTO (O)	D08
HAYDN, J.-LELOIR. CONCERTO (2 HN) (OP)	D11
HAYDN, J. CONCERTO #1 (OP)	A78
HAYDN, J. CONCERTO #1 (P)	B53
HAYDN, J.-MANDYCZEWSKI. CONCERTO #1 (P)	A89
HAYDN, J.-MANDYCZOWSKI. CONCERTO #1 (P)	A78

```
HAYDN, J.-CERMINARO.  CONCERTO #1                                   C91
HAYDN, J.-BUSHOUSE.  CONCERTO #2 (FIRST MOV'T) (P)                  D14
HAYDN, J.-MANDYCZEWSKI.  CONCERTO #2 (OP)                           A89
HAYDN, J.  CONCERTO #2 (P)                                          D81
HAYDN, J.-MANDYCZOWSKI.  CONCERTO #2 (P)                            A78
HAYDN, J.-POTTAG.  CONCERTO #2 (P)                                  B53
HAYDN, J.-CERMINARO.  CONCERTO #2                                   C91
HAYDN, J.-STEVES.  CONCERTO NO. 2 (P)                               A78
HAYDN, J.-WOLLHEIM.  KONZERT (O)                                    A83
HAYDN, J.  KONZERT (2 HN) (OP)                                      C60
HAYDN, J.  KONZERT #1 (OP)                                          A89
HAYDN, J.-LELOIR.  KONZERT FUR ZWEI HORNER (OP)                     C60
HAYDN, M.-LELOIR.  CONCERTO IN D (P)                                C60
HENSELT, A.VON.  CONCERTINO, OP. 80                                 D81
HESS, W.  KONZERT, OP. 65 (P)                                       C03
HINDEMITH, P.  CONCERTO (1949) (OP)                                 F31
HODDINOTT, A.  CONCERTO (O)                                         E51
HOFFMEISTER, F.A.-CHAMBERS.  CONCERTO (2 HN) (OP)                   C91
HOVHANESS, A.S.  ARTIK. CONCERTO (OP)                               E65
HOVHANESS, A.S.  CONCERTO #3 (DIRAN) (O)                            D16
HOVHANESS, A.S.  CONCERTO #3 DIRAN (O)                              D16
HUBLER, H.  CONCERTO FOR 4 HORNS (O)                                D11
JACOB, G.P.  CONCERTO (O)                                           G26
JONG, DE.  CONCERTO (P)                                             B12
KARADIMCHEV.  CONCERTO (P)                                          D11
KARKOFF, M.  KONSERT, OP. 40 (P)                                    B90
KOMAROVSKY, A.  CONCERTO (P)                                        D81
KORN, P.J.  CONCERTINO, OP. 15 (P)                                  A78
KREK, U.  KONZERT (O)                                              C41
KRICKA, J.  CONCERTO, OP. 102 (P)                                   A33
KROL, B.  CADENZAS TO MOZART HN CONCERTOS #3&4                      F52
KROL, E.  CONCERTO (STUDY IN JAZZ), OP.29 (P)                       F52
KUDELSKI, K.M.-SANSONE.  FRENCH HORN CONCERTINO (OP)               F60
LANG.  CONCERTO BUCOLICO (P)                                        B84
LARSSON, L.E.V.  CONCERTINO, OP. 45/5 (OP)                          C39
LECLERCQ, M.  CONCERTO (O)                                          D67
LEUTWILER.  CONCERTINO (O)                                          E37
LEWIS, A.C.  CONCERTO (P)                                           D42
MANIET, R.  CONCERTINO (O)                                          D67
MANZO, S.  CONCERTO (P)                                             G38
MATYS, K.  CONCERTO #3, OP. 39                                      F60
MENGELBERG, K.  CONCERTO (OP)                                       B74
MERCADANTE.  CONCERTO (P)                                           G95
MEULEMANS, A.  CONCERTO (OP)                                        B12
MEULEMANS, A.  CONCERTO #2 (OP)                                     B12
MOULAERT, R.  EROICA (OP)                                           B12
MOYSE, L.  MARLOBORIAN CONCERTO (2 HN) (O)                          D55
MOZART, L.-LELOIR.  CONCERTO (2 HN) (OP)                            D11
MOZART, L.-LELOIR.  CONCERTO, HN IN D (OP)                          D11
MOZART, W.A.  ADAGIO (P)                                            B53
MOZART, W.A.  ADAGIO AUS KONZERT, OP.107 (P)                        B99
MOZART, W.A.-KROL.  CADENZAS TO MOZART'S HN CONCERTOS #3 & 4        F60
MOZART, W.A.-BLAAUW.  CONCERT #1 (P)                                D64
MOZART, W.A.  CONCERTO #1 (P)                                       D81
MOZART, W.A.  CONCERTO #1, K. 412 (BOP)                             F60
MOZART, W.A.  CONCERTO #1, K. 412 (O)                               D08
MOZART, W.A.-KLING.  CONCERTO #1, K. 412 (O)                        A89
MOZART, W.A.-KLING.  CONCERTO #1, K. 412 (OP)                       A89
MOZART, W.A.  CONCERTO #1, K. 412 (P)                               B53
MOZART, W.A.-CHAMBERS.  CONCERTO #1, K. 412 (P)                     C91
MOZART, W.A.  CONCERTO #1, K.412 (BOP)                              F60
```

MOZART, W.A. CONCERTO #2	D64
MOZART, W.A.-VOXMAN. CONCERTO #2 (P)	F07
MOZART, W.A.-VOXMAN. CONCERTO #2 (3RD MOV'T) (P)	F07
MOZART, W.A.-SANSONE. CONCERTO #2, K. 417 (BOP)	F60
MOZART, W.A. CONCERTO #2, K. 417 (O)	D08
MOZART, W.A.-KLING. CONCERTO #2, K. 417 (OP)	A89
MOZART, W.A. CONCERTO #2, K. 417 (P)	B53
MOZART, W.A.-CHAMBERS. CONCERTO #2, K. 417 (P)	C91
MOZART, W.A. CONCERTO #3, K. 447 (O)	D08
MOZART, W.A. CONCERTO #3, K. 447 (OP)	F60
MOZART, W.A.-KLING. CONCERTO #3, K. 447 (OP)	A89
MOZART, W.A. CONCERTO #3, K. 447 (P)	B53
MOZART, W.A. CONCERTO #3, K. 447 (P)	C19
MOZART, W.A.-CHAMBERS. CONCERTO #3, K. 447 (P)	C91
MOZART, W.A.-FAULX. CONCERTO #3, K. 447 (P)	A96
MOZART, W.A.-OUSSOV. CONCERTO #3, K. 447 (P)	D81
MOZART, W.A.-POTTAG. CONCERTO #3, K. 447 (P)	C11
MOZART, W.A.-REINECKE. CONCERTO #3, K. 447 (P)	C11
MOZART, W.A.-SALOMON. CONCERTO #3, K. 447 (P)	A78
MOZART, W.A. CONCERTO #3, K.447 (SCORE ONLY) (O)	C03
MOZART, W.A.-VOXMAN. CONCERTO #3, K.447 (2ND MOV'T) (P)	F07
MOZART, W.A. CONCERTO #4, K. 495 (O)	D08
MOZART, W.A. CONCERTO #4, K. 495 (O)	D11
MOZART, W.A. CONCERTO #4, K. 495 (OP)	F60
MOZART, W.A.-KLING. CONCERTO #4, K. 495 (OP)	A89
MOZART, W.A. CONCERTO #4, K. 495 (P)	B53
MOZART, W.A. CONCERTO #4, K. 495 (P)	D81
MOZART, W.A.-CHAMBERS. CONCERTO #4, K. 495 (P)	C91
MOZART, W.A.-SALOMON. CONCERTO #4, K. 495 (P)	A78
MOZART, W.A.-KLING. CONCERTO IN D MAJOR (P)	E11
MOZART, W.A. CONCERTO, K. 417 (P)	A78
MOZART, W.A. 4 CONCERTOS & CONCERT RONDO (P)	F23
MOZART, W.A. 4 HORN CONCERTOS AND CONCERT RONDO (P)	F23
NEULING, H. KONZERT-CADENZ (P)	E81
PASSANI. CONCERTO (P)	F87
PATTERSON, P. CONCERTO (P)	A78
PAUER, J. KONZERT (OP)	A51
PORRET, J. CONCERTINO #5 (P)	D64
PORRET, J. CONCERTINO #6 (P)	D64
PUNTO, G. (SEE STICH)	
RISTORI, E. CONCERTO IN A MINOR (P)	A96
ROESSLER, F.A. (SEE ROSETTI)	
ROSETTI, F.A.-WEELINK. CONCERTO #II(15) IN E-FLAT (OP) (2 HN)	D11
ROSETTI, F.A.-WEELINK. CONCERTO #V(18) IN E-FLAT (OP) (2 HN)	D11
ROSETTI, F.A.-LELOIR. CONCERTO #1 IN E-FLAT (OP)	D11
ROSETTI, F.A.-LELOIR. CONCERTO #2 IN E-FLAT (OP)	D11
ROSETTI, F.A.-LELOIR. CONCERTO #3 IN E-FLAT (OP)	D11
ROSETTI, F.A.-LELOIR. CONCERTO #4 IN F (OP)	D11
ROSETTI, F.A.-LELOIR. CONCERTO #5 IN E (OP)	D11
ROSETTI, F.A.-LELOIR. CONCERTO #6 IN D (OP)	D11
ROSETTI, F.A.-WEELINK. CONCERTO #6	D11
ROSETTI, F.A. CONCERTO FOR 2 HN IN E-FLAT (OP)	D61
ROSETTI, F.A.-KROL. CONCERTO IN D MINOR (P)	F52
ROSETTI, F.A.-DAMM. CONCERTO IN E (2 HN)(OP)	D11
ROSETTI, F.A.-STEFAN. CONCERTO IN E MAJOR (2 HN) (P)	F52
ROSETTI, F.A.-CHAMBERS. CONCERTO IN E MAJOR (2 HN)	C91
ROSETTI, F.A. CONCERTO IN E-FLAT (O)	A89
ROSETTI, F.A.-CHAMBERS. CONCERTO IN E-FLAT (P)	C91
ROSETTI, F.A.-DAMM & HAUER. CONCERTO IN E-FLAT MAJOR (P)	B69
SABATINI, G. CLASSICAL CONCERTO (O)	B44
SANSONE, L. CADENZA FOR ANY MOZART E-FLAT CONCERTO	F60
SANSONE, L. CONCERTINO (BP)	F60

```
SCHOECK, O.  CONCERTO, OP. 65 (OP)                                    A78
SIKORSKI, K.  CONCERTO (O)                                           A 31
SIKORSKI, K.-LACHOWSKA.  CONCERTO (P)                                 E72
SKROUP.  KONZERT (O)                                                 A51
SMYTH, E.  CONCERTO FOR HN & VN (OP)                                  G58
STAMITZ, K.-LEBERMANN & MAY.  CONCERTO, E-FLAT (P)                    F31
STICH, J.W.-LELOIR.  CONCERTO #5, F MAJOR (OP)                        D11
STICH, J.W.  HORN CONCERTO #7 IN F (P)                                E02
STRAUSS, F.-BUIANOVSKY.  CONCERTO (P)                                 E 19
STRAUSS, F.  CONCERTO, OP. 8 (OP)                                     F97
STRAUSS, F.  CONCERTO, OP. 8 (P)                                      B53
STRAUSS, F.  CONCERTO, OP. 8 (P)                                      C11
STRAUSS, F.  CONCERTO, OP. 8 (P)                                      F60
STRAUSS, R.-PERRY.  2ND CONCERTO (OP)                                 A78
STRAUSS, R.  CONCERTO #1, OP. 11 (P)                                  C91
STRAUSS, R.  CONCERTO #1, OP. 11 (P)                                  F23
STRAUSS, R.  CONCERTO, OP. 11 (OP)                                    F97
STRAUSS, R.  CONCERTO, OP. 11 (P)                                     B53
TELEMANN, G.P.  CONCERTO FOR 2 HNS IN D (OP)                          D 11
TELEMANN, G.P.-WINSCHERMANN & BUCH.  CONCERTO IN D (P)                F50
TELEMANN, G.P.-SEIFFERT.  CONCERTO IN E-FLAT MAJOR (2 HN)             A89
TELEMANN, G.P.-LELOIR.  KONZERT, D MAJOR (OP)                         C60
TELEMANN, G.P.  KONZERT, D MAJOR (P)                                  F50
THATCHER, H.R.  CONCERTO (O)                                          B44
TOLDI, J.  KONZERT (OP)                                               F31
TOMASI, H.  CONCERTO (P)                                              D36
VAN DOREN, T.  CONCERTO (P)                                           D80
VASSILENKO, S.N.  CONCERTO, OP. 136 (P)                               D81
VEREMANS, R.  CONCERTO (O)                                            D67
VIVALDI, A.-SABATINI.  CONCERTO (OP)                                  B44
WEBER, C.M.V.  CONCERTINO E MINOR, OP. 45 (P)                         D46
WEBER, C.M.V.-CERMINARO.  CONCERTINO IN E-FLAT, OP. 45 (P)            C91
WEBER, C.M.V.-KLING.  CONCERTINO IN E MINOR, OP. 45 (P)               A89
WEBER, C.M.V.  CONCERTINO IN F, OP. 45 (P)                            D46
WEBER, C.M.V.-LELOIR.  CONCERTINO, OP. 45 (O)                         D11
WEBER, C.M.V.  CONCERTINO, OP. 45 (P)                                 B53
WEBER, C.M.V.-KLING.  CONCERTINO, OP. 45 (P)                          D 11
WEINER, S.  CONCERTO (OP)                                             D71
WERNER, J.J.  CONCERTO (P)                                            C01
WINSCHERMANN (ARR).  KONZERT ES-DUR (2 HN)(OP)(POSSIBLY HAYDN)        F50
```

0112   HORN SONATAS AND SONATINAS

```
ADAMS, L.  LARGO (FR. EMPIRE SONATA)                                  A38
ADLER, S.H.  SONATA                                                   D16
AMBROSIUS, H.  SONATA                                                 D81
AMBROSIUS, H.  SONATE F MAJOR                                         C75
AUBAIN.  SONATINE                                                     B24
BASSETT, L.R.  SONATA                                                 D16
BEETHOVEN, L.V.  SONATA IN F, OP. 17                                  A38
BEETHOVEN, L.V.  SONATA, OP. 17                                       B53
BEETHOVEN, L.V.  SONATA, OP. 17                                       C11
BEETHOVEN, L.V.  SONATA, OP. 17                                       C91
BEETHOVEN, L.V.  SONATA, OP. 17                                       D41
BEETHOVEN, L.V.  SONATA, OP. 17                                       E65
BEETHOVEN, L.V.-LELOIR.  SONATA, OP. 17                               F52
BEETHOVEN, L.V.-WOLFF.  SONATA, OP. 17                                A78
BENTZON, N.V.  SONATA, OP. 47                                         H30
```

```
BEVERSDORF, T.  MODERN SONATA                                    F60
BOISMORTIER-SHAW.  SONATA                                        C78
BORRIS, S.  SONATE                                              F53
BORROFF.  SONATA                                                D16
BUSSER, H.P.  CONCERT PIECE IN D                                F60
CAZDEN, N.  SONATA, OP. 33                                      F62
CHERUBINI, L.-CHAMBERS.  2 SONATAS                              C91
CHERUBINI, L.-WOJCIECHOWSKI.  2 SONATAS                         F50
COPE, D.  SONATA                                                B35
CORELLI, A.-SABATINI.  SONATA (OP)                              B44
CORELLI, A.  SONATA IN F                                        B85
CORELLI, A.  SONATA IN G MINOR                                  B85
CORTESE, L.  SONATA                                             D84
CORTESE, L.  SONATA, OP. 34                                     B07
DANZI, F.-CHAMBERS.  SONATA IN E-FLAT, OP. 28                   C91
DANZI, F.-WOJCIECHOWSKI.  SONATE CONCERTANTE, OP. 44            F50
DANZI, F.-HAUSSWALD.  SONATE IN E-FLAT MAJOR, OP. 28            C75
DAUPRAT, L.F.  SONATE IN F                                      B24
DONATO, A.  SONATA                                             E11
ECCLES, H.-EGER.  SONATA IN G MINOR                             C91
EDER, H.  SONATINE, OP 34#6                                     B73
FINKE, F.F.  SONATA                                            A89
FRICKER, P.R.  SONATA, OP. 24                                   F31
GENZMER.  SONATINE                                              D48
GIPPS, R.  SONATINA, OP. 56                                     C25
GRAAP.  SONATINE                                                C75
GUILLOU, R.  SONATINA POUR SAX ALTO OU COR                      D36
GWILT.  SONATINA                                                P24
HAAS, J.  SONATE, OP. 29                                        F31
HADDAD, D.  SONATA                                              F43
HAMILTON, I.  SONATA NOTTURNA                                   F31
HANDEL, G.F.  3RD SONATA (ORIGINALLY FOR VIOLIN)               F60
HANDEL, G.F.-EGER.  SONATA IN G MINOR                           A38
HAYDN, J.-MULLER.  SONATINE                                     D67
HEIDEN, B.  SONATA                                             A38
HINDEMITH, P.  SONATA FOR ALTO HORN                             A38
HINDEMITH, P.  SONATA FOR HORN                                  F31
HODDINOTT, A.  SONATA, OP. 78/2                                 E51
HUGHES, M.  SONATA                                             F80
KAZANDJIEV.  SONATA                                             D11
KILAR, W.  SONATA                                              E72
KOEHLER.  SONATE, OP. 32                                        B69
KORN, P.J.  SONATA, OP. 18                                      F52
KREISLER.  SONATINA                                            F60
KROL, B.  SONATE, OP. 1                                         E81
LEROUX, X.H.N.-CHAMBERS.  SONATA                                C91
LEROUX, X.H.N.  SONATE                                          D36
LOEILLET, J.B.  SONATA IN G MINOR                              C91
MANZO, S.  SONATA (CONCERTO A FORM DI SONATA)                   G38
MOZART, W.A.  HOORNSONATA #1                                    D92
MOZART, W.A.  HOORNSONATA #2                                    D92
MOZART, W.A.  SONATA #6                                         F60
MOZART, W.A.-EHRLICH.  SONATA #6, K. 332                        B99
MOZART, W.A.-SANSONE.  SONATA #6                                F60
MOZART, W.A.  SONATA IN E-FLAT FOR 2 HNS                        B44
MOZART, W.A.-PLOYHAR.  SONATA THEME                             G85
MOZART, W.A.-MULLER.  SONATINE                                  D67
MULDER, H.  SONATE #4, OP. 43                                   B74
PASCAL, C.  SONATE                                             B92
PETERSON, H.  SONATINA                                          P31
PILSS, K.  3 PEZZI IN FORMA DI SONATA                          B73
```

```
PISK, P.A.   SONATA, OP. 77                                    E68
PORTER, Q.   SONATA                                           D16
PORTER, Q.   SONATA                                           E11
FOSER, H.   SONATA, OP. 8                                     F30
PURCELL, H.   SONATA IN G MINOR                               B85
REITER, A.   SONATINE                                        B73
REYNOLDS, V.   SONATA                                        F60
RHEINBERGER, J.-KASTNER.  SONATE IN E-FLAT MAJOR, OP. 178    F31
RIES, F.  SONATA IN F MAJOR, OP. 34                          F31
RUSSELL, R.  SONATA IN ONE MOVEMENT                          C40
RYCHLIK.  PUPIL'S SONATINE                                   C40
RYELANDT, J.  SONATE, OP. 18                                 B12
SANDERS, R.L.  SONATA IN E-FLAT                              D16
SCHREITER, H.  SONATINE, OP. 12                              A83
SCHUMANN, G.  SONATINE                                       F53
STEIN, L.  SONATA (UNACC.)                                   B36
STEVENS, H.  SONATA                                          E68
TELEMANN, G.P.-EGER.  SONATA IN F MINOR                      C91
TUROK, P.  SONATA, OP. 36                                    M80
VALLIER, J.  SONATINE, OP. 55                                C01
VERRALL, J.  SONATA                                          E68
VIGNERY, J.  SONATA, OP. 7                                   A96
WILDER, A.  SONATA #1                                        B14
WILDER, A.  SONATA #2                                        B14
WILDER, A.  SONATA #3                                        H09
WILDGANS, F.  SONATINE, OP. 5                                B73
ZVEREV, V.I.  SONATA                                         E19
```

0113   HORN SOLOS WITH BAND ACCOMPANIMENT

```
BENNETT, D.  HORNASCOPE (B)                                       F60
CONCONE, G.-SANSONE.  ROCCONTO (A LITTLE STORY) (B)              F60
FOX, F.A.  ESSAY FOR HN & WIND ENS (B)                           G89
FRANZ, O.-SANSONE.  CONCERT PIECE, OP. 4 (2 HN)                  F60
FRANZ, O.-SANSONE.  CONCERT PIECE, OP. 4 FOR 2 HNS (B)          F60
GODARD, B.-SANSONE.  BERCEUSE FROM "JOCELYN" (B)                F60
GOTTWALD, H.-SANSONE.  FRIENDSHIP (BP)                          F60
HADDAD, D.  ADAGIO & ALLEGRO (B)                                F78
LEVERMANN, W.  SERENADE ESPAGNOLA (BOP)                         F60
MALTBY.  BLUES ESSAY (B)                                        D63
MOZART, W.A.-BARDEEN.  ROMANZA (BP)                             D14
MOZART, W.A.-BARDEEN.  RONDO (B)                                D14
PERGOLESI, G.B.-SANSONE.  NINA (BO)                             F60
RIMSKY-KORSAKOV, N.A.-WRIGHT.  CHANSON INDOUE FROM "SADKO" (B)  E59
ROSSINI, G.  CUJUS ANIMAM (STABAT MATER) (B)                    E83
SAINT-SAENS, C.-CAILLIET.  ROMANCE IN F (B)                     F60
SCHMITT, F.  LIED ET SCHERZO, OP. 54 (P)                        B81
STREET, A.(CMPL).  4 SOLOS (B)                                  E59
TCHAIKOVSKY, P.I.-SANSONE.  CHANSON TRISTE, OP. 40 (BOP)        F60
```

0114   HORN SOLOS WITH ORCHESTRAL ACCOMPANIMENT

```
ARMANDO, G.  KOMZERTSTUCK (O)                                F34
BERGHMANS, J.  LES LUTTEURS (OP)                             D36
```

BERGHMANS, J. LUTTEURS (OP)	D36
BONNEAU, P. SOUVENIR (OP)	D36
BORRESEN, H. SERENADE (O)	D32
BOZZA, E. EN FORET (OP)	D36
BRUNEAU, A. ROMANCE EN FA (OP)	C55
BRUSSELMANS, M. LEGENDE DU GAPEAU (O)	F16
BRUSSELMANS, M. RHAPSODIE (OP)	B12
BUSSER, H.P. PIECE EN RE, OP. 39 (OP)	D36
BUTT, J.B. SUITE (OP)	C71
BUTTERWORTH, A.E. ROMANCE (OP)	C71
CATELINET, P.B. 10 LITTLE INDIANS (OP)	C71
CHABRIER, E.-FROSETH. LARGHETTO (O)	D18
CHERUBINI, L.-WAJCIECHOWSKI. 2 SONATAS (O)	F50
CLERISSE, R. CHANSON A BERCER (OP)	D36
CORELLI, A. SONATA (OP)	B44
DIMMIER, A.-SCHERCHEN. CONCERTANTE FUR 2 HN (OP)	F31
FELD, J. PIECES DE CONCERT (OP)	D36
FRANZ, O.-SANSONE. CONCERT PIECE, OP. 4 FOR 2 HNS (O)	F60
GLAZUNOV. IDYLL (O)	B44
GLAZUNOV, A.K. REVERIE, OP. 24 (O)	A58
GLAZUNOV, A.K. SERENADE #2 (O)	B44
GOCK, E. KONZERTFANTASIE (O)	E43
HAMILTON, I. VOYAGE (O)	E77
HERBERIGS, R. CYRANO DE BERGERAC (OP)	B12
KRUKA, R.F. BALLAD, OP. 36 (OP)	G17
LEFEBVRE, C.E. ROMANCE, OP. 30 (OP)	C55
LESCHETIZKY, T.H. SCHERZO (O)	F97
LEVERMANN, W.-SANSONE. SERENADE ESPAGNOLE (BOP)	F60
LIPKIN, M. PASTORALE (O)	B23
MANIET, R. PIECE (O)	D67
MONTICO, M. CACCIA (O)	B07
MONTICO, M. ELEGIA (O)	B07
MORAIS, M.-BRAIN. LE BASQUE (FUNF ALTE FRANZOSISCHE TANZE)*	B23
MORTELMANS, L. LYRISCHE PASTORALE (O)	D80
MOZART, W.A.-KLING. CONCERT RONDO IN E-FLAT, K. 371 (OP)	A89
MOZART, W.A.-PAUMGARTNER. CONCERT RONDO, K. 371 (O)	F97
MUTH, F. EPISODE (OP)	C30
MUTH, F. RESIGNATION (OP)	C30
MUTH, F. ROMANZE (OP)	C30
NORDEN, H. PASSACAGLIA (OP)	B23
PERGOLESI, G.B.-SANSONE. NINA (BO)	F60
PORPORA, N.A. ARIOSO (OP)	B44
REGER, M. SCHERZINO (O)	A89
ROGERS, B. FANTASIA (O)	E77
SABATINI, G. ELEGIA (OP)	B44
SAINT-SAENS, C. MORCEAU DE CONCERT, OP. 94 (OP)	B81
SAINT-SAENS, C. ROMANCE IN MI, OP.67 (OP)	C55
SAINT-SAENS, C. ROMANCE, OP. 36 (O)	B81
SCHOEMAKER, M. VARIAZIONI (OP)	A96
SCHOLLUM. DIALOG (O)	B73
SCHUMANN, R.-ANSERMET. ADAGIO & ALLEGRO (O)	F97
SEARLE, H. AUBADE, OP. 28 (OP)	F31
SEIBER, M. NOTTURNO (O)	F31
STRAUSS, F.-SPIES. NOCTURNO (O)	F97
STRAUSS, F.-SPIES. ROMANZE, OP. 12 (O)	F97
SYDEMAN, W. CONCERT PIECE (O)	D63
TCHAIKOVSKY, P.I.-SANSONE. CHANSON TRISTE, OP. 40 (BOP)	F60
TOMASI, H. DANSE PROFANE (OP)	D36
WENNING, H. FROHLICHEN HORNERKLANG (O)	F34
ZUPKO, R. PROLOGUE, ARIA & DANCE (O)	B42

0116   HORN SOLOS WITH PIANO ACCOMPANIMENT

ABBOT, A. ALLA CACCIA	A26
ABSIL, J. RHAPSODIE #6	D41
ADAMS, L. LARGO	A38
AKIMENKO, F.S.-SINGER. MELODIE	D37
ALBERT. PERMUTATIONS	E10
ALFVEN, H. NOTTURNO ELEGIACO, OP. 5	C39
AMELLER, A.C. BELLE PROVINCE-RIMOUSKI	D36
AMELLER, A.C. CANZONE (3 EASY PIECES)	C71
AMELLER, A.C. CORADIEUX	E66
AMELLER, A.C. PRELUDE (3 EASY PIECES)	C71
AMELLER, A.C. RONDE (3 EASY PIECES)	C71
ANDERSEN, A.O. NOCTURNE	C11
ANDRE-BLOCH. EN FORET D'ILE DE GRANCE	C49
ARBAN, J.J.B.L. OBERTO FANTAISIE	D92
ARBAN, J.J.B.L.-JAKMA. OBERTO FANTAISIE	D64
ASAFIEV, B.V. VARIATIONS ON A THEME OF MOZART	D81
AUBER, D.F.E.-LUREMAN. TERRACINA KLANKEN FROM "FRA DIAVOLO"	F81
AUCLERT, P. LIED	D36
BACH, J.C. LAMENT	B85
BACH, J.S.-VUILLERMOZ. ARIA	D36
BACH, J.S.-GOUNOD. AVE MARIA	B53
BACH, J.S. SICILIANO	B85
BACH, K.P.E. LAMENT	B85
BACHELET, A.-THEVET. DANS LA MONTAGNE	D36
BACON, E. SONG AFTER THE RAIN	F03
BAKALEINIKOFF, V.R. CANZONA	A62
BAKALEINIKOFF, V.R. CAVATINA	A62
BAKER. CANTILENA	B23
BALAY, G. CHANSON DU FORESTIER	D36
BALL, E. MOUNTAIN MELODY	F24
BALLATORE, P.-SANSONE. SERENATA	F23
BARAT, J.E. FANTAISIE	D92
BARBE. FANTASIE ORIGINALE IN D	D92
BARET, J.E. FANTAISIE	D36
BARON, M. NIRVANA	A56
BARRAINE, E. CREPUSCULES	C49
BARRAINE, E. FANFARE	C49
BECK, C. INTERMEZZO	C65
BEETHOVEN, L.V. ADAGIO CANTABILE	F60
BEETHOVEN, L.V. ADAGIO FROM "SONATA PATHETIQUE"	B53
BEETHOVEN, L.V. ADELAIDE	B44
BEETHOVEN, L.V. ADELAIDE	B53
BEETHOVEN, L.V.-POOLE. ANDROMEDA	A62
BEETHOVEN, L.V. CAVATINE AUS QUARTETT, OP. 130	B99
BEETHOVEN, L.V.-SANSONE-BALLATORE. LITTLE RONDO	F23
BEETHOVEN, L.V.-LEIDZEN. RONDINO ON A THEME OF BEETHOVEN	C18
BEETHOVEN, L.V. RONDO, OP. 17	B85
BENNETT, D. HORNASCOPE	F60
BERG-SANSONE. SHEPHERD, THE	F60
BERGHMANS, J. LUTTEURS, LES	D36
BERNSTEIN, L. ELEGY FOR MIPPY I	F23
BERTHELOT. FRERE JACQUES	B92
BERTHELOT. FRERE JACQUES	D36
BERTHELOT. VARIATIONS BREVES	D36
BIGOT, E.V. PIECE #2	B92

BIGOT, E.V. PIECE #2	D41
BIGOT, E.V. RECIT, SCHERZO ET FINAL	D41
BITSCH, M. CHORAL	D36
BITSCH, M. VARIATIONS SUR UNE CHANSON FRANCAISE	D36
BITTS. BALLAD	A55
BIZET, G. AGNUS DEI	D92
BLAND, W.K. SONIC NOCTURNES	B35
BODNAR, I. 21 EASY SHORT PIECES	D29
BONNEAU, P. SOUVENIR (OP)	D36
BORKOVEC. INTERMEZZO	E54
BOUCARD. LEGENDE RUSTIQUE	A71
EOUSQUET, F. AGROTERA	C49
EOUTRY, R. CHASSACOR	D36
BOZZA, E. CHANT LOINTAIN	D36
BOZZA, E. EN FORET (OP)	D36
BOZZA, E. EN IRLANDE	D36
BOZZA, E. SUR LES CIMES	D36
BRADFORD-ANDERSON, M. PRELUDE IN CANON	A78
BRADFORD & ANDERSON. MARCH IN CANON	A78
BRAGA, F. ANGEL'S SERENADE	B53
BRAHMS, J.-PHILLIPS. INTERMEZZO	E51
BRAHMS, J.-ANDREONI. LULLABY, OP. 49, #4	E98
BRAHMS, J.-BAUDRIER. POPULAR SONG	D92
BRAHMS, J.-POOLE. SARABANDE	A62
BRAHMS, J.-PHILLIPS. SCHERZO FROM SERENADE IN D	E51
BREHM-LEIDZEN. HORNS-A-HUNTING	C25
BREMOND, F. SOLO #1	D41
BRETON. PIEZA CONCERTANTE	F95
BROWN, C.L.G. LEGENDE	D36
BRUCH, M.-EGER. KOL NIDREI, OP. 47	A38
BRUNEAU, A. ROMANCE IN F (OP)	C55
ERUNEAU, A. SUR LA MONTAGNE	A71
BRUSSELMANS, M. LEGENDE DU GAPEAU	F16
BUCCHI. 3 LIEDER	D36
BUCHGEL, F.L. PRINCE RUPERT	D18
BUCHTEL, F.L. ARCADIA	D18
EUCHTEL, F.L.(ARR). CIELITO LONDO	D18
BUCHTEL, F.L. ELEGY	D18
BUCHTEL, F.L.(ARR). HOLY CITY	D18
BUCHTEL, F.L. JANUS	D18
BUCHTEL, F.L. MY BUDDY	D18
BUCHTEL, F.L. REVERIE	D18
BUCHTEL, F.L. SOLITUDE	D18
BURKHARD, W. ROMANZE	A51
EUSH, A.D. AUTUMN POEM, OP. 45	F31
BUSH, A.D. TRENT'S BROAD REACHES, OP. 36	F31
EUSSER, H.P. CANTECOR, OP. 77	D36
BUSSER, H.P. LA CHASSE DE ST. HUBERT (OP)	D36
BUSSER, H.P. PIECE EN RE, OP. 39 (OP)	D36
BUTT, J.B. SUITE (OP)	C71
BUTTERWORTH, A.E. ROMANZA (OP)	C71
BUTTERWORTH, D.N. PRELUDE & SCHERZO	B20
BUTTS, C.M. ANDANTE AND RONDO	D14
CAISSONS GO ROLLING ALONG.	D18
CAMPOLIETO, L. ANDANTE, PASTORALE ET ALLEGRO	E98
CANIVEZ, L. FANTAISIE DE CONCERT, OP. 127	F81
CAPDEVIELLE, P. ELEGIE DE DUINO	D36
CARLES, M. CHORAL	D36
CARSE, A. 2 EASY PIECES	C33
CATELINET, P.B. CAPRICE "ENCORE"	C71
CATELINET, P.B. 10 LITTLE INDIANS	C71
CECCONI. AUTOMNE	E66

```
CECCONI.  SCHERZETTO                                             E66
CELLIER, A.  BALLADE                                             D36
CESARE-SMITH.  HIERONYMA FROM MUSICALI MELODIE, 1621            D16
CHABRIER, E.-LABEY.  LARGHETTO                                   F16
CHALLAN, H.  VARIATIONS                                          D36
CHAMBERS.  CAVATINA                                              G13
CHARPENTIER, J.  POUR DIANE                                      D36
CHEVILLARD, C.  ALLEGRO, OP. 18                                  D36
CHILDS, B.  INTERBALANCES VI (OPT. MAGNETIC TAPE)               E68
CHOPIN, F.  CAVATINA                                             D18
CHOPIN, F.-ANDRAUD.  NOCTURNE CELEBRE                            F60
CHOPIN, F.  NOCTURNE, OP.9, #2                                   B53
CHOPIN, F.-POTTAG.  NOCTURNO, OP.9, #2                           A62
CHRISTOL.  LE COEUR DE MA VIE                                    D92
CLERGUE, J.  PRELUDE, LIED ET RONDO                             D41
CLERISSE, R.  CHANSON A BERCER (OP)                              D36
CLERISSE, R.  CHANT SANS PAROLES                                 D36
CLERISSE, R.  L'ABSENT                                           D36
CLERISSE, R.  LE CHANT DU SONNEUR                                A71
CLERISSE, R.  LE CHANT DU SONNEUR                                D64
CLERISSE, R.  MATINES                                            D36
COHEN, S.B.  FANTASY IN F MAJOR                                  A62
COHEN, S.B.  LEGEND OF THE HILLS                                 A62
COHEN, S.B.  PASTORALE                                          A62
COLOMER, B.M.  FANTAISIE-LEGENDE                                 D36
CONCERT & CONTEST COLLECTION.                                    F07
CONCONE, G.-SANSONE.  ROCCONTO (BP)                              F60
CONSTANT.  COULEUR PROVENCALE                                    M67
COOKE, A.A.  RONDO IN B-FLAT                                     F31
CORELLI, A.  SUITE IN B-FLAT MAJOR                               B85
CORIOLIS.  NOCTURNE                                              D36
COX.  HORNISTE                                                   B53
COX.  LULLABY FOR 2ND HN                                         F62
CREPY, DE.  SYNOPSE                                              F87
CRISWELL, J.  4 INTERLUDES                                       C33
CZERNY-GABLER.  ANDANTE E POLACCA                                B73
DAMASE, J.M.  BERCEUSE, OP. 19                                   D36
DAMASE, J.M.  PAVANE VARIEE                                      D41
DANBURG.  POEME                                                  F60
DAUCE.  ROMANCE                                                  E66
DAUPRAT, L.F.  3 SOLOS, OP. 11                                   D41
DAUPRAT, L.F.  3 SOLOS, OP. 16                                   D41
DAUPRAT, L.F.  3 SOLOS, OP. 17                                   D41
DAUPRAT, L.F.  3 SOLOS, OP. 20                                   D41
DAUPRAT, L.F.  THEME VARIE #2, OP. 24                            D41
DAUTREMER, M.  THEME VARIE                                       D36
DEARNLEY, C.H.  8 EASY PIECES BY CLASSICAL COMP.                D23
DEARNLEY, C.H.  MORE EASY PIECES BY CLASSICAL COMP.            D23
DEFAYE.  ALPHA                                                   D36
DELERUE, G.  POEME FANTASQUE                                     D36
DELMAS, M.J.B.  BALLADE FEERIQUE                                A71
DELMAS, M.J.B.  CLAIR DE LUNE                                    A71
DEMESSIEUX, J.  BALLADE                                          B81
DEPELSENAIRE, J.M.  NOCTURNE                                     D41
DESENCLOS, A.  CANTILENE ET DIVERTISSEMENTS                     D36
DESENCLOS, A.  PREAMBULE, COMPLAINTE ET FINALE                  B81
DESPORTES, Y.  BALLADE NORMANDE                                  D36
DESPORTES, Y.  IMPROVISATION                                     D36
DESPORTES, Y.  SICILIENNE ET ALLEGRO                             D36
DIERCKS, J.  FANTASY                                             F80
DOMENICO, O.DI.  VARIAZIONI                                      D36
DONIZETTI, G.  RECITATIV II & CAVATINE AUS LINDA DE CHAMOUNIX   B99
```

```
DOUANE, J.   DANS LES ALPES                                         E66
DOUANE, J.   EN FORET D'OLONNE                                      D41
DUBOIS, P.M.   COR ET A CRI                                         D36
DUBOIS, P.M.   CORNOUAILLE                                          N50
DUBOIS, P.M.   POURSUITE                                            N50
DUBOIS, P.M.   ROMANCE SANS PAROLES                                 D36
DUCK, L.   SILVER HUNTRESS                                          B20
DUCLOS, R.   SUR LA MONTAGNE                                        D36
DUKAS, P.   VILLANELLE                                              B81
DUKAS, P.-CHAMBERS.   VILLANELLE                                    C91
DUPUIS, A.   VARIATIONS SUR UN THEME POPULAIRE                      D36
DURKO.   SYMBOLS                                                    B84
DVORAK, A.-ADAMS.   MELODY IN F MINOR                               G10
DVORAK, A.-ADAMS.   MEMORIES IN C MINOR                             G10
DVORAK, A.-BUTTERWORTH.   SLAVONIC DANCE #10, OP. 7/2               B20
ECHEVARRIA, V.   INTERMEZZO                                         D36
EFFINGER.   RONDINO                                                 F23
EGER.   ORIGINAL FRENCH HORN SOLOS                                  B41
ELGAR, E.-AKERS.   THEME FROM POMP & CIRCUMSTANCE, OP. 39, #1       C11
EMMERT.   BETA ASSOCIACE                                            D11
ERNST, H.W.   ELEGIE                                                B53
FAITH.   MOVEMENTS                                                  F43
FATTAKH, A.   LYRIC PIECE                                           D81
FELD, J.   PIECES DE CONCERT (OP)                                   D36
FEVRIER-VUILLERMOZ.   10 PIECES MELODIQUES #4                       D36
FIEVET, P.   CHANT LYRIQUE                                          B66
FIRST DIV BAND COURSE.   ANDANTE                                    A62
FIRST DIV BAND COURSE.   ANDROMEDA                                  A62
FIRST DIV BAND COURSE.   CHALET                                     A62
FIRST DIV BAND COURSE.   COUNT DOWN                                 A62
FIRST DIV BAND COURSE.   GYPSY LOVE SONG                            A62
FIRST DIV BAND COURSE.   HUNTSMAN                                   A62
FIRST DIV BAND COURSE.   NOBILITY                                   A62
FIRST DIV BAND COURSE.   OUR FAVORITE                               A62
FIRST DIV BAND COURSE.   SARABANDE                                  A62
FIRST DIV BAND COURSE.   SONG OF A CITY                             A62
FIRST DIV BAND COURSE.   TELESTAR                                   A62
FIRST DIV BAND COURSE.   TO SPRING                                  A62
FLEGIER, A.-VOXMAN.   LE COR                                        F07
FOURNIER, G.   BROWN & GOLD                                         G13
FOURNIER, G.   MELODIE, CHANT DU MATIN                              G13
FOX, F.A.   SEQUENCE                                                G89
FRANCAIX, J.   CANON IN OCTAVE                                      C91
FRANCAIX, J.   DIVERTIMENTO                                         F87
FRANCK, C.-BOYD.   PANIS ANGELICUS                                  G31
FRANTZ-OUSSOV.   4 PIECES                                           D81
GABAYE, P.   SERENADE DE PRINTEMPS (SPRING SERENADE)               D36
GABELLES.   ANDANTE APASSIONATO                                     A71
GABELLES.   FANTAISIE                                               A71
GAGNEBIN, H.   AUBADE                                               D36
GALLAY, J.F.   3 CAPRICES, OP. 60                                   D41
GALLAY, J.F.   ECHOS, OP. 59                                        D41
GALLAY, J.F.   ELISIRE D'AMORE DONIZETTI, OP. 46                    D41
GALLAY, J.F.   REGRETS                                              D41
GALLAY, J.F.   SOLO #10, OP. 45                                     D41
GALLAY, J.F.   SOLO #12, OP. 55                                     D41
GALLAY, J.F.   SOLO #9, OP. 39                                      D41
GALLOIS-MONTBRUN.   BALLADE                                         D36
GARFIELD, B.   SOLILOQUY                                            B85
GARTENLAUB, O.   POUR LE COR                                        N50
GEIST, C.   ANDANTE PASTORALE                                       B53
GIGGY, F.D.   THEME & 4 VARIATIONS                                  B35
```

```
GILLAM.  RONDINO                                               D 14
GLAZUNOV, A.K.  REVERIE, OP. 24                                B 53
GLAZUNOV, A.K.-SINGER.  REVERIE                                D 37
GLIERE, R.M.-SHELDON.  INTERMEZZO, OP. 35, #11                 D 37
GLIERE, R.M.-SINGER.  NOCTURNE, OP. 35, #10                    D 37
GLOVER, C.W.  ROSE OF TRALEE                                   D 92
GLUCK, C.W.  ACH ICH HABE SIE VERLOREN                         D 92
GLUCK, C.W.  LARGO                                             C 19
GLUCK, C.W.-ELKAN.  O DEL MIO DOLCE ARDOR                      B 91
GODARD, E.  BERCEUSE                                           D 18
GODARD, E.  BERCEUSE FROM JOCELYN                              B 53
GODARD, B.  BERCEUSE FROM JOCELYN                              D 92
GODARD, B.-HAUSER.  BERCEUSE FROM JOCELYN                      C 11
GOLTERMANN, G.E.  ANDANTE                                      B 53
GOTTWALD, H.  FANTASIE HEROIQUE, OP. 25                        B 53
GOTTWALD, H.  FRIENDSHIP (BP)                                  F 60
GOUNOD, C.F.-HAUSER.  AVE MARIA                                C 11
GOUNOD, C.F.-ABT.  BERCEUSE (SING, SMILE, SLUMBER)            B 53
GRANADOS-PHILLIPS.  SPANISH DANCE #5                           E 51
GRANT, W.P.  ESSAY, OP. 25 (G)                                 A 13
GRANT, W.P.  POEM, OP. 15 (G)                                  A 13
GRAZIOLI-REYNOLDS.  ADAGIO                                     F 60
GRETRY, A.E.M.-VUILLERMOZ.  SERENADE                           D 36
GRIEG, E.H.-PHILLIPS.  BALLADE, OP. 65/5                       E 51
GRIEG, E.H.-WILSON.  I LOVE THEE                               E 11
GRIEG, E.H.-BOYD.  NORTHERN BALLADE, OP. 65, #5                G 31
GRIEG, E.H.-PHILLIPS.  NOTTURNO                                E 51
GRUDZINSKI, C.  MINIATURES                                     E 72
GUILBERT, R.  PUZZLE                                           D 36
GUILLCU, R.  MON NOM EST ROLANDE                               A 71
GYRING, E.  ANDANTE CANTABILE                                  E 68
HACOUT, E.  IMPRESSION D'AUTOMNE                               C 49
HADDAD, D.  ADAGIO AND ALLEGRO                                 F 43
HADDAD, D.  ALLEGRO GIOCOSO                                    F 43
HAHN-VUILLERMOZ.  10 PIECES MELODIQUES #7                      D 36
HAJDU & SZERVANSZKY & SZEKELY.  5 HORN PIECES                  B 84
HALLER, H.  NOVELLETTA, OP. 38                                 F 53
HAMILTON, I.  ARIA                                             F 31
HANDEL, G.F.-BRISSET.  CELEBRE LARGO                           A 71
HANDEL, G.F.-MOLENAAR.  LARGO                                  D 92
HANDEL, G.F.-VUILLERMOZ.  LARGO                                D 36
HARRIS, F.O.  SHORT SUITE                                      D 52
HARRIS, F.O.  VESPER MOODS                                     D 52
HARTMANN, J.  BEAUTIFUL AMERICAN, THE                          D 64
HARTMANN, J.-MOLENAAR.  LE DESIR                               D 64
HARTMANN, J.  RETURN, AIR VARIE                                D 92
HARVEY, R.  MENUETTO                                           G 13
HAUGLAND, A.O.  SUITE OF TWO PIECES                            A 62
HAUSER, E.  AT THE FAIR                                        C 11
HAUSER, E.  MODERN HORN REPERTOIRE ALBUM                       C 11
HAUSER, E.  SOLDIER SONG                                       C 11
HAUSER, E.  TWILIGHT THOUGHTS                                  C 11
HAUSER, E.  WOODLAND MEMORIES                                  C 11
HAUSER, E. (ARR).  LULLABY, OP.49 (BRAHMS), & OP.10 (MASSENET) C 11
HAYDN, J.-WOOD.  ROSES OF PICCARDY                             D 92
HAYES, J.  RECITATIVE                                          B 44
HEAD.  SCHERZO                                                 A 78
HERBERIGS, R.  CYRANO DE BERGERAC (OP)                         B 12
HERBERT, V.-MACLEAN.  GYPSY LOVE SONG                          G 31
HERFURTH, W.-VOXMAN.  FAREWELL SERENADE, OP. 85                F 07
HESSENBERG.  NOCTURNE ET RONDO                                 D 36
HLOBIL, E.  ANDANTE PASTORALE                                  A 51
```

MOZART, W.A.-WILCOX. ALLEGRO FROM HN QUINTET	A62
MOZART, W.A.-PLOYHAR. ALLELUIA	A62
MOZART, W.A.-WILCOX. ANDANTE FROM HN QUINTET	A62
MOZART, W.A. ARIA FROM MAGIC FLUTE	B53
MOZART, W.A.-O'NEILL. ARIA FROM MAGIC FLUTE	G13
MOZART, W.A.-CERMINARO. CONCERT RONDO K 371	C91
MOZART, W.A.-POTTAG. CONCERT RONDO, K. 371	F60
MOZART, W.A.-SANSONE. CONCERT RONDO, K. 371	F60
MOZART, W.A.-KLING. CONCERT RONDO	D81
MOZART, W.A.-KLING. CONCERT-RONDO IN E-FLAT, K. 371 (OP)	A89
MOZART, W.A. LARGHETTO AUS STADLER QT.	B99
MOZART, W.A.-VUILLERMOZ. LARGHETTO	D36
MOZART, W.A.-FRANTZ & OUSSOV. 3 PIECES	D81
MOZART, W.A.-JONES. QUINTET IN E-FLAT	F23
MOZART, W.A.-BARDEEN. ROMANZA	D14
MOZART, W.A.-BARDEEN. RONDO	D14
MUELLER, O. LA CHASSE	B44
MUELLER, O. LYRICAL ROMANCE	B44
MULLER, B. GEBET, OP. 65A	G43
MULLER, B. MELANCHOLIE, OP. 68	G43
MULLER, B.E. ANDANTE, OP. 74	G43
MULLER, J.P. NOCTURNE	D67
MURPHY, J. ARCOLA (EASY JAZZ)	F74
MUSGRAVE, T. MUSIC FOR HORN AND PIANO	B23
MUSSORGSKY, M.P.-HANSON. TEAR	D52
MUTH, F. EPISODE (OP)	C30
MUTH, F. RESIGNATION (OP)	C30
MUTH, F. ROMANZE (OP)	C30
NELHYBEL, V. SCHERZO CONCERTANTE	C40
NEULING, H. BAGATELLE	C59
NEULING, H. KONZERT-KADENZ	C59
NIVERD, L. CHANT MELANCOLIQUE	A71
NIVERD, L. COMPLAINTE	A71
NIVERD, L. CREPUSCULE D'AUTOMNE	B66
NIVERD, L. HISTORIETTE DRAMATIQUE	A71
NIVERD, L. HYMNE	A71
NIVERD, L. 6 PIECES DE STYLE	A71
NIVERD, L. ROMANCE SENTIMENTALE	A71
NIVERD, L. SCHERZETTO	A71
NOEL-GALLON. ANDANTE ET PRESTO	B92
NOLL, D. VARIATIONEN UND BAGATELLEN	C75
NORDEN, H. PASSACAGLIA (OP)	B23
NYQUIST, M.A. GOLDEN SUMMER	A62
NYQUIST, M.A. MAZURKA IN A MAJOR	A62
NYQUIST, M.A. MELODY	A62
C'NEILL. MELODIC PHANTASIE	G13
OLLONE, M.D. PIECE MELODIQUE	D36
CRR, R. SERENADE	F31
OSTRANDER, A. CONCERT ALBUM	B85
OSTRANSKY, L. BALLADE	F07
OUBRADOUS, F. (CMPL). CONTEMPORARY FRENCH RECITAL PIECES	C91
OUSSOV, A. 5 PIECES BY RUSSIAN COMPOSERS	D81
OUSSOV, A. (CMPL). 13 PIECES BY RUSSIAN COMPOSERS	D81
OUSSOV, A. (CMPL). 7 PIECES BY RUSSIAN COMPOSERS	D81
OUSSOV, A. (CMPL). 4 PIECES BY WESTERN CLASSICAL COMPOSERS	D81
OUSSOV, A. & SOLODUYEV (ARR). 3 PIECES	D81
PAGE, N.C. (CMPL). 18 CONCERT PIECES	B72
PAINTER, P. SYLVAN COLORS	C11
PANNIER, O. SERENADE, OP. 45	C54
PASCAL, A. FANTAISIE ELEGAIQUE	E66
PASSANI. SARABANDE ET BOUREE	D36
PELZ, W. BALLAD	A62

```
RZAYEV, G.  PIECE                                             D81
SABATINI, G.  PUPPET WALTZ (OP)                              B44
SAGAEV, D.  TUNE FROM RHODOPE                                F36
SAINT-SAENS, C.  LE CYGNE                                    B92
SAINT-SAENS, C.  MORCEAU DE CONCERT                          E11
SAINT-SAENS, C.  MORCEAU DE CONCERT, OP. 94                  C91
SAINT-SAENS, C.  MORCEAU DE CONCERT, OP. 94 (OP)            B81
SAINT-SAENS, C.  ROMANCE                                     B85
SAINT-SAENS, C.  ROMANCE, OP. 36                             C91
SAINT-SAENS, C.  ROMANCE, OP. 36 (OP)                       B81
SAINT-SAENS, C.-VOXMAN.  ROMANCE, OP. 36                     F07
SAINT-SAENS, C.  ROMANCE, OP. 67 (OP)                        C55
SAMUEL-ROUSSEAU.  ROMANCE                                    D36
SCHAEFER.  SPRING IN THE FOREST                              C11
SCHEURER, R.  ELEGIE                                         A62
SCHLEMM, G.A.  VARIATIONEN                                   C54
SCHMID, H.K.  IM TIEFSTEN WALDE, OP. 34, #4                 F31
SCHMITT, F.  LIED ET SCHERZO, OP. 54                         B81
SCHOEMAKER, M.  VARIAZIONI (OP)                              A96
SCHOUWMAN, H.  2 LEGENDEN, OP. 35, #1, #2                   B74
SCHUBERT, F.P.-SMITH & FARKAS.  ANDANTE                      A62
SCHUBERT, F.P.-VUILLERMOZ.  AVE MARIA                        D36
SCHUBERT, F.P.-BAUDIER.  BERCEUSE                            D92
SCHUBERT, F.P.-EGER.  FAVORITE COLOR, THE                   A38
SCHUBERT, F.P.  POST, THE, OP. 89, #13                       B53
SCHUBERT, F.P.  SERENADE                                     D92
SCHUBERT, F.P.-VUILLERMOZ.  SERENADE                         D36
SCHULLER, G.  NOCTURNE                                       D84
SCHUMANN, R.  ADAGIO & ALLEGRO, OP. 70                       A89
SCHUMANN, R.  ADAGIO & ALLEGRO, OP. 70                       C91
SCHUMANN, R.  ADAGIO & ALLEGRO, OP. 70                       D81
SCHUMANN, R.  ADAGIO & ALLEGRO, OP. 70                       E65
SCHUMANN, R.  ADAGIO & ALLEGRO, OP. 70                       F60
SCHUMANN, R.-REYNOLDS.  ALBUM                                F23
SCHUMANN, R.-HILFIGER.  2 CHILDHOOD SCENES                  D14
SCHUMANN, R.  EVENING SONG (ABENDLIED) & TRAUMEREI          C11
SCHUMANN, R.-VUILLERMOZ.  EVENING SONG                       D36
SCHUMANN, R.-ANDREONI.  IL CONTADINO ALLEGRO, OP. 68, #10   E98
SCHUMANN, R.  TRAUMEREI & ROMANCE                            B53
SCHUMANN, R.-TOBANI.  VOICE OF LOVE                          C11
SCHWARTZ, G.  INTERNATIONAL FOLK SUITE                       F60
SCRIABINE, A.N.-SINGER.  ROMANCE                             D37
SEARLE, H.  AUBADE, OP. 28 (OP)                              F31
SEELENNE, T.  BERCEUSE                                       A96
SEIBER, M.-BANKS.  NOTTURNO                                  F31
SEIGLE, F.  LEGENDE                                          D36
SEMINI.  INVENZIONI                                          B95
SEMLER-COLLERY, J.  PIECE CONCERTANTE                        D36
SENAILLE, J.B.-EGER.  ALLEGRO SPIRITOSO                      A38
SENAILLE, J.B.-EGER.  SARABANDE & ALLEMANDE                 C91
SERRADELL.  GOLONDRINA                                       D92
SERVAIS.  CANTILENE SICILIENNE                               D67
SERVAIS, T.  PREMIER SOLO                                    A96
SHCHELOKOV, V.-VOXMAN.  SCHERZO                              F07
SHEPHERD, W.S.  NOCTURNE AND RONDOLETTE                      F60
SIEBERT.  SCHERZETTO                                         C03
SINIGAGLIA, L.  ROMANCE, OP. 3                               E98 0
SIQUEIRA, J.  3 ETUDEN                                       B69
SLAVICKY.  CAPRICCI                                          C40
SMOLANOFF.  ESSAY                                            E67
SOLODUYEV, V.N.-OUSSOV.  3 PIECES                            D81
SOMETINES I FEEL.                                            D92
```

```
SOUFFRIAU, A.  BALLADE, OP. 15                              A96
SOUSA, J.P.  STARS & STRIPES FOREVER                       D18
SPORCK.  TONE POEM                                         A10
SPORCK.  VIRELAI                                           A71
STACHE & REMA (PSEUD).  ROMANCE                            A96
STACHE, H.  CREPUSCULE                                     D67
STEKKE, L.  POEME SYLVESTRE, OP. 21                        A96
STEVENS, H.  4 PIECES                                      B44
STEWART, K.D.  MUSIC FOR HORN AND PIANO                    B42
STOUT, A.  PRELUDE, TOCCATA & POSTLUDE                     E68
STRAUSS, F.-MEEK.  ADIEUX, LES                             D16
STRAUSS, F.-POTTAG.  FANTASIE UBER BEETHOVEN, OP. 2        A62
STRAUSS, F.  THEMA U. VARIATIONEN, OP. 13                  G43
STRAUSS, R.-VOXMAN.  ALLERSEELEN, OP. 10, #8               F07
STRAUSS, R.  ANDANTE, OP. POSTH.                           A78
STRAUSS, R.-SINGER.  WIEGENLIED, OP. 41, #1                D44
SULLIVAN, A.S.  LOST CHORD                                 D92
SUTTNER, J.  ERINNERUNGEN                                  C54
SWINSON, L.  SOLILOQUY (IN JAZZ-BALLAD STYLE)              F74
SYLVIUS.  ROMANZA                                          N95
TCHAIKOVSKY, P.I.-SEREDY.  ANDANTE CANTABILE (SYM. #5)     C11
TCHAIKOVSKY, P.I.-SEREDY.  ANDANTE CANTABILE FROM 5TH SYM  C11
TCHAIKOVSKY, P.I.  CHANSON TRISTE, OP. 40                  F60
TCHAIKOVSKY, P.I.-SMITH.  HUMORESAUE                       A62
TCHAIKOVSKY, P.I.-HANSON.  KAMARINSKAYA                    D52
TCHAIKOVSKY, P.I.-WEBER.  MARCH SLAV                       A62
TCHAIKOVSKY, P.I.-SOLODUYEV & LEONOV.  3 PIECES            D81
TELEMANN, G.P.-CHIDESTER.  ADAGIO PRESTO                   F60
TELEMANN, G.P.-CHIDESTER.  ALLEGRO FROM SONATA IN D MINOR  F60
TELEMANN, G.P.-BARNES.  ARIE FROM "PIMPINONE"              F62
TENAGLIA, A.F.  ARIA                                       C19
IENAGLIA, A.F.  ARIA ANTICA                                B85
THOME, F.  SIMPLE AVEU                                     D92
TILLOTSON, N.  FANTASY                                     B15
TILLOTSON, N.  FANTASY                                     C25
TISNE, A.  LIED, OP. 32, #3                                D36
TITL, A.E.-ROBERTS.  SERENADE                              C11
TOMASI, H.  DANSE PROFANE FROM "CINQ DANSES" (OP)          D36
TOMOV, T. (CMPL).  PIECES                                  F36
TOSELLI, E.  CELEBRE SERENATA                              B66
TOURNEMIRE, C.  FANTAISIE                                  D36
UBER, D.A.  4 SKETCHES                                     B85
UYTTENHOVE, Y.  PETITE PIECE                               D67
VAN EECHAUTE, P.  POEME NOCTURNE                           D80
VANDERCOOK, H.A.  ALTAIR                                   F07
VANDERCOOK, H.A.  VEGA                                     F07
VIDAL, P.  PIECE DE CONCERT                                D36
VILLA-LOBOS-SIMON.  SONG OF THE BLACK SWAN                 D63
VINTER, G.  HUNTER'S MOON                                  A78
VIVALDI, A.  RAIN (THE SEASONS)                            B85
VOXMAN, H.  CONCERT & CONTEST COLLECTION                   F07
VUILLERMOZ.  NUMBER 8 FR. 10 PIECES MELODIQUES             B92
WAGNER, R.-MASSO.  WALTHER'S PRIZE SONG                    D14
WALTERS, H.L.  TARANTELLE (BP)                             D52
WARREN, D.  MEDITATION                                     D52
WEBBER.  SUMMER PASTURES                                   A35
WEBBER (ARR).  FIRST SOLO ALBUM                            E77
WEBER, A.  IMPROVISATION                                   D36
WEBER, C.M.V.  ADAGIO AUS OP. 73                           B99
WEBER, C.M.V.  CAVATINE AUS FREISCHUTZ                     B99
WEBER, C.M.V.-KLING.  CONCERTINO IN MINOR, OP. 45          A89
WEBER, C.M.V.-PLOYHAR.  MELODIES FROM "DER FREISCHUTZ"     A62
```

WEBER, C.M.V. RECITATIV UND GEBET AUS FREISCHUTZ	B99
WEBER, C.M.V. ROMANZA APPASSIONATA	B53
WEBER, F. ABOVE THE CLOUDS	A62
WEBER, F. MIGHTY MAJOR	A62
WEBER, F. (ARR). 2 PIECES	A62
WEIGEL, E. MAINE SKETCHES	B52
WERNER. 3 INVENTIONS	A71
WERNER. PASTORALE	A71
WESSEL. SCHERZO	C11
WHEAR, P.W. PASTORALE LAMENT	B52
WIEDEMANN, L. NOCTURNO	B53
WIEDEMANN, L.-POTTAG. NOCTURNO	A62
WIGY, F. ELEGIE ET DANSE	D67
WILDER, A. SUITE	B14
WILLNER, A. (ARR). CLASSICAL ALBUM	A78
WITTMANN, R. BARCAROLLE, OP. 50	C11
WOLFF, C. DUET II	E65
WUENSCH, G. LENTO & VIVACE	G21
WURMSER. BADINERIES	A71
WURMSER. PIECETTES	A71
ZELLER. SCHENKT MAN SICH ROSEN IN TIROL	D92
ZENOBIA.	D92
ZIMMERMAN (ARR). PLAY A SONG OF AMERICA	E77
ZIMMERMAN (ARR). PLAY A SONG OF CHRISTMAS	E77
ZIRING, V. ADAGIO, OP. 17	D81
ZITZMANIS, Y.(CMPL). 7 PIECES BY LATVIAN COMPOSERS	D81

0117   HORN SOLOS, UNACCOMPANIED

APOSTEL, H.E. SONATINA, OP. 39B	F97
BACH, J.S.-HOSS. VIOLONCELLO SUITES	F60
BUTT, J.B. SUITE	C71
CHILDS, B. 5 CONSIDERATIONS	E68
CHILDS, B. VARIATIONS FOR DAVID RACUSEN	E68
DAUPRAT, L.F. 3 SOLOS	D41
DUFOUR, O. PRELUDE, AIR ET MARCHE	C49
GALLAY, J.F. 22 MELODIC FANTAISIES, OP. 58 (2 VOL)	D41
GALLAY, J.F. 18 MELODIES, OP. 53 (2 VOL)	D41
GALLAY, J.F.-THEVET. 39 PRELUDES, BARRED & UNBARRED, OP. 27	B92
GAUDERFROY. DANS LA CAMPAGNE ENSOLEÏLLEC	C49
GAUDERFROY. PETITE PIECE D'EXAMEN	C49
GERSCHEFSKI, E. SUITE, OP. 52, #1-5	B36
GOLDSTEIN, A.E. FIRST BOOK OF SOLOS	B44
GOLDSTEIN, A.E. SECOND BOOK OF SOLOS	B44
GUARNIERI, M.C. ETUDE	F03
KROL, B. LAUDATIO	F52
KROL, B. SOLOBOOK (2 VOL)	F52
PELLEMEULLE. PIECE D'EXAMEN	C49
PERSICHETTI, V. PARABLE FOR SOLO HORN	B52
PHILIPPE. ALLEGRO ET ANDANTE	C49
POTTAG, M.P. PREPARATORY MELODIES TO SOLO WORK (SCHANTL)	A62
PRESSER, W.H. 3 PIECES	G83
RAPHLING, S. CONCERT ETUDES	B85
RAPHLING, S. SONATA FROM "CONCERT ETUDES"	B32
ROSENTHAL. PARTITA	G21
SCHANTL, J.-POTTAG. PREPARATORY MELODIES	A62
SOMBRUN. RECUEIL DE FANFARES	D41

STEIN, L. SONATA   B36
VUILLERMOZ. 10 PIECES MELODIQUES (ORGINALLY BY HETTICH)   D36
WELLESZ, E. FANFARES, OP. 78   F03

0121   TROMBONE CONCERTOS AND CONCERTINOS

ALBRECHTSBERGER. CONCERTO FOR ALTO TROMBONE (O)	B84
ALBRECHTSBERGER-DARVAS. CONCERTO FOR ALTO TROMBONE (P)	B84
ALSCHAUSKY, S. KONZERT #1 IN B-DUR (O)	C10
BARTA. CONCERTINO (P)	A33
BERGHMANS, J. CONCERTINO (OP)	D36
BLAZHEVICH, V.M. CONCERTO #10 (P)	C91
BLAZHEVICH, V.M. CONCERTO #10 (P)	D81
BLAZHEVICH, V.M. CONCERTO #2 (P)	B53
BLAZHEVICH, V.M.-LAFOSSE. CONCERTO #2 (P)	C91
BLAZHEVICH, V.M. CONCERTO #5 (P)	D81
BLAZHEVICH, V.M.-OSTRANDER. CONCERTO #5 (P)	C91
BOUTRY, R. CONCERTO (P)	D36
BRESGEN, C. KONZERT IN G MINOR (OP)	G09
BRINK. CONCERTO (P)	B30
BROOKS, E. CONCERTINO (THE MESSAGE) (P)	C11
BUCCI. CONCERTO FOR A SINGING INSTRUMENT (P)	F27
BUETTNER. CONZERTO (P)	E89
CIMERA, J. CONCERTO, 1ST MVT (ALLEGRO) (P)	E11
CIMERA, J. CONCERTO, 2ND MVT (ANDANTE) (P)	E11
CIMERA, J. CONCERTO, 3RD MVT (ALLEGRO) (P)	E11
CIMERA, J. & SARES. CONCERTINO PETITE (P)	A62
COKER, W. CONCERTO (BP)	E77
DAVID, F.V. CONCERTINO (P)	D92
DAVID, F.V.-MUELLER. CONCERTINO, OP. 4 (OP)	G43
DAVID, F.V. CONCERTINO, OP. 4 (P)	B53
DAVID, F.V. CONCERTINO, OP. 4 (P)	C75
DAVID, F.V. CONCERTINO, OP. 4 (P)	D81
DAVID, F.V.-GIBSON. CONCERTINO, OP. 4 (P)	C91
DAVID, F.V.-GRUBE. CONCERTINO, OP. 4 (P)	A63
DAVID, F.V.-MUELLER. CONCERTINO, OP. 4 (P)	C11
DEFOSSEZ, R. CONCERTO (B)	B47
DEFOSSEZ, R. CONCERTO (P)	D80
DOMAZLICKY. CONCERTO (P)	C41
DUBOIS, P.M. CONCERTO DIT "L'IRRESPECTUEUX" (P)	D36
FITELBERG, J. CONCERTINO (O)	D63
FREHSE, A. STUDIENKONZERT (P)	C95
GRAFE, F. CONCERTO (P)	C91
GRONDAHL, L. KONCERT (OP)	D32
HANDEL, G.F.-LAFOSSE. CONCERTO IN F MINOR (P)	D36
HANDEL, G.F.-MARSTELLER. CONCERTO IN F MINOR (P)	F60
HANDEL, G.F.-BROWN. CONCERTO IN G MINOR (P)	C91
HASSLER, L. CONCERTO, OP. 14, ALLEGRO MODERATO (P)	B53
HASSLER, L. CONCERTO, OP. 14, ANDANTE AND RONDO (P)	B53
HAYDN, J.-SHUMAN. ADAGIO (CELLO CONCERTO) (P)	H06
HAYDN, J. ANDANTE FROM CONCERTO (P)	F62
HENNEBERG, A. BASUNKONSERT (P)	B90
HOVHANESS, A.S. CONCERTO #3 (DIRAN) (O)	A13
HOVHANESS, A.S. CONCERTO #3 (DIRAN) (C)	D16
HUBER-PRICE. CONCERTINO #4, OP. 8, THEME (P)	C11
JOCOB, G.P. CONCERTO (OP)	G26
KARKOFF, M. KONSERT, OP. 35 (P)	B90
KUBIN. KONCERT (P)	D11
KUNKEL, M.J. CONCERTINO (P)	B53
LARSSON, L.E.V. CONCERTINO, OP. 45/7 (OP)	C39
LAUGA, E. CONCERTO IN F MINOR (P)	B85

LEBEDEV, A. CONCERTO IN ONE MOVEMENT (P)	B85
LECLERCQ, E. 2ND CONCERTINO (P)	C49
LECLERCQ, E. 1ST CONCERTO (P)	F60
LEYDEN, N. CONCERTO FOR TRBS & BAND (B)	E70
MAGNAN, G. CONCERTO (P)	B53
MANFREDINI, F.-TONI. CONCERTO (O)	B07
MANFREDINI, F. CONCERTO (2 TRB)(GO)	B07
MANZO, S. CONCERTINO (P)	G38
MATEJ, J. KONZERT (O)	A51
MEULEMANS, A. CONCERTINO (OP)	B12
MICHALSKY. CONCERTINO (O)	G21
MILHAUD, D. CONCERTINO (O)	F31
MILHAUD, D. CONCERTINO D'HIVER (OP)	A38
MILHAUD, D. CONCERTINO D'HIVER (P)	C01
MOZART, W.A.-FOTE. CONCERTO IN B-FLAT, K. 191 (RONDO)(P)	D14
MOZART, W.A. CONCERTO, K. 191 (P) (ORIG. FOR BASSOON)	B85
MOZART, W.A. HORN CONCERTO #1 (P)	F60
MULLER, J.P. CONCERTINO (O)	D67
MULLER, J.P. CONCERTINO GIOCOSO, OP. 47 (OP)	C75
MULLER, J.P. CONCERTO-MINUTE, OP. 4 (P)	D67
NATANSON, T. CONCERTO BREVE	A31
NESTEROV, A.A.-GIBSON. CONCERTO (P)	C91
NESTEROV, A.A. CONCERTO, OP. 11 (P)	D81
NOVAKOVSKY, J.-KRUGER. CONCERTINO (AIR VARIE) (P)	B53
NOVAKOVSKY, J.-GIBSON. CONCERTINO (P)	C91
OSTRANSKY, L. CONCERTINO (P)	F07
PARROTT, I. CONCERTO FOR TRB & WIND BAND (BOP)	E14
PLATANOV, N.I. CONCERTO (P)	D81
PORRET, J. CONCERTINO #23 (P)	D64
PORRET, J. CONCERTINO #24 (P)	D64
PORRET, J. CONCERTINO #7 (P)	D64
PORRET, J. CONCERTINO #8 (P)	D64
PREMRU, R.E. CONCERTINO (D)	E14
RASSE, F. CONCERTINO (OP)	C04
REICHE, E.-SATZ. CONCERTO #2 IN A MAJOR (P)	D37
REICHE, E. KONZERT #2 IN A MAJOR (OP)	G43
RIMSKY-KORSAKOV, N.A. CONCERTO (P)	A78
RIMSKY-KORSAKOV, N.A. CONCERTO (P)	F50
RIMSKY-KORSAKOV, N.A.-FEDOSEYEV. CONCERTO (P)	D37
RIMSKY-KORSAKOV, N.A.-FEDOSSEJEW. CONCERTO (P)	C75
RIMSKY-KORSAKOV, N.A.-GIBSON. CONCERTO (P)	C91
ROGISTER, F. CONCERTINO (P)	A82
ROTA. CONCERTO (OP)	E98
SACHSE, E. CONCERTINO (P)	C91
SACHSE, E.-MAUSEBACH. CONCERTINO (P)	B53
SARES, I.R. & CIMERA. CONCERTINO PETITE (P)	A62
SERLY, T. CONCERTO (OP)	F59
SEROCKI, K. CONCERTO (O)	A31
SEROCKI, K. CONCERTO (O) (SCORE ONLY)	A31
SEROCKI, K.-KISIELEWSKI. CONCERTO (P)	A31
SOUKUP. CONCERTO (P)	E54
SPILLMAN, R.A. CONCERTO (P)	B85
SPISAK, M. CONCERTINO (OP)	D36
SPISAK, M. CONCERTINO (P)	D81
STRAUWEN, J. CONCERTINO, OP. 167 (P)	F81
TANNER, P. CONCERTO FOR 2 TROMBONES (BP)	G21
TELEMANN, G.P.-LUMSDEN. CONCERTO (4 TRB)	E14
TOMASI, H. CONCERTO (P)	D36
TOWNSEND. CHAMBER CONCERTO #2 (P)	D74
TUTHILL, B.C. CONCERTO (P)	M98
VASILIEV, S. CONCERTO (P)	E19
VIVALDI, A. CONCERTO IN A MINOR (P)	B85

WAGENSEIL, G.C. CONCERTO IN E-FLAT MAJOR (P)   E02
WALKER, G. CONCERTO (O)   B35
WEBER, A. CONCERTO (OP)   D36
WILLIAMS, E. CONCERTO #2 (P)   B31
WILLIAMS, E. CONCERTO #5 (P)   B31
ZADOR, E. CONCERTO (OP)   D71

0122   TROMBONE SONATAS AND SONATINAS

AMBROSIUS, H. SONATE   C75
AMES, W. SONATINA   A13
ANDERSEN. SONATINA   C71
BACH, J.S.-BROWN. 3 SONATAS   C91
BASSETT, L.R. SONATA   E68
BERTALI, A. SONATA (TRB, 2 VLN, C)   E14
BERTALI, A.-HILL-BLOCK. SONATA A3 #1 (TRB, 2 VLN,G)   E14
BERTALI, A.-WIGNESS-BLOCK. SONATA A3 #2 (TRB, 2 VLN, G)   E14
BIBER, H.I.F.-JANETZKY. SONATA A TRE (TRB,2 VLN, BC)   E14
BODA, J. SONATINA   N70
CAPDEVILLE, C. SONATE CONCERTANTE   D36
CASTEREDE, J. SONATINE   D36
CORELLI, A.-BROWN. SONATA #10 IN F MAJOR   C91
CORELLI, A.-BROWN. SONATA #3 IN F MAJOR   C91
CORELLI, A.-BROWN. SONATA #6 IN E MAJOR   C91
CORELLI, A.-BROWN. SONATA #7 IN D MINOR   C91
CORELLI, A.-BROWN. SONATA #9 IN A MAJOR   C91
CORELLI, A.-GIBSON. SONATA IN D MINOR   C91
CORELLI, A. SONATA IN F   B85
CORELLI, A. SONATA IN G   B85
DAVISON, J. SONATA   F43
ECCLES, H.-BROWN. SONATA IN G MINOR   C91
FARINA. SONATA AL DIVINO CLAUDIO   B07
FASCH, J.F.-FROMME. SONATA IN C MAJOR   D55
GALLIARD, J.E.-BROWN. 6 SONATAS (2 VOL)   C91
GALLIARD, J.E.-CLARK. 6 SONATAS (2 VOL)   D55
GEISSLER, F. SONATINE   C75
GIFFELS, A.-BEVERSDORF. SONATA   F60
HANDEL, G.F. SONATA #3 IN F MAJOR   C91
HANDEL, G.F.-POWELL. SONATA #3   F60
HANDEL, G.F. SONATA #6 IN E MAJOR   C91
HARTLEY, W.S. SONATA CONCERTANTE   B52
HINDEMITH, P. SONATA   E19
HINDEMITH, P. SONATA   F31
JONES, R.W. SONATINA   B52
KELLY, R. SONATA   E68
KOETSIER. SONATINA   B74
KRECJI, M.-HEJDA. SONATINE   A33
KREISLER, VON. SONATINA   F60
LEHNER, F.X. SONATINE   A51
LUENING, O. SONATA   C33
LUENING, O. SONATA   E68
MARCELLO, B.-FOTE. SONATA III   D14
MARCELLO, B. SONATA IN A MINOR   C91
MARCELLO, B. SONATA IN C MAJOR   C91
MARCELLO, B. SONATA IN D MAJOR   C91
MARCELLO, B. SONATA IN E MINOR   C91
MARCELLO, B. SONATA IN F MAJOR   C91
MARCELLO, B.-BROWN. SONATA IN G MAJOR   C91

```
MARCELLO, B.  SONATA IN G MINOR                                  C91
MATEJ, J.  SONATA                                               E54
MC KAY, G.F.  SONATA                                           E11
MITSCHA, A.  SONATA                                            E72
MONACO, R.  SONATA                                             G83
MOZART, W.A.  HOORNSONATE #2 & 3                               D92
MOZART, W.A.  HOORNSONATE #4                                   D92
MOZART, W.A.-BROWN.  SONATA IN B-FLAT, K. 292                  C91
PRESSER, W.H.  SONATINA                                        F80
RAGWITZ.  SONATINE                                             B69
RIVARD.  SONATA                                                F80
ROY, K.G.  SONATA, OP. 13                                      D26
RUSSELL, R.  SONATA IN ONE MOVEMENT                            C40
SANDERS, R.L.  SONATA IN E-FLAT                                E11
SCHMUTZ, A.D.  SONATINE                                        D52
SEROCKI, K.  SONATINA                                          E72
SPEER, D.  SONATA FOR 3 TROMBONES                              E14
STEIN, L.  SONATA (UNACC)                                      B36
STEVENS, H.  SONATA                                            E68
STEVENS, H.  SONATINA                                          E61
TAKACS, J.  SONATA, OP. 59                                     D84
TELEMANN, G.P.-OSTRANDER.  SONATA IN F MINOR                   C91
TREVARTHEN, R.  SONATA                                         G83
UBER.  SONATA                                                  F59
VIVALDI, A.  SONATA #1 IN B-FLAT MAJOR                         C91
VIVALDI, A.-BROWN.  SONATA #2 FROM IL PASTOR FIDO              C91
VIVALDI, A.  SONATA #2 IN F MAJOR                              C91
VIVALDI, A.-OSTRANDER.  SONATA #3 IN A MINOR (OP)              C91
VIVALDI, A.  SONATA #4 IN B-FLAT MAJOR                         C91
VIVALDI, A.  SONATA #5 IN E MINOR                              C91
VIVALDI, A.  SONATA #6 IN B-FLAT MAJOR (O)                     C91
VIVALDI, A.  SONATA IN G MINOR, OP. 2/1                        C91
WATSON, W.  SONATINA                                           F43
WHEAR, P.W.  SONATA                                            D52
WHITE, D.  SONATA                                              F60
WILDER, A.  SONATA                                             B14
```

0123   TROMBONE SOLOS WITH BAND ACCOMPANIMENT

```
ADAM, A.C.-BOUSQUET.  CELEBRE NOEL (B)                         D64
ADES, H.(ARR).  LONDONDERRY AIR (BP)                           F43
ANDRIEU.  ANGELUS DU SOIR, MELODIE (B)                         D64
ANDRIEU.  UNE ETOILE, REVERIE (B)                             D64
BARAT, J.E.-MARSTELLER.  ANDANTE & ALLEGRO (B)                 F60
BIZET, G.-HARDING.  FLOWER SONG FROM CARMEN (B)               D18
BIZET, G.-OUGHTON.  ROMANCE FROM FAIR MAID OF PERTH (B)       E59
BLEMANT, L.  TROIMPHE, FANTASIE (B)                           D64
BOCCALARI.  FANTASIA DI CONCERTO (SOUNDS FR THE RIVIERA) (BP)  C11
BOULCOURT, A.  TROMBONE POLKA (B)                             A78
BRAHE, M.H.  BLESS THIS HOUSE (B)                             A78
BUCHTEL, F.L.  JUPITER (B)                                    D18
BUSCH, M.  BALLAD (B)                                         D18
CARDILLO.  CATARI-CATARI (B)                                  D92
CLARKE, H.L.  STARS IN A VELVETY SKY (BP)                     C11
CLOUGH, T.H.  WINNING SPURT (B)                               A78
CODE, P.  EMPEROR (B)                                         A78
COPIELD, F.D.  CHARTREUSE (B)                                 F07
COKER, W.  CONCERTO (B)                                       E77
```

COOK, E.-RICHARDSON. BOLIVAR (B)	A78
DAVIS, A.O. DESERT STAR (BP)	D52
DEDRICK, A.(ARR). VIENNESE REFRAIN (B)	D14
DEFOSSEZ, R. CONCERTO (BP)	B47
DELBECQ, A. SUR LA SEILLE, REVERIE (B)	D64
DELUCA, J. BEAUTIFUL COLORADO (BP)	C11
FERNAND. BALLADE DE L'AVEUGLE (B)	D64
FLEGIER, A.-DELBECQ. COR, LE (B)	D64
FRACKENPOHL, A.R. PASTORALE (B)	F02
FRANCK, C. PANIS ANGELICUS (B)	D64
GILLIS, D. DIALOGUE (BP)	D84
GODARD, E. BERCEISE FROM JOCELYN (B)	F60
GODARD, E. BERCEUSE DE JOCELYN (BP)	F54
GODFREY, F. LUCY LONG (B)	A78
GOUBLIER-FERNAND. L'ANGELUS DE LA MER (B)	D64
GUILLEMENT. BASQUE, LE (B)	D64
HADRABA, J. KUH-LANDLER ("MIT JAZZORCHESTER")	D20
HARTZELL, D. EGOTISTICAL ELEPHANT (BP)	F43
HEMMERLE. TROMBONE SENTIMENTAL (B)	D64
HUBERT. ELEGIE (B)	D64
HUME, J.O. VICTORY (B)	E83
LAKE, M.L. NAIDA (BP)	D52
LEGENDRE-BOUSQUET. AIR VARIE (B)	D64
MARSAL. RACHEL (B)	D64
MASTEN, I.J. BONNIE ELOISE (BP)	D52
MELLISH. DRINK TO ME ONLY WITH THINE ICE (B)	A91
METEHEN, E. RAMSES (B)	D64
MEUNIER. DUE DES TROMBONES (B)	D64
MORRISSEY, J.J. SONG FOR TROMBONE (B)	D63
MOSS, H. JOKER (B)	A78
MOSS, H. KANGAROO (B)	A78
MOSS, H. MOSQUITO (B)	A78
MOZART, W.A. SARASTRO-ARIE AUS "DIE ZAUBERFLOTE" (B)	F10
NESTICO, S. REFLECTIVE MOOD (B)	D14
PARES, G.P.C. CREPUSCULE (B)	D64
PONIATOWSKI, J. YEOMAN'S WEDDING SONG (B)	A78
PRESSEL, G.A.-BREUER. AN DER WESER (B)	B99
PRYOR, A. BLUE BELLS OF SCOTLAND (BP)	C11
PRYOR, A. THOUGHTS OF LOVE (BP)	C11
SIMON, F. WILLOW ECHOES (BP)	C09
SIMONS, G. ATLANTIC ZEPHYRS (BP)	C11
STREET, A.(CMPL). 4 SOLOS (B)	E59
TANNER, P. ARIA (BP)	G21
THAYER, P. I TRAVEL THE ROAD (B)	E83
WALTERS, H.L. TARANTELLE (BP)	D52
WINDSOR, B. BARNACLE BILL (B)	A78

0124 TROMBONE SOLOS WITH ORCHESTRAL ACCOMPANIMENT

BERGHMANS, J. FEMME A BARBE (#4 DES "TABLEAUX FORAINS) (OP)	D36
BIGOT, E.V. IMPROMPTU (OP)	D36
BLOCH, E. SYMPHONIE FUR POSAUNE & ORCH (O)	F31
BLOCH, E. SYMPHONY FOR TRB & ORCH (OP)	A98
BONNEAU, P. FANTAISIE CONCERTANTE (OP)	D36
BORSCEEL, E. CANZONETTA (OP)	C30
BOSSI, R. TEMPO DI CONCERTO (O)	B07
BOZZA, E. BALLADE, OP. 62 (OP)	D36
BRICCETTI, T. ECLOGUE #2 (O)	G89

```
DEDRICK.  AWAKENING (O)                                        M65
GABAYE, P.  SPECIAL (O)                                        D36
HARTLEY, W.S.  CAPRICCIO (O)                                   G83
HARTZELL, D.  BALLAD FOR YOUNG CATS (O)                        F43
HERF, F.  KONZERTSTUCK (OP)                                    D44
HOVHANESS, A.S.  OVERTURE (O)                                  E65
JORGENSEN, A.  SUITE, OP. 22 (OP)                              H30
KWIATKOWSKI, R.  SERENADE (O)                                  A31
LENZ, M.  TANZENDE KOBOLD, DER (OP)                            C30
LOHMANN, G.-MIELENZ.  POSAUNEN TEUFEL (OP)                     C30
MAES, J.  CONCERTSTUK (O)                                      B12
MALTBY.  BLUES ESSAY (O)                                       E67
MARTIN, F.  BALLADE (OP)                                       F97
MEIER, A.-BOHME.  UNTER DEN STERNEN (OP)                       C30
MEULEMANS, A.  RHAPSODIE (OP)                                  B12
NELHYBEL, V.  CONCERT PIECE (O)                                G68
PRESSER, W.H.  RONDO (O)                                       F88
RESCHOFSKY, A.  KONZERT-PHANTASIE (OP)                         D44
SCHOEMAKER, M.  PIECE CONCERTANTE (OP)                         C42
SERERBRIER, J.  VARIATIONS ON A THEME FROM CHILDHOOD (O)       F59
VILLETTE, P.  FANTAISIE CONCERTANTE (OP)                       D36
WILCKEN, E.  BLAUER MOHN (OP)                                  C30
```

0126   TROMBONE SOLOS WITH PIANO ACCOMPANIMENT

```
ABSIL.  BERCEUSE                                               C42
ABSIL, J.  SUITE, OP. 78                                       F21
ADAMS, S.  HOLY CITY                                           D92
ADAMS, S.-FRANGKISER.  HOLY CITY                               A62
ADAMS, S.-GLENN.  HOLY CITY                                    A78
ADES, H.  LONDONDERRY AIR                                      F43
AERTS, F.  FANTAISIE ORIGINALE                                 F81
AHL, G.  GALANTE POSAUNE                                       C30
ALEXANDER, H.  SHUR DODI                                       C94
ALLAN, W.  ECLIPSE                                             D92
AMELLER, A.C.  HAUTERIVE                                       D36
AMELLER, A.C.  KRYPTOS (ETUDE)                                 C71
AMELLER, A.C.  RIVIERE DU LOUP                                 D36
ANNA LAURIE.                                                   D92
ARBAN, J.J.B.L.  FANTASIE BRILLANTE                            B53
ARLEN-SEARS.  BLUES IN THE NIGHT                               H06
ARNDT.  NOLA                                                   C25
ARNE, T.A.  DRINK TO ME ONLY                                   D92
ARNOLD, J.  EVERYBODY'S FAVORITE SERIES: #106 EASY SOLOS       A18
ARRIEU, C.  MOUVEMENTS                                         A16
ASCHER, J.  ALICE, WHERE ARE YOU?                             D92
ASH GROVE.                                                     D92
ASHLEY (PUB).  EASY TO PLAY PIECES                             A37
ASHLEY (PUB).  INTERMEDIATE PIECES FOR TRB                     A37
AUBAIN.  ARIA, SCHERZO ET FINALE                              D36
BACH, J.S.-SINGERLING.  AIR (ON THE G STRING)                 D92
BACH, J.S.-FOTE.  AIR FROM SUITE #3                            D14
BACH, J.S.-FITZGERALD.  ARIA "BIST DU BEI MIR"                B32
BACH, J.S.-KENT.  ARIOSO                                       C11
BACH, J.S.  AVE MARIA                                          D92
BACH, J.S.-KRANE.  BACH FOR TRB (9 SOLOS)                      F62
BACH, J.S.-BEVERSDORF.  ENDURE! ENDURE! (PASSION, ST. MATTHEW) F60
BACH, J.S.-FIGERT.  FOR HE THAT IS MIGHTY                      D14
```

```
BACH, J.S.-BEVERSDORF.  HASTE, YE SHEPHERDS (XMAS ORATORIO)      F60
BACH, J.S.   JESU, JOY OF MAN                                    D92
BACH, J.S.   PATRON OF THE WIND                                  B85
BACH, J.S.-SIEGRIST.  PLAISIR DU TROMBONISTE, BK 1               F87
BACH, J.S.-HUTCHERSON.  SARABANDE...GIGUE (CELLO SUITE #1)       C11
BACH, J.S.-FOTE.  SINFONIA                                       D14
BACH, J.S.-LOEB.  6 SUITES                                       D64
BACH, J.S.   THOU WHO SITS TO THE FATHER'S RIGHT                 B31
BACH, J.S.-BEVERSDORF.  TIS THEE I WOULD BE PRAISING             F60
BACHELET, A.  CONCERTPIECE                                       C91
BACHELET, A.  MORCEAU DE CONCOURS                                D36
BAERVOETS, R.  IMPROMPTU                                         D67
BAEYENS, H.  INTRODUCTION & CANTABILE                            A96
BAKALEINIKOFF, V.R.  ANDANTINO CANTABILE                         A62
BAKALEINIKOFF, V.R.  MEDITATION                                  A62
BAKALEINIKOFF, V.R.  VALSE TRISTE                                A62
BALFE, M.W.   KILLARNEY                                          D92
BARAT, J.E.   ANDANTE & ALLEGRO                                  C91
BARAT, J.E.   ANDANTE ALLEGRO                                    F60
BARAT, J.E.   ANDANTE ET ALLEGRO                                 B53
BARAT, J.E.   ANDANTE ET ALLEGRO                                 D36
BARAT, J.E.   PIECE EN MI-FLAT                                   D36
BARATI, G.  LUMBERJACK                                           A13
BARBE.  1 FANTASIE ORIGINALE                                     D92
BARILLER, R.  ENTERREMENT DE SAINT-JEAN                          D36
BARNARD, G.D.  MOANA WALTZ                                       A55
BARNARD, G.D.  PUNCH & JUDY                                      A55
BARNES, C.P.  YOUNG ARTIST                                       A78
BARNES, C.P.  YOUNG GENIUS                                       A78
BARNES, C.P.  YOUNG MAESTRO                                      A78
BARNES, C.P.  YOUNG VIRTUOSO                                     A78
BARNHOUSE, C.L.  GOD BE WITH YOU                                 A55
BARNHOUSE, C.L.  LET THE LOWER LIGHTS BE BURNING                 A55
BARNHOUSE, C.L.  MEDITATION RELIGIOSO FROM "LAST HOPE"           A55
BARNHOUSE, C.L.  REFUGE                                          A55
BARNHOUSE, C.L.  SWEET BY AND BY                                 A55
BARNHOUSE, C.L.  TRAMP, TRAMP, TRAMP                             A55
BARON.  NIRVANA                                                  A56
BARRAINE, E.  ANDANTE & ALLEGRO                                  F16
BARRAINE, E.  CHIENS DE PAILLE                                   D00
BARTLETT, H.H.-HUMMEL.  DREAM, A                                 F07
BARTOK, B.-HARRIS.  EVENING IN THE COUNTRY                       D52
BARTOLOMEO.  FANTASIA                                            N92
BAUMGARTNER.  NOCH SIND DIE TAGE DER                             D92
BEACH, B.C.  SUITE                                              A38
BECHER, H.  CAPRICCIO                                            C54
BEELER, W.R. (CMPL).  CHRISTMAS FAVORITES                        F23
BEETHOVEN, L.V.-KREISLER.  RONDINO ON A THEME OF BEETHOVEN       C18
BEETHOVEN, L.V.  RONDO, OP. 17                                   B85
BELLINI, V.  DASTA DIVA                                          B53
BELLSTEDT, H.-SIMON.  AMERICAN BOY                               F60
BELLSTEDT, H.-SIMON.  BETTY LEE                                  F60
BELLSTEDT, H.-SIMON.  CAPRICCIO BRILLANTE (CARNIVAL OF NAPLES)   F60
BELLSTEDT, H.-SIMON.  CARMEN FANTASIE                            F60
BELLSTEDT, H.-SIMON.  CARNIVAL OF VENICE                         F60
BELLSTEDT, H.-SIMON.  COQUETTE                                   F60
BELLSTEDT, H.-SIMON.  FANTASIA #1                                F60
BELLSTEDT, H.-SIMON.  HERMAN BELSTEDT SOLOS (15 SOLOS)           F60
BELLSTEDT, H.-SIMON.  INTRO. & TARANTELLE                        F60
BELLSTEDT, H.-SIMON.  MANDOLINATA                                F60
BELLSTEDT, H.-SIMON.  NAPOLI                                     F60
BELLSTEDT, H.-SIMON.  PIECE DE CONCERTE (ON A CHOPIN MELODY)     F60
```

```
BELLSTEDT, H.-SIMON.  PRINCESS ALICE                               F60
BELLSTEDT, H.-SIMON.  SKYROCKET                                    F60
BELLSTEDT, H.-SIMON.  STUDENT'S SWEETHEART                         F60
BENNETT, C.W.  LITTLE BLUE CAP                                     C11
BENNETT, C.W.  ROMANCE                                             C11
BENNETT, D.  TROMBOGRAPHIC                                         C11
BENOIT.  ANDANTE                                                   D92
BENSON, W.F.  AUBADE                                               E67
BERGHMANS, J.  FEMME A BARBE (#4 DES "TABLEAUX FORAINS") (OP)      D36
BERLIOZ, H.  RECITATIVE & PRAYER, OP. 15                           D74
BERLIOZ, H.  3 SONGS (DAMNATION OF FAUST)                          B85
BERLIOZ, H.  UNKNOWN ISLE                                          B85
BERTHELOT.  ROI RENAUD, LE                                         D36
BERTHOLON.  VARIETES                                               D36
BEY, R.  KINDERLIEDER VARIATIONEN                                  C30
BEY, R.  ROMANZE                                                   C30
BIGOT, E.V.  CARILLON ET BOURDON                                   D36
BIGOT, E.V.  IMPROMPTU (OP)                                        D36
BIGOT, E.V.  VARIATIONS                                            D36
BISSELINK.  IZEGRIM                                                D92
BITSCH, M.  RICERCARE                                              D36
BIZET, G.  AGNUS DEI                                               B85
BIZET, G.  AGNUS DEI                                               D92
BLAAUW, L.  BALLET SCENE                                           F81
BLAAUW, L.  CAVATINE                                               F81
BLAAUW, L.  CHANT D'AMOUR                                          D92
BLAAUW, L.  INTRODUCTIE...EEN ST. NICOLAASLIEDJE                   D92
BLATTER.  5 SKETCHES                                               N29
BLAZHEVICH, V.M.  CONCERT PIECE #5                                 A62
BLAZHEVICH, V.M.-SATZ.  CONCERT SKETCH #5                          D37
BLAZHEVICH, V.M.-SHUMAN.  ETUDE #86                                F62
BLAZHEVICH, V.M.-SHUMAN.  ETUDE #92                                F62
BLAZHEVICH, V.M.  KONZERTSTUCK #5                                  F50
BLEGER, M.  SOUVENIR DE VALENCE                                    D92
BLEMANT, L.  TRIOMPHE                                              D64
BLOCH, E.  SYMPHONY FOR TROMBONE & ORCHESTRA (OP)                  A98
BOCCALARI.  FANTASIA DI CONCERTO (SOUNDS FROM THE RIVIERA) (BP)    C11
BOEDIJN, G.H.  ODE AAN EEN VETTE KIP                               D92
BONNEAU, P.  CAPRICCIO                                             D36
BONNEAU, P.  FANTAISIE CONCERTANTE (OP)                            D36
BOOS, L.F.-BUCHTEL.  CHARMER, THE                                  D18
BORMANN, C.E.  VOLLEN ZUGEN, IN                                    C30
BORSCHEL, E.  CANZONETTA (OP)                                      C30
BOTTJE, W.G.  RECITATIVE, ARIOSO & FINALE                          A13
BOUILLON.  SOUVENIR D'OSTENDE                                      D92
BOUTRY, R.  CAPRICCIO                                              D36
BOUTRY, R.  CHORAL VARIE                                           D36
BOZZA, E.  ALLEGRO ET FINALE                                       D36
BOZZA, E.  BALLADE, OP. 62 (OP)                                    D36
BOZZA, E.  CIACONNA                                                B92
BOZZA, E.  CIACONNA                                                D36
BOZZA, E.  HOMMAGE A BACH                                          D36
BRAHE, M.H.-GLENN.  BLESS THIS HOUSE                               A78
BRAHMSTEDT, N.K.  STUPENDO (CONCERT POLKA)                         F07
BREARD, R.  PIECE DE CONCOURS                                      D41
BRIEGEL, G.F.  BASSO PROFUNDO                                      A91
BRIEGEL, G.F.  LITTLE SHEPHERD                                     A91
BRIEGEL, G.F.  MULBERRY STREET TARANTELLA                          A91
BROGI-ANDREONI.  VISIONE VENEZIANA                                 E98
BROOKS, E.  MESSAGE, THE                                           D18
BROWN, C.L.G.  MEDITATION                                          D36
BROWN, K.  ALBUM OF CLASSICAL PIECES                               C91
```

```
BRUCKNER, A.   AVE MARIA                                          B85
BUCHTEL, F.L.   APOLLO                                            D84
BUCHTEL, F.L.   AROGANT WALTZ                                     D18
BUCHTEL, F.L.   BALL, AT THE                                      D18
BUCHTEL, F.L.   BEAU BRUMMEL                                      D18
BUCHTEL, F.L.   BLUE BELLS OF SCOTLAND WITH VARIATIONS           D84
BUCHTEL, F.L.   BOLERO                                            D18
BUCHTEL, F.L.   CHROMATICA WALTZ                                  D18
BUCHTEL, F.L.   CIELITO LINDO                                     D18
BUCHTEL, F.L.   DREAMER, THE                                      D18
EUCHTEL, F.L.   DRUM MAJOR MARCH                                  D18
BUCHTEL, F.L.   GLADIATOR                                         D18
BUCHTEL, F.L.   GOLDEN DREAMS WALTZ                               D18
BUCHTEL, F.L.   HARLEQUIN                                         D18
EUCHTEL, F.L.   HOLY CITY                                         D18
EUCHTEL, F.L.   INTERMEZZO                                        D18
BUCHTEL, F.L.   INTRODUCTION & RONDO                              A55
EUCHTEL, F.L.   JOVIAL MOOD                                       D18
BUCHTEL, F.L.   JUPITER                                           D18
BUCHTEL, F.L.   MARINES HYMN                                      D18
BUCHTEL, F.L.   MAY NOON                                          D18
BUCHTEL, F.L.   MEDITATION (SONATINA IN F)                       D18
BUCHTEL, F.L.   MINSTREL BOY                                      D18
BUCHTEL, F.L.   PIED PIPER                                        D18
BUCHTEL, F.L.   SENTIMENTAL SAM                                   D18
BUCHTEL, F.L.   WALTZ MEDLEY                                      D18
BUCHTEL, F.L.   YOUNG JACKANAPES                                  D18
BURKE, J.F.-SMITH.   HOCUS POCUS                                  E77
BURKE, J.F.-SMITH.   PROM WALTZ                                   E77
EURKE, J.F.-SMITH.   SERENADE IN 6/8                             E77
BURKE, J.F.-SMITH.   STRICTLY G.I.                               E77
BURKE, J.F.-SMITH.   TWILIGHT TUNE                               E77
BUSSER, H.P.   CANTABILE ET SCHERZANDO, OP. 51                    D36
BUSSER, H.P.   CONCERTPIECE IN E-FLAT                             C91
BUSSER, H.P.   ETUDE DE CONCERT, OP. 79                          C04
BUSSER, H.P.   PHOEBUS(VARIATIONS SUR UN AIR PYRENEEN),OP.87      D36
BUSSER, H.P.   PIECE EN MI BEMOL, OP. 33                         D36
BUTTNER, M.K.   IMPROVISATIONEN, OP. 6                            C75
BUTTS, C.M.   ARIA                                                G90
BUZZI-PECCIA, A.-ANDREONI.   LOLITA                               E98
CABUS, P.N.   FUGA ET TOCCATA                                     D67
CADMAN, C.W.   DAWNING, AT                                        B72
CAISSCNS GO ROLLING ALONG.                                       D18
CANIVEZ, L.   AIR VARIE, OP. 6                                    F81
CARDILLO-ANDREONI.   CORE 'NGRATO. CANZONE NAPOLETANA            E98
CARISSIMI, G.G.-BARNES.   HEART VICTORICUS                       F62
CASEY.   HONEYSUCKLE POLKA                                        D18
CASEY.   REMEMBRANCE OF LIBERATI                                  D18
CASINIERE, Y. DE LA.   THEME VARIE                               D36
CASTLETON.   9 PROGRAM SOLOS                                      E77
CATELINET, P.B.   OLD MACDONALD HAD A FARM                        C71
CESARE-SMITH.   HIERONYMA FROM MUSICALI MELODIE, 1621            D16
CHAMBERS.   COMMODORE                                             D18
CHARLES.   CORTEGE ET DANSE                                       F87
CHAYNES, C.   IMPULSIONS                                          D36
CHENETTE, E.S.   MAGIC WAND                                       A62
CHERUBINI, L.   AVE MARIA                                         B85
CHILDS, B.   MUSIC FOR TRB & PA                                   E68
CHOPIN, F.-MARSTELLER.   NOCTURNE IN F MINOR                      F60
CHOPIN, F.-ANDREONI.   TRISTEZZA (DALLA STUDIO, OP. 10/3)        E98
CHRISTOPHE, J.   AIR VARIE #2                                     D92
CHRISTOPHE, J.   AIR VARIE #2                                     F81
```

```
CIMERA, J.-GANGWARE.  BEMIDJI ZEPHYRS                        A62
CIMERA, J.  BETSY WALTZ                                      A62
CIMERA, J.  CAPRICE CHARMANTE                                D18
CIMERA, J.  CARNIVAL OF VENICE                               E11
CIMERA, J.  CATHERINE                                        D18
CIMERA, J.  IMPROVISATION                                    E11
CIMERA, J.  ISABELLA                                         D18
CIMERA, J.  JOAN OF ARC                                      D18
CIMERA, J.  LIBUSE                                           D18
CIMERA, J.  MARY                                             D18
CIMERA, J.  POLKA CAPRICE                                    G85
CIMERA, J.  POLONAISE CHARMOUNT                              D18
CIMERA, J.  SPRING CAPRICE                                   D18
CIMERA, J.  VALSE LA RUE (SARES)                             D18
CIMERA, J.  VALSE PETITE                                     E11
CIMERA, J.  VALSE ROMANTIQUE                                 E11
CIMERA, J.  VICTORIA                                         D18
CIMERA, J.  WALTZ HELEN                                      A62
CIMERA, J. & SARES.  LITTLE CARNIVAL                         A62
CIMERA, J. & SARES.  MARGARET WALTZ                          A62
CIMERA, J. & SARES.  SLIDING ON ICE                         A62
CIRRI, G.B.  ARIOSO                                          B85
CLARIBEL-DE ROOY.  COME BACK TO ERIN                         F81
CLARKE, E.  AT THE SHRINE                                    C11
CLARKE, E.  CHIMES                                           C11
CLARKE, E.  DEVOTION                                         C11
CLARKE, E.  DRIFTING IN THE MOONLIGHT                        C11
CLARKE, E.  EVENING SHADOWS                                  C11
CLARKE, E.  GARDEN FESTIVAL                                  C11
CLARKE, E.  STROLLING MINSTRELS                              C11
CLARKE, H.L.  ARTEMIS POLKA                                  C09
CLARKE, H.L.  BRIDE OF THE WAVES                             H06
CLARKE, H.L.  MAID OF THE MIST                               H06
CLARKE, H.L.  SOUTHERN CROSS                                 H06
CLARKE, H.L.  STARS IN A VELVETY SKY (BP)                    C11
CLEMENT, F.W.  EVENING ZEPHYR                                A55
CLERGUE, J.  IMPROMPTU                                       D41
CLERISSE, R.-SMITH.  IDYLLE                                  F60
CLERISSE, R.  POEME                                          A71
CLERISSE, R.  POEME                                          D64
CLERISSE, R.  PRELUDE ET DIVERTISSEMENT                      A71
CLERISSE, R.-VOXMAN.  PRELUDE ET DIVERTISSEMENT              F07
CLERISSE, R.  PRIERE                                         D36
CLERISSE, R.  THEME DE CONCOURS                              D36
COFIELD, F.D.  CHARTREUSE                                    F07
CONCONE, G.-GOWER.  BERCEUSE                                 F07
CONCONE, G.-GOWER.  MEDITATION                               F07
CONCONE, G.-CRAMER.  15 VOCALISES, OP. 12                    N70
COOK, E.  BOLIVAR                                            A78
COOLIDGE, R.  ARIOSO                                         G83
COOLIDGE, R.-BAKER.  CURVES OF GOLD                          D14
COOLS, E.  ALLEGRO DE CONCERT                                A71
CORELLI, A.-POWELL.  PRELUDE & MINUET                        F60
CORIOLIS.  ARIA                                              D36
CORIOLIS.  4 PEICETTES                                       A71
COVINGTON.  TIPSY TROMBONE                                   D84
COVINGTON.  TROMBONANZA                                      D84
COWELL, H.D.  HYMN & FUGUING TUNE #13                        A38
COWLES, E.  FORGOTTEN                                        E77
CRESTON, P.  FANTASY, OP. 42                                 F23
CROCE-SPINELLI.  SOLO DE CONCOURS                            A62
CROCE-SPINELLI.  SOLO DE CONCOURS                            D36
```

CUI, C.A.   ORIENTALE   B53
CUNNINGHAM, M.G.   STATEMENTS, OP. 43   G66
CUSTER, A.R.   MARCH   D33
DAGNELIES.   LINDA   D92
DAKE, F.   MEET YOUR SLIDE   G43
DANEELS, F.   PETITE PIECE   D67
DAUTREMER.   COULISSIANA   B24
DAVIS, A.O.   DESERT STAR (BP)   D52
DAVIS, A.O.   (ARR).   CARNIVAL OF VENICE   F37
DAWES, C.G.-SEARS.   MELODY   E11
DE HERVE, A.   INTRODUCTION & FINALE   A82
DE JONG, M.   CONCERT PIECE, OP. 50   A96
DE LAMATER, E.   BRILLIANT POLKA   F07
DE LUCA, J.-ROBERTS.   BEAUTIFUL COLORADO (BP)   C11
DE LUCA, J.-ROBERTS.   BEAUTIFUL COLORADO   C11
DE LUCA, J.   MINUET SCHERZO   A55
DE SCHRIJVER.   6 PETITS MORCEAUX   F21
DEARNLEY, C.H.   8 EASY PIECES BY CLASSICAL COMPOSERS   B23
DEARNLEY, C.H.   MORE EASY PIECES BY CLASSICAL COMPOSERS   B23
DEBAAR, M.   LEGENDE ET CAPRICE   A96
DEBUSSY, C.   AIR DE LIA   B85
DEDRICK.   AWAKENING   M65
DEDRICK, A.   (ARR).   VIENNESE REFRAIN   D14
DEEP RIVER.   D92
DEFAY, J.M.   2 DANCES   D36
DEFAYE.   MOUVEMENT   D36
DELBECQ, L.   JULIANA   D92
DELHAYE.   SILVER THREADS   D92
DEMERSSEMAN-STEWART.   CAVATINA   B53
DEMERSSEMAN.   CAVATINE   A71
DEMERSSEMAN.   INTRODUCTION ET POLONAISE   A71
DENMARK, M.F.   INTRODUCTION & POLONAISE   D52
DENZA, L.-ANDREONI.   FUNICULI-FUNICULA   E98
DEPELSENAIRE.   IMPROMPTU   F31
DEPELSENAIRE.   JEUX CHROMATIQUES   E66
DEPELSENAIRE.   LEGENDE NERVIENNE   E66
DEPELSENAIRE.   VIEUX BERGER RACONTE, LE   E66
DEPELSENAIRE, J.M.   FUNAMBULES   E77
DEPELSENAIRE, J.M.   FUNAMBULES   F87
DEPELSENAIRE, J.M.   RECITATIF ET AIR   B66
DEPREZ.   PIECE DE CONCOURS   D67
DES PREZ, J.   PIECE DE CONCOURS   D67
DESENCLOS, A.   PLAIN CHANT ET ALLEGRETTO   D36
DESPORTES, Y.   FANTAISIE   D36
DESPORTES, Y.   FANTAISIE   B53
DESPREZ, F.   FANTAISIE CONCERTANTE   D67
DEVILLE-GOLDMAN.   BLUE BELLS OF SCOTLAND   C11
DEWANGER, A.   HUMORESQUE, OP. 89   D36
DHOSSCHE, R.A.   INVOCATION   F60
DITTMER (ARR).   DARK EYES   B13
DIWISCH, F.   GROTESKE   C30
DIWISCH, F.   SCHACH MATT   C30
DOMROESE.   2 EPIGRAMME   A80
DOMROESE.   6 KLEINE STUECKE   A80
DOMROESE.   KLEINE SUITE   A80
DOMROESE.   OURS, LES   D36
DOMROESE.   SAKURA IMPRESSIONS JAPONAISES   D36
DONDEYNE, D.   CANTABILE ET CAPRICE   D36
DONIZETTI, G.-PAQUE.   CAVATINE D'ANNA BOLENA   F81
DONIZETTI, G.-ANDREONI.   FURTIVA LAGRIMA, UNA   A62
DONIZETTI, G.-RIMMER.   STILL SO GENTLY   D92
DORSEY, T.   3 MOODS   A70

DORSSELAER, W.VAN.	GRAND DUC, LE	A71
DORSSELAER, W.VAN.	INTRODUCTION ET ALLEGRO MARTIAL	A71
DORSSELAER, W.VAN.	JERICHO	D92
DORSSELAER, W.VAN.	LONHCHAMP, A	A71
DORSSELAER, W.VAN.	POUR LA PROMOTION	A71
DOULIEZ, V.	ANDANTE, OP. 53	A96
DOULIEZ, V.	INTRODUCTION & ANDANTE, OP. 54	A96
DRIGO, R.	SERENADE, MILLIONS OF HARLEQUIN	B13
DUBOIS, P.M.	CORTEGE	D36
DUBOIS, P.M.	COULISSE, EN	N50
DUBOIS, P.M.	2 MARCHES	D36
DUBOIS, P.M.	POUR LE TROMBONE MOYEN	D36
DUBOIS, P.M.	POUR LE TROMBONE PREPARATOIRE	D36
DUBOIS, P.M.	SUITE	B92
DUBOIS, P.M.	SUITE	D36
DUBOIS, T.	CONCERTPIECE IN A-FLAT MAJOR	C91
DUBOIS, T.	SOLO DE CONCERT	D36
DUCKWORTH.	STATEMENTS & INTERLUDES	F80
DUCLOS, R.	DOUBLES SUR UN CHORAL	D36
DUCLOS, R.	SA MAJESTE LE TROMBONE	D36
DUPORT, J.L.	ROMANCE	F62
DURAND & AUDARD, P.	DIALOGUE	D36
DUTILLEUX, H.	CHORAL, CADENCE ET FUGATO	D36
DVARIONAS, B.	THEME WITH VARIATIONS	E19
DVORACEK.	INVENZIONI	E54
ECKARD, W. (ARR).	HIGHLIGHTS OF FAMILIAR MUSIC	E77
ENDRESEN, R.M.	ACHILLES	F07
ENGLEMANN, H.	MELODY OF LOVE	E77
EVANS.	LADY OF SPAIN	C25
FABRE, C.	REVERIE #2	B53
FALCONE.	2 PIECES	F60
FAURE, G.U.-OSTRANDER.	APRES UN REVE	C91
FAURE, G.U.-STOUTAMIRE.	AURORA	D14
FAURE, G.U.	EN PRIERE	B85
FAURE, G.U.	PALMS	C11
FAURE, G.U.-BROWN.	SICILIENE, OP. 78	C91
FERNANDEZ, O.L.	BEAUTIFUL HEAVEN	A91
FERSTL, E.	ROMANZETTA	C30
FIBICH, Z.	POEM (ROMANCE)	B13
FIBICH, Z.-ANDREONI.	POEMA	E98
FIEVET, P.	LEGENDE CELTIQUE	A71
FILLMORE, H.	LASSUS TROMBONE	C09
FILLMORE, H.	SHOUTIN' LIZA TROMBONE	C09
FIRST DIV BAND COURSE.	CAMPING OUT	A62
FIRST DIV BAND COURSE.	DOWNTOWN	A62
FIRST DIV BAND COURSE.	ELEGIE	A62
FIRST DIV BAND COURSE.	MARSHALL	A62
FIRST DIV BAND COURSE.	MOODS FROM DORIAN	A62
FIRST DIV BAND COURSE.	ROMANCE	A62
FIRST DIV BAND COURSE.	SHEPHERD'S DANCE	A62
FIRST DIV BAND COURSE.	SONG WITHOUT WORDS	A62
FIRST DIV BAND COURSE.	SPOKANE	A62
FIRST DIV BAND COURSE.	TOUCHDOWN	A62
FIRST DIV BAND COURSE.	VISCOUNT	A62
FISHER, W.A.	DEEP RIVER	B72
FLOTOW, F.V.	MARTHA ARIA	D92
FORESTIER, J.J.	BELLONA	D92
FOSTER, S.C.	BEAUTIFUL DREAMER	D92
FOSTER, S.C.	JEANIE WITH THE LIGHT BROWN HAIR	D92
FOX (PUB).	FOX ALBUM OF TROMBONE SOLOS	C25
FRACKENPOHL, A.R.	PASTORALE	E87
FRANCK, C.	PANIS ANGELICUS	D92

```
FRANCK, M.  FANFARE, ANDANTE ET ALLEGRO                          F16
FRANCL.  DUMKA, ELEGY & DANCE                                    A33
FRANCO, J.  DUO LIRICO                                           B36
FRANCOEUR-BOSWELL.  SYMPHONIA SACRA                              N42
FRANGKISER, C.  AUTUMN SOLILOQUY                                 A62
FRANGKISER, C.  FIRESIDE SOLILOQUY                               A62
FRAZEUR.  DIVERTIMENTO                                           B98
FRESCOBALDI, G.-BROWN.  TOCCATA                                  C91
FROST, G.  GRAND FANTASY OBLIGATO                                D92
FROTHEY, F.  TANZENDE TRAUM, DER                                 C30
FUHLISCH, G.  POSAUNENERFOLGE                                    F50
GABAYE, P.  COMPLAINTE                                           D36
GABAYE, P.  SPECIAL                                              D36
GADE, J.-SEARS.  JALOUSIE                                        C58
GALIEGUE & DUPIN.  QUELQUES CHANTS (4 BKS)                       D36
GALLET.  LEGENDE                                                 A71
GALLOIS-MONTBRUN, R.  ARIA                                       D36
GARDNER, J.L.  ROMANCE                                           F31
GAUBERT, P.  MORCEAU SYMPHONIQUE                                 D36
GAUBERT, P.  MORCEAU SYMPHONIQUE                                 F60
GAUBERT, P.  SYMPHONIC PIECE                                     C91
GEDALGE, A.  CONTEST PIECE                                       C91
GEDALGE, A.  SOLO DE CONCOURS                                    C38
GERMAN-SMITH.  SHEPHERD'S DANCE                                  A62
GERSCHEFSKI, E.  SUITE FOR TRB ALONE, OP. 49, NOS. 1-5          A13
GERSHWIN, G.-SEARS.  AMERICAN IN PARIS, AN                       H06
GERSHWIN, G.  ANDANTE & FINALE (RHAPSODY IN BLUE)               H06
GERSHWIN, G.-STERLING.  FASCONATING RHYTHM                       E11
GILLIS, D.  DIALOGUE (BP)                                        D84
GIORDANI, T.  CARO MIO BEN                                       D92
GIORDANI, T.-FELIX.  CARO MIO BEN (AN 18TH CEMTURY AIR)          B85
GIORDANI, T.-CONLEY.  CARO MIO BEN                               D14
GLANTZ, H.  6 GREAT MODERN SOLOS                                 B31
GLINKA, M.I.  ROMANCE MELODY                                     F62
GLOVER, C.W.  ROSE OF TRALEE                                     D92
GLOVER, E.N.  PAN'S REVELS                                       D18
GLUCK, C.W.  ACH ICH HABE SIE VERLOREN, ARIA UIT ORPHEUS         D92
GLUCK, C.W.  2 CLASSIC AIRS                                      B85
GO DOWN MOSES.                                                   D92
GODARD, B.  BERCEUSE DE JOCELYN                                  D92
GODARD, B.  BERCEUSE DE JOCELYN (BP)                             F54
GODARD, B.-DUBOIS.  BERCEUSE DE JOCELYN                          B24
GOLDMAN, E.F.  AMERICAN CAPRICE                                  C11
GOLDMAN, E.F.  TRAMP, TRAMP, TRAMP                               C11
GOLDSTEIN, A.E.  COLLOQUY                                        C25
GORDON, S.  ICEBERG, THE                                         A78
GOTTWALD, H.  FANTASIE HEROIQUE                                  B53
GOUNOD, C.F.  CALF OF GOLD                                       B85
GOUNOD, C.F.-WALTERS.  MARCH OF A MARIONETTE                     F07
GOVAERT.  AIR VARIE                                              D92
GOWER, W.  BALLAD                                                F07
GRETRY, A.E.M.-PAQUE.  AIR DE RICHARD COEUR DE LION              F81
GRIEG, E.H.-TOBANI.  HAIL STAR OF HEAVEN...                      C11
GRIEG, E.H.  ICH LIEBE DICH                                      D92
GRIEG, E.H.  LETZTER FRUHLING                                    D92
GRIEG, E.H.  SOLVEJGS LIED                                       D92
GRILLAERT.  AMOROSO                                              D67
GUERINI-KINNEY.  PRESTO                                          N61
GUIDE, R. DE.  SUITE "LES CARACTERES DU TROMBONE," OP.32/3       D36
GUILMANT, A.  MORCEAU SYMPHONIQUE                                F31
GUILMANT, A.-FALAGUERRA.  MORCEAU SYMPHONIQUE                    E11
GUILMANT, A.  SYMPHONIC PIECE, OP. 88                            C91
```

```
GUMPERT, E.-VOXMAN.  ROMANZE, OP. 19                            FC7
HADRAEA, J.   LYDDI                                             D20
HADRABA, J.   RHAPSODIA ROMANTICA (OP)                         D20
HADRABA, J.   SCHNUCKS, DAS POSAUNENBABY (MARSCH-INTERMEZZO)   D20
HALEVY, J.F.  CARDINAL'S AIR (LA JUIVE)                        B85
HANDEL, G.F.  ARIA FROM THE MESSIAH                            D92
HANDEL, G.F.  ARM, ARM YOU BRAVE                               B85
HANDEL, G.F.  ART THOU TROUBLED                                D92
HANDEL, G.F.  CATILENA                                         D18
HANDEL, G.F.-BEVERSDORF.  ENEMY SAID, THE (ISRAEL IN EGYPT)    F60
HANDEL, G.F.-BEVERSDORF.  EV'RY VALLEY (MESSIAH)               F60
HANDEL, G.F.-BEVERSDORF.  FROM CELESTIAL SEATS DESCENDING      F60
HANDEL, G.F.  HONOR & ARMS                                     B85
HANDEL, G.F.  I KNOW THAT MY REDEEMER LIVETH                   D92
HANDEL, G.F.  LARGO                                            D92
HANDEL, G.F.-MORRIS.  REVENGE TIMOTHEUS CRIES                  D52
HANDEL, G.F.-GOWER.  SARABAND                                  F07
HANDEL, G.F.-LETHBRIDGE.  SOLO ALBUM                           E51
HANDEL, G.F.-BARNES.  SOUND AN ALARM                           F62
HANDEL, G.F.-OSTRANDER.  TOTAL ECLIPSE FROM SAMSON             F60
HANDEL, G.F.  WHERE EVER YOU WALK                              D92
HANDEL, G.F.-LAYCOCK.  WHERE'ER YOU WALK (SEMELE)              A78
HANDEL, G.F.-HARVEY.  WHERE'ER YOU WALK                        F23
HANDEL, J.-OSTRANDER.  THUNDER, LIGHTING & WHISTLING WIND      D14
HARLOW-REEVES.  WANDERER                                       C11
HARRIS, F.O.  BRASS BANGLES                                    D52
HARRIS, F.O.  CHARMING BALLERINA                               A55
HARRIS, F.O.  GAY LIEUTENANT, THE                             A55
HARRIS, F.O.  KING'S JESTER                                    D52
EARRIS, F.O.  LITTLE CAESAR                                    D52
HARRIS, F.O.  MARILEE                                          A55
HARRIS, F.O.  OCEAN BEACH VALSE                                D52
HARRIS, F.O.  2 REVERIES                                       A55
HARRIS, F.O.  SPARKLES                                         D52
HARRIS, F.O.  2 YOUNG BRAVADOS                                 A55
HARRIS, F.O.  YOUNG PRINCE                                     D52
HARTLEY, W.S.  CAPRICCIO                                       G83
HARTMANN, J.  ALEXIS, AIR VARIE                                D92
HARTMANN, J.  AULD LANG SIJNE                                  D92
HARTMANN, J.  BEAUTIFUL AMERICAN                               D92
HARTMANN, J.  FANTASIE BRILLANTE SUR LE CONQUERING HERO        D92
HARTMANN, J.  FATHERLAND                                       D92
HARTMANN, J.  GIPSY'S WARNING                                  D92
HARTMANN, J.  OLD FOLKS                                        D92
HARTMANN, J.  ON THE BANKS OF ALLAN WATER                      D92
HARTMANN, J.  RETURN, THE                                      D92
HARTMANN, J.  ROBIN ADAIR                                      D92
HARTMANN, J.  SEHNSUCHT NACH DER HEIMAT                        D92
HARTZELL, D.  BALLAD FOR YOUNG CATS                            F43
HARTZELL, D.  EGOTISTICAL ELEPHANT (BP)                        F43
HASSE, J.A.-GOWER.  MENUET & BOUREE                            F07
HASSE, J.A.-GOWER.  SUITE                                      F07
HAUSDOERFER, F.  DORPSBURGEMEESTER, DE                         D92
HAYDN, J.-SHUMAN.  ADAGIO FROM CELLO CCNCERTO                  G31
HAYDN, J.-BEVERSDORF.  AND NOW REVIVED HE SPRINGS (SEASONS)    F60
HEISER, W.  GRAB AUF DER HEIDE, OP. 30                         D46
HEKHUIS, J.  3 BAGATELLEN                                      F81
HEKKER.  RECITATIEF EN ARIA UIT "HERALD DE ONVERSAAGDE"        F81
HENDERSON-SEARS.  JUST A MEMORY                                C58
HERBERT-GOSSETTE.  I WANT WHAT I WANT WHEN I WANT IT           G31
HERBERT, V.  CZARDAS                                           D18
HERBERT, V.  GYPSY LOVE SONG                                   D18
```

HERF, F. KONZERTSTUCK (OF)	D44
HERMAN. AIR VARIE, OP. 37	F81
HEUBERGER, R.-KREISLER & LEIDZEN. MIDNIGHT BELLS	C18
HICH, T. SINGVOGELCHEN AUS DEM THURINGERWALD	D92
HIGUET, N. LARGHETTO E ALLEGRETTO	D67
HILGEMAN, P. BAROQUE IS BACK	B31
HOCH, T. FANTAISIE CONCERTANTE	D92
HOCH, T. PERLE DE L'OCEAN	D92
HOCH, T. REVE D'AMOUR (LIEBESTRAUM)	D92
HOFFMAN, E. BIG HORN	F60
HOFMANN, R.-HERBST. MELODISCHE STUDIEN	C75
HOLMES, G.E. & KIEFER. ELENA POLKA	A55
HOROVITZ. ADAM-BLUES	E41
HOSKINS, W.B. RECITATIVE & ARIA	E68
HOUDY, P. LARGO ET TOCCATA	D36
HOVHANESS, A.S. WORLD, O	E65
HOWARD. STILL WATERS	B85
HUBER, B.E.-GABRIEL. TOMMY	C30
HUBERT. DANS LES PINS	D64
HUBERT. ELEGIE	D64
HUDADOFF. MARCHES, MARCHES, MARCHES	E83
HUGHES, D.-PELZ. ENTRANCE OF THE NOBLEMEN	C25
HUGON, G. INTRODUCTION ET ALLEGRO	F87
HUME, J.O. HARMONIOUS BLACKSMITH	D92
HURRELL, C.E. SUMMER SERENADE	F07
IMBRIE. 3 SKETCHES	F43
JACOBI, F. MEDITATION	F59
JAFFE. CENTONE BUFFO CONCERTANTE	F60
JAKMA, F. CAVATINE	F81
JAKMA, F. DANS DER TEDDYBEREN	F81
JAKMA, F. HERFSTBLOEMEN	F81
JAKMA, H. TOOTER, THE	F81
JAMES, W. ELEGY	D52
JOHNSON. SACRED SOLOS	F07
JOHNSON, C.W. LYRIC INTERLUDE	F07
JOHNSON, C.W. PASTEL PRAIRIES	A62
JOHNSON, C.W. SUNSET SERENADE	A62
JONGEN, J.J. ARIA & POLONAISE, OP. 128	C42
JORGENSEN, A. SUITE, OP. 22 (OP)	H30
KATCHER, R.-SEARS. WHEN DAY IS DONE	C58
KENNEDY, A.-HUMMEL. STAR OF THE EAST	F07
KENNEDY, A.-HUMMEL. SWEETEST STORY EVER TOLD	F07
KETELBY, A.W.-TEAGUE. IN A MONASTERY GARDEN	H06
KIEFER & HOLMES. ELENA POLKA	A55
KING, K.L. NIGHT IN JUNE	A55
KINYON, J.L. (ARR). PROGRAM PIECES FOR TROMBONE	G31
KINYON, J.L. (ARR). RECITAL PIECES FOR TROMBONE	G31
KLUGHARDT, A. ROMANZE	B53
KLUGHARDT, A. ROMANZE	F62
KLUGHARDT, A.-MULLER. ROMANZE	C11
KREISLER, F.-LEIDZEN. LIEBESLIED	C18
KREK. THEME VARIE	C41
KRENEK. 5 PIECES	A51
KROL, B. CAPRICCIO DA CAMERA, OP. 35	F52
KROTOV-BLAZHEVICH. CONCERT ETUDE	D81
KRYL, B. KING CARNEVAL	C11
KURPINSKI, K.-BURKIEWICZ. CAVATINA	E72
KUTSCH, B. (ARR). POSAUNENKLANGE, EINE SAMMLUNG BELIEBIER...	G43
LAFOSSE, A. (CMPL). 3 PIECES DE STYLE	D36
LAKE, M.L. NAIDA (BP)	D52
LALO. ROY D'YS, LE	D92
LAMY, F. CHORAL VARIE	D36

```
LANCEN.  MENUET POUR UN OURS                                        A71
LANGLOIS, L.  AIR VARIE                                             F81
LANGLOIS, L.  GRAND AIR VARIE                                       D92
LASSEN, E.  DEVOTIONS, AT                                           B85
LAUBE.  CONTEST ALBUM                                               B53
LAURENT, L.-BILLAULT.  CARNIVAL OF VENICE                           C38
LAVALLE & TARTO.  TRUMPET POLKA                                     C25
LAVROV, N.  CANZONETTA                                              D81
LAVROV, N.  CANZONETTA                                              D97
LAWTON, S.M.  YOUNG TROMBONIST (3 BKS)                              E51
LAYCOCK, H.A. (ED).  TROMBONE SOLO ALBUM                            A78
LEDUC, J.  ARIOSO ET DANSE, OP. 3                                   D67
LENZ, M.  TANZENDE KOBOLD, DER (OP)                                 C30
LEPETIT, P.  PIECE DE CONCERT                                       D36
LIAGRE.  SOUVENIR DE CALAIS                                         A71
LIAGRE.  SOUVENIR DE CALAIS                                         D64
LIBERATI, A.-BARNES.  VALSE CAPRICE                                 D52
LINCKE, P.  GLOW WORM                                               D18
LINCKE, P.-WALTERS.  GLOW WORM                                      F07
LISZT, F.-MASSO.  CONSOLATION #5                                    D14
LISZT, F.  LIEBESTRAUM                                              D92
LISZT, F.-SMITH.  LIEBESTRAUM                                       A55
LLEWELLYN, E.  MY REGARDS                                           H06
LLEWELLYN, E.  PREMIER POLKA                                        E11
LOHMANN, G.-PERL.  BAYRISCHE POLKA                                  C30
LOHMANN, G.  DORFMUSIK                                              C30
LOHMANN, G.  EWIGE ZECHER, DER                                      C30
LOHMANN, G.-MUNSENINS.  HOPPLA, JETZT KOMM ICH                      C30
LOHMANN, G.-MIELENZ.  HUMORESKE (DAS VERHEXTE ECHO)                 C30
LOHMANN, G.-MUNSENINS.  POSAUNEN LANDLER                            C30
LOHMANN, G.-MIELENZ.  POSAUNEN TEUFEL (OP)                          C30
LONDON, P.  TROMBONE SERENADE                                       H30
LONDONDERRY AIR.                                                    D92
LONG, LONG AGO.                                                     D92
LONQUE, A.  SCHERZO CAPRICCIOSO, OP. 68                             D67
LOOSER, R.  VARIATIONENFANTASIE UBER EIN EIGENES CHORALTHEMA        C61
LOSEY, F.H.  AT THE DAWN                                            A55
LOTTI.  ARIETTA                                                     B85
LOTZENHISER, G.W.  DESERT SHADOWS                                   A62
LOTZENHISER, G.W.  PETITE VALSE                                     A62
LULLY, J.B.  DANCES FOR THE KING                                    B85
LUREMAN.  GROOTVADER'S KLOK                                         D92
LUYPAERTS.  SUITE                                                   D67
MACDOWELL, E.A.-MASSO.  DESERTED FARM, OP. 15                       E83
MACDOWELL, E.A.  TO A WILD ROSE                                     D92
MAES, J.  CONCERT PIECE                                            A96
MAES, J.  CONCERT PIECE                                            B91
MAGANINI, Q.  I'LL BE GOING HOME                                    B85
MAGANINI, Q.  SONNET                                                B85
MAHLER-MAGANINI.  PRIMEVAL LIGHT                                    B85
MAHLER, G.  SOLO FROM 3RD SYMPHONY                                  B85
MAHY, A.  CANTILENE                                                 D92
MAHY, A.  SOLO DE CONCERT                                           D92
MALTBY.  BLUES ESSAY                                                D63
MAN OF HARLECH.                                                     D92
MANIET, R.  MARZIALE                                                D67
MANIET, R.  PIECE IN C                                              A96
MANIET, R.  POCO ALLEGRO                                            A96
MARCHETTI-HURRELL.  FASCINATION                                     F07
MARITANA.                                                           D92
MARTEAU, H.-BARNES.  MORCEAU VIVANT                                 F62
MARTELLI, M.  SUITE FOR TROMBONE OR TUBA, OP. 83                    C01
```

```
MARTIN.  ELEGY                                             C11
MARTIN.  NOVELETTE                                         C11
MARTIN, F.  BALLADE                                        F97
MARTINI.  CANZONA                                          D92
MARTINI, J.P.E.  PLAISIR D'AMOUR                           B85
MASCAGNI, P.-GASTON.  SICILIANA                            E11
MASSENET, J.  HEROD'S AIR                                  B85
MASSENET, J.  2 OPERATIC SCENES                            B85
MASSENET, J.  VALSE DES ESPRITS                            B85
MASSIS, A.  IMPROMPTU                                      D36
MASSO, G.  SUITE FOR LOUISE                                D14
MASTEN, I.J.  BONNIE ELOISE (BP)                           D52
MATEJ, J.  INFORMATORIUM                                   E54
MAURAT, E.  PETITES INVENTIONS                             C01
MAZELLIER, J.  SOLO DE CONCOURS                            C91
MAZELLIER, J.  SOLO DE CONCOURS                            D36
MC KAY, F.H.  BUCKBOARD BLUES                              A55
MC KAY, F.H.  DREAM WALTZ                                  A55
MC KAY, F.H.  HERNANDO'S HOLIDAY                           A55
MC KAY, F.H.  JIF FOR JEANINE                              A55
MC KAY, F.H.  POWDERED WIG                                 A55
MC KAY, F.H.  TRAVELING TROUBADOR                          A55
MEACHAM-HUMMEL.  AMERICAN PATROL                           F07
MEIER, A.-BOHME.  UNTER DEN STERNEN (OP)                   C30
MELLERS, W.H.  GALLIARDE                                   F31
MENDELSSOHN, F.  ARIA UIT ELIAS                            D92
MENDELSSOHN, F.  FLUGELN DES GESANGES, AUF                 D92
MENDELSSOHN, F.  FRUHLINGSLIED                             D92
MENDELSSOHN, F.-OSTRANDER.  IF WITH ALL YOUR HEARTS        F60
MENDELSSOHN, F.  IT IS ENOUGH                              B85
MENDELSSOHN, F.  ON WINGS OF SONG                          D18
MENDELSSOHN, F.-LAYCOCK.  ON WINGS OF SONG                 A78
MEULEMANS, A.  RHAPSODIE (OP)                              C42
MEVER, P.V.  3 PIECES                                      D92
MEVIN-HUMMEL.  MIGHTY LAK' A ROSE                          F07
MEYER, J.H.  CORDELINETTE                                  D41
MIGNION.  ANDANTE ET ALLEGRO                               A71
MIGNION.  REVERIE ET BALLADE                               A71
MIKULICZ-LOHMANN.  POSAUNEN WALZER                         C30
MISSA, E.J.L.  MORCEAU DE CONCOURS                         D36
MITSCHA, A.  ROMANS                                        E72
MOLLEY.  LOVE'S OLD SWEET SONG                             D92
MONGER (ARR).  FIRST ENSEMBLE ALBUM                        E77
MONTAGNE.  AIR VARIE                                       D92
MONTI-ANDREONI.  AUBADE D'AMOUR                            E98
MOQUIN, A.  SAILING THE MIGHTY DEEP                        C09
MOREL.  PIECE EN FA MINEUR                                 A71
MORRISSEY, J.J.  SONG                                      E67
MOSS, H.  FIREFLY                                          A78
MOSS, H.  JOKER                                            A78
MOUQUET, J.  LEGENDE HEROIQUE                              C11
MOZART, W.A.-POWELL.  ARIETTA & ALLEGRO                    F60
MOZART, W.A.  AVE VERUM                                    D92
MOZART, W.A.  CONCERT-RONDO, K. 371                        F60
MOZART, W.A.-LETHBRIDGE.  MOZART SOLO ALBUM                E51
MOZART, W.A.-BARNES.  QUESTA BELLA MANO, PER, K. 612       F62
MOZART, W.A.  SERENADE (DON GIOVANNI)                      B85
MUCK, F.  PAUERN WALZER                                    C30
MUHLFELD, W.  CONCERTSTUECK, OP. 7                         A62
MULLER, J.I.-OSTRANDER.  PRAELUDIUM, CHORALE...AND FUGUE   B85
MULLER, R.  SOLOSTUCKE (2 VOL)                             G43
MULLINS (ARR).  12 EASY CLASSICS                           F72
```

```
MURPHY, J.  ARCOLA (EASY JAZZ IN THE BOSSA NOVA STYLE)        F74
MUSSORGSKY, M.P.  SONG OF THE FLEA                            B85
NAGEL, R. & TRUCHET.  IMPROMPTU                               N66
NELHYBEL, V.  CONCERT PIECE                                   G68
NELHYBEL, V.  SUITE                                           C50
NESTICO, S.  REFLECTIVE MOOD                                  D14
NEUKOMM, S.R.-KAPLAN.  ARIA                                   F62
NEVIN, E.W.  MIGHTY LAK' A ROSE                               D92
NEVIN, E.W.  NARCISSUS                                        D92
NEVIN, E.W.-HUMMEL.  NARCISSUS                                F07
NIVERD, L.  CHANT MELANCOLIQUE                                A71
NIVERD, L.  COMPLAINTE                                        A71
NIVERD, L.  HISTORIETTE DRAMATIQUE                            A71
NIVERD, L.  HYMNE                                             A71
NIVERD, L.  LEGENDE                                           A71
NIVERD, L.  LEGENDE                                           F60
NIVERD, L.  6 PETITES PIECES DE STYLE                         A71
NIVERD, L.  ROMANCE SENTIMENTALE                              A71
NIVERD, L.  SCHERZETTO                                        A71
NIVERD, R.  MAESTOSO & SCHERZANDO                             B66
NOBODY KNOWS.                                                 D92
NUX, P.V. DE LA.  SOLO DE CONCOURS                            D36
NUX, P.V. DE LA.  SOLO DE CONCOURS                            F60
NYQUIST, M.A.  SPRING ENCHANTMENT                             A62
C LOVELY NIGHT.                                               D92
O'NEILL.  HARVEST TIME                                        G13
OFFENBACH, J.  WALTZ "LA PERICHOLE"                           D18
OLCOTT, C.  WILD IRISH ROSE                                   D18
OLCOTT, C.-HUMMEL.  WILD IRISH ROSE                           F07
OLD HCME DOWN ON THE FARM.                                    D18
CSTRANDER, A.  ANTIQUE AIRS                                   B85
OSTRANDER, A.  CONCERT ALBUM                                  B85
OSTRANDER, A.  CONCERT PIECE IN FUGAL STYLE                   B85
OSTRANDER, A.  ON THE FAIR GROUNDS                            B85
OSTRANDER, A.  PARIS SOIR                                     B85
OSTRANDER, A. (CMPL).  ALBUM OF 12 CLASSICAL PIECES           C91
OTT, J.  TOCCATA                                             A65
FALA, J.  GREEN HILLS                                         D64
PALA, J.  GREEN HILLS                                         D92
FANELLA.  JOLLY TWO                                           G10
PANELLA.  TOM & JERRY                                         G10
FAQUE, J.  VARIATIONS BRILLANTES                              D92
PARES, G.P.C.  CREPUSCULE                                     A71
PASCAL, C.  IMPROVISATION EN FORME DE CANON                   B81
PASCAL, C.R.G.  PASTORALE HEROIQUE                            B81
PAUDERT, E.  FANTASIE MAZAILE                                 B53
PEARSON (COMP).  LET US HAVE MUSIC FOR TROMBONE               C11
PELZ, W.  GLORY AND SPLENDOR                                  A62
PELZ, W.  SILVER SKATES WALTZ                                 A62
PERCK, W. VAN.  BEAU JOUR, UN                                 F81
FERGOLESI, G.B.-BARNES.  CANZONA                              F62
PERL, M.  MAUERBLUMCHEN                                       C30
PERL, M.  5 MINUTEN VOR MITTERNACHT                           C30
PERL, M.  SCHLENDRIAN                                         C30
PERL, M.  TANZ CAPRICCIO                                      C30
PERRIN, C.  INTRODUCTION ET ALLEGRO                           A71
PERRY.  CLASSICAL ALBUM                                       A78
PETER, GO RING THE BELLS.                                     D92
PETRIE, H.W.  ASLEEP IN THE DEEP                              D18
PFEIFFER, G.J.  SOLO                                          D36
PFEIFFER, G.J.  SOLO                                          F60
PHILLIPS, D.  TROMBONE SERENADE                               D84
```

PHILLIPS, H. 8 BEL CANTO SONGS		F43
PHILLIPS, I.C. CLASSICAL AND ROMANTIC ALBUM		E51
PINARD, A. AUTUMN		C11
PINARD, A. CRUSADER, THE		C11
PINARD, A. POLKA PETITE		C11
PINARD, A. VALOR		C11
PLAY¬ALONG SING (3 VOL).		E77
PONARD. A VOUS		C11
POOT, M. ETUDE DE CONCERT		D36
POOT, M. IMPROMPTU		C01
PORRET, J. 6 ESQUISSES		A56
PORRET, J. SOLO DE CONCOURS #15		D92
PORRET, J. SOLO DE CONCOURS #16		D92
PORRET, J. SOLO DE CONCOURS #21		D92
PORRET, J. SOLO DE CONCOURS #22		D92
PORRET, J. SOLO DE CONCOURS #25		D92
PORRET, J. SOLO DE CONCOURS #26		D92
PORRET, J. SOLO DE CONCOURS #29		D92
PORRET, J. SOLO DE CONCOURS #30		D92
PORRET, J. SOLO DE CONCOURS #31		D92
PORRET, J. SOLO DE CONCOURS #32		D92
PRESSER, W.H. RONDO		F80
PRYOR, A.-SMITH. ANNIE LAURIE		D52
PRYOR, A. BLUE BELLS OF SCOTLAND (BP)		C11
PRYOR, A. FANTASTIC POLKA		C11
PRYOR, A.-JOHNSON. LOVE THOUGHTS		F07
PRYOR, A. PATRIOT, THE		C11
PRYOR, A. PETITE SUZANNE, LA		C11
PRYOR, A. STARLIGHT		C11
PRYOR, A. SUPERVISOR, THE		C11
PRYOR, A. THOUGHTS OF LOVE		C11
PRYOR, A. TIP TOPPER, THE		C11
PUCCINI, G.-ANDREONI. GELIDA MANINA, CHE (LA BOHEME)		E98
PUCCINI, G.-ANDREONI. TOSCA: E LUCEVAN LE STELLE		E98
PUCCINI, G.-ANDREONI. TURANDOT: NON PIANGERE, LIU!		E98
PURCELL, H. SUITE IN F		B85
RACHMANINOFF, S.V.-GOWER. VOCALISE		F07
RAFF, J.J. CAVATINA		D92
RAKOV, N.P. ARIA		D81
RAPH, A. RUSSIAN SAILOR'S DANCE		B85
RAPHLING, S. LYRIC PRELUDE		B85
RAVEL, M. PAVANE		B53
RAVEL, M.-WALTERS. PAVANE		F07
RAVEL, M. PAVANNE		B85
RAWLINGS. HIATUS II		N92
REICHE, E. CONCERT PIECE #2		A62
REICHE, E.-SEYFFARTH. STUDIENKONZERT (BASED ON CONCERTO #2)		C75
REINHARDT, B. MUSIC FOR TRB SOLO		C94
REUTER, F. SUITEN FUR VC & PA (ARR FOR TRB)		C75
REUTTER. ETUDE POLYPHONIQUE		D36
REUTTER, H. OSTINATO		D36
REYNAUD, J. ADAM AND EVE		C38
REYNAUD, J. GRANDE FANTASIE		C38
RICHARDS, J.J. FALCARO		A55
RICHARDS, J.J. SUNBEAMS		A55
RICHARDS, J.J. VILLETTA		A55
RILEY. TEXTURES		F43
RIMSKY¬KORSAKOV, N.A. CHANSON HINDOE		D92
RIMSKY¬KORSAKOV, N.A. SONG OF INDIA		D18
RIVIERE, J.P. BURLESQUE		D36
ROBERT, J. AIR NOBLE		E77
ROGERS (ED). TREASURY OF WORLD'S GREAT SOLOS		B31

```
ROGERS, W.  TALKING TWINS                                          B31
ROGERS, W.  WAR SONG                                              B31
ROGERS, W.B.  AULD LANG SYNE                                      B31
ROGERS, W.B.  HARP OF TARA                                        B31
ROGERS, W.B.  LULLE                                               B31
ROGISTER, F.  PIECE CONCERTANTE                                   F81
ROLLINSON, T.H.  COLUMBIA                                         D18
RONKA, E.  FANTASETTE                                             C09
ROPARTZ, J.G.  ANDANTE ET ALLEGRO                                 B53
ROPARTZ, J.G.  PIECE EN E-FLAT MINOR                             D36
ROPARTZ, J.G.  PIECE IN E-FLAT MINOR                             C91
ROPARTZ, J.G.  PIECE IN E-FLAT MINOR                             D81
ROSS.  CRYPTICAL TRIPTYCH                                         A78
ROSSINI, G.  COJUS ANIMAN, ARIA BY LISZT                         F31
ROSSINI, G.  CUJUS ANIMAN                                         B53
ROSSINI, G.-MARSTELLER.  DANZA, LA                               F60
ROSSINI, G.  LARGO AL FACTOTUM (BARBER OF SEVILLE)              E98
ROSSINI, G.-ANDREONI.  LARGO AL FACTOTUM (BARBER OF SEVILLE)    E98
ROSSINI, G.  LORD PRESERVE ME                                    B85
ROSSINI, G.  STABAT MATER                                        D92
ROSY MORN, THE.                                                  D92
ROUSSEAU, S.A.  PIECE CONCERTANTE                                B53
ROUSSEAU, S.A.  PIECE CONCERTANTE                                C65
RUBANK CONCERT AND CONTEST COLLECTION.                          F07
RUBINSTEIN, A.G.  MELODIE                                        D92
RUBINSTEIN, A.G.  ROMANCE                                        C25
RUEFF, J.  RHAPSODIE                                             D36
RZAYEV, G.  PIECE                                                D81
SAEYS, E.  BALLADE, OP. 216                                      D67
SAINT-SAENS, C.-WHEAR.  AMOUR VIENS AIDER                        D52
SAINT-SAENS, C.  CAVATINE, OP. 144                               B81
SAINT-SAENS, C.  ROMANCE, OP. 36                                 B85
SAINT-SAENS, C.-TRINKAUS.  SWAN (LE CYGNE)                       C09
SAINT-SAENS, C.-FALCONE.  SWAN, THE                              F60
SALZEDO, C.  PIECE CONCERTANTE, OP. 27                           C91
SALZEDO, C.  PIECE CONCERTANTE, OP. 27                           D36
SAMAZEUILH.  EVOCATION                                           B81
SARES, I.R. & CIMERA.  LITTLE CARNIVAL                           A62
SARES, I.R. & CIMERA.  MARGARET WALTZ                            A62
SARES, I.R. & CIMERA.  SLIDING ON ICE                           A62
SCARLATTI, A.-BARNES.  ARIA FROM OPERA TIGRAINE                 F62
SCARLATTI, D.-MARSTELLER.  CAT'S FUGUE                           F60
SCARMOLIN, A.L.  RECITATIVE & ROMANCE                            A62
SCHAD.  58 MASTERPIECES                                          A62
SCHAEFER, A.H.  DAVID'S DREAM                                    C09
SCHAMPAERT, J.  DRAMATIC FANTASY                                 D80
SCHEVENHALS.  2 PIECES                                           F31
SCHIBLER.  SIGNAL, BESCHWORUNG & TANZ                            A08
SCHNEIDER, H.  MELODIE                                           C30
SCHOEMAKER, M.  PIECE CONCERTANTE (CONCERTSTUK) (OP)            C42
SCHRODER, W.  ANDANTE CANTABILE                                  H30
SCHUBERT, F.P.-TRAXLER.  AVE MARIA                               A78
SCHUBERT, F.P.-BOETTGER.  BY THE SEA                             C11
SCHUBERT, F.P.-ANDREONI.  MOMENTO MUSICALE, OP. 94/3            E98
SCHUBERT, F.P.  ROSAMUNDE                                        D92
SCHUBERT, F.P.-MOSES.  SERENADE                                  C11
SCHUBERT, F.P.-ANDREONI.  SERENATA                               E98
SCHUBERT, F.P.  SWAN SONG (MY LAST ABODE)                       B85
SCHUMANN, R.  LOTOSBLUME, DIE                                    D92
SCHUMANN, R.-ANDREONI.  SOGNO (SONG), OP. 15/7                  E98
SCHWARTZ, G.  INTERNATIONAL FOLK SUITE                          F60
SCULL.  BENEATH THY WINDOW                                       G10
```

SEMLER-COLLERY, J. ETUDES LYRIQUES	C01
SEMLER-COLLERY, J. FANTAISIE LYRIQUE	C01
SENAILLE, J.B.-FALCONE. ALLEGRO	F60
SHEPHERD, W.S. NOCTURNE & RONDOLETTE	F60
SHERIFF, N. PIECE FOR RAY	C93
SHOSTAKOVICH, D. DANSES FANTASTIQUES	B85
SHOSTAKOVICH, D. 4 PRELUDES	B85
SHUMAN, D. 3 GYMNASTICS	G17
SIENNICKI. WOODLAND WALTZ	D18
SIMON. MISS BLUE BONNET	F60
SIMON, F. WILLOW ECHOES (BP)	C09
SIMONS, G. ATLANTIC ZEPHYRS (BP)	C11
SKOLNIK. LITTLE SUITE IN A-FLAT	F80
SMITA, V. KONZERTARIE	A51
SMITE. CAPRICCIO	M69
SMITH. FRIENDS	F07
SMITH. HAPPY MAN, THE	D92
SMITH, C. AMONG THE SYCAMORES	A55
SMITH, C. ANNIE LAURIE	A55
SMITH, C. CLAY SMITH SOLOS (ALBUM)	A55
SMITH, C. FANCY FREE	A55
SMITH, C. HARBOR LIGHTS	A55
SMITH, C. IMOGENE, REVERIE	A55
SMITH, C. ITALIANA, VALSE	A55
SMITH, C. LIFE'S LIGHTER HOURS	A55
SMITH, C. MEMORIES OF THE PAST	A55
SMITH, C. MILADY'S PLEASURE	A55
SMITH, C. MIRAFLORES	A55
SMITH, C. OLD FOLKS AT HOME	A55
SMITH, C. OLD KENTUCKY HOME	A55
SMITH, C. PHILISTINE	A55
SMITH, C. PIPES O' PAN	A55
SMITH, C. RAINBOW HUES	A55
SMITH, C. SATELLITE	A55
SMITH, C. SMITHSONIAN	A55
SMITH, C. SOUL OF THE SURF	A55
SMITH, C. THOUGHTS OF YESTERDAY	C11
SMITH, C. TRUMPETER, THE	A55
SMITH, C. WATER WITCH	A55
SMITH, C. WINGS OF THE MORNING	A55
SMITH, C. & HOLMES. CALL OF THE SEA	A55
SMITH, C. & HOLMES. MASSA'S IN THE COLD, COLD GROUND	A55
SMITH, C. & HOLMES. SILVER THREADS AMONG THE GOLD	A55
SMITH, C. & HOLMES. THROUGH SHADOWED VALES	A55
SMITH, C. & HOLMES. WAYFARER	A55
SMITH, H.C. FIRST SOLOS FOR THE TROMBONE PLAYER	F23
SMITH, L.B. ECSTASY WALTZ	C11
SMITH, L.B. SPANISH CAPRICE	B31
SMOTH, R. TREASURE WALTZ	B31
SOLOMON. 2 CONTRASTS	F60
SOUSA, J.P. STARS AND STRIPES FOREVER	D18
SOUSA, J.P.-WALTERS. STARS AND STRIPES FOREVER	F07
SPEARS. RECITATIVE	G83
STALMEIER, P. REVERIE ET ALLEGRO	D92
STEINBACHER, E.-EISBRENNER. LUMPENSAMMLER	C30
STEINER-SCHOENFELD. TARA THEME (MY OWN TRUE LOVE)	H06
STILLMAN & WRIGHT. SMALL TOWN BLUES	D84
STOJOWSKI, S. FANTAISIE	D36
STOJOWSKI, S.-SZALESKI. FANTASIA	E72
STOJOWSKI, S.-BROWN. FANTASY	C91
STORM, C.W. GLEN EDEN	F07
STORM, C.W. KENDRICKIS	A55

STOUT, A.   AUS TIEFER NOTH: BACH (G)   A13
STOUT, A.   JESUS CHRISTUS UNSER HEILAND; F. TUNDER (G)   A13
STOUTAMIRE, A.L.   PRELUDE & FUGUE   D52
STRADELLA, A.   PIETA, SIGNORE!   B85
STRAUSS, R.-WALTERS.   ALLERSEELEN, OP. 10/8   F07
STRAUSS, R.   TOMORROW   B85
STRAUSS, R.   ZUEIGNUNG   B85
STRAVINSKY, I.   BERCEUSE (FIREBIRD)   B85
STRAVINSKY, I.   DANCE OF THE PRINCESSES   B85
STRAVINSKY, I.   PALLID MOONLIGHT   B85
STULTZ, R.M.   SWEETEST STORY EVER TOLD   B72
SWING LOW.   D92
SWINSON, L.   SOLILOQUY (SOLO IN JAZZ-BALLAD STYLE)   F74
SYLVIUS.   ROMANZA   N95
TAMBA, A.   FANTAISIE   D36
TANNER.   ADVENTURES IN 5/4   A62
TANNER.   I AM A POOR WAYFARING STRANGER   A62
TANNER.   KALEIDOSCOPE   A62
TANNER, P.   ARIA (BP)(OPT. BASS TRB)   G21
TARTINI, G.   ADAGIO   C91
TAYLOR.   SHEPHERD'S DREAM   F07
TCHAIKOVSKY, P.I.   ANDANTE CANTABILE   B53
TCHAIKOVSKY, P.I.   CHANSON TRISTE   D92
TCHAIKOVSKY, P.I.   CHANSON TRISTE, OP. 40/2   B13
TCHAIKOVSKY, P.I.   SONG OF PRAISE   B85
TCHAIKOVSKY, P.I.-FOTE.   SWEET DREAMS   D14
TCHEREPNIN, A.N.   ANDANTE   A78
TCHEREPNIN, A.N.   ANDANTE, OP. 64   A58
TEIFENBOCK, A.   LUSTIG UND FIDEL   C30
TELEMANN, G.P.-BARNES.   ARIE FROM "PIMPINONE"   F62
TENAGLIA, A.F.   ARIA ANTICA   B85
THOMAS, A.   ARIA UIT MIGNON   D92
THOMAS, S.F.   TORERO, EL   F27
THOMAS, S.F.   TRUMPET OF DAIRWOOD, THE   F27
THOMAS, S.F.   WALTZ PASTEL   F27
THOME, F.   SIMPLE AVEU   D92
TIEFENBOCK, A.   BITTE RECHT FREUNDLICH   C30
TIEFENBOCK, A.   ROTER MOHN   C30
TISNE, A.   ELEGIE ET BURLESQUE   D36
TODOROV, G. (CMPL).   ETUDES & PIECES FOR SLIDE TROMBONE   F36
TOMASI, H.   DANSE SACREE   D36
TORELLI, G.   SINFONIA   N62
TOSTI-ANDREONI.   IDEALE   E98
TOURNEMIRE, C.   LEGENDE   D36
TOURNIER.   AEREME   N50
TROWBRIDGE, L.   CHROMATICO   B38
TUEFENBOCK, A.   LIED OHNE WORTE   C30
TUTHILL, B.C.   PHANTASY PIECE, OP. 10/2   C11
UBER.   GOLDEN LEAVES   D14
UBER, D.A.   AUTUMN SKETCHES, 1965, OP. 56   B98
UBER, D.A.   CHOICE COLLECTION OF SONGS FOR SOLO TRB   AC3
UBER, D.A.   MISSISSIPPI LEGEND   A03
UBER, D.A.   PANORAMA   A03
VACHEY, H.   2 INTERLUDES   D36
VALLIER.   ARIA   N50
VAN DER MAESBRUGGE, M.   PRELUDE ET DANSE   D67
VAN HOOF, J.   DIVERTIMENTO   D80
VANDERCOOK, H.A.   AMETHYST   F07
VANDERCOOK, H.A.   ARBUTUS   D18
VANDERCOOK, H.A.   CARNATIONS   C11
VANDERCOOK, H.A.   CHRYSANTHEMUM   D18
VANDERCOOK, H.A.   COLUMBINE   D18

```
VANDERCOOK, H.A.   DAISIES                                              D18
VANDERCOOK, H.A.   DIAMOND                                             F07
VANDERCOOK, H.A.   EMERALD                                             F07
VANDERCOOK, H.A.   GARNET                                              F07
VANDERCOOK, H.A.   HELIOTROPE                                          D18
VANDERCOOK, H.A.   HYACINTHE                                           D18
VANDERCOOK, H.A.   IVY                                                 D18
VANDERCOOK, H.A.   LILY                                                C11
VANDERCOOK, H.A.   LILY                                                D18
VANDERCOOK, H.A.   MAGNOLIA                                            D18
VANDERCOOK, H.A.   MARIGOLD                                            D18
VANDERCOOK, H.A.   MORNING GLORY                                       C11
VANDERCOOK, H.A.   MORNING GLORY                                       D18
VANDERCOOK, H.A.   MOSS ROSE                                           D18
VANDERCOOK, H.A.   OPAL                                                F07
VANDERCOOK, H.A.   PANSIES                                             D18
VANDERCOOK, H.A.   PEARL                                               F07
VANDERCOOK, H.A.   PEONY                                               D18
VANDERCOOK, H.A.   ROSEBUDS                                            D18
VANDERCOOK, H.A.   RUBY                                                F07
VANDERCOOK, H.A.   SAPPHIRE                                            F07
VANDERCOOK, H.A.   TOPAZ                                               F07
VANDERCOOK, H.A.   TULIP                                               D18
VANDERCOOK, H.A.   TURQUOISE                                           F07
VANDERCOOK, H.A.   WILD ROSE                                           D18
VANDERCOOK, H.A.   WILD ROSE POLKA                                     C11
VASILIEV, S.-ENKE.  CONCERT PIECE                                      D81
VERDI, G.  ARIA (DON CARLOS)                                           B85
VERDI, G.  ATILLA GRAND AIR                                            D92
VERDI, G.  BALEN DEL SUO SORRISO, IL (IL TROVATORE)                    E98
VERDI, G.  DONNA E MOBILE, LA (RIGOLETTO)                              E98
VERDI, G.-ANDREONI.  ERNANI: OH! DE' VERD'ANNI MIEI                    E98
VERDI, G.-ANDREONI.  FORZA DEL DESTINO, LA                            E98
VERDI, G.  GRAND AIR (MASKED BALL)                                     B85
VERDI, G.-ANDREONI.  NABUCCO: VA, PENSIERO, SULL'ALI DORATE           E98
VERDI, G.  OH. DE' VERD'ANNI MIEI (FR ERNANI)                          E98
VERDI, G.  PROVENZA IL MAR, IL SUOL, DI (LA TRAVIATA)                  E98
VERDI, G.  QUELLA PIRA, DI (IL TROVATORE)                              E98
VERDI, G.-ANDREONI.  QUESTA O QUELLA PER ME PARI SONO                 E98
VERDI, G.-ANDREONI.  RIGOLETTO: CORTIGIANI, VIL RAZZA DANNATA         E98
VERDI, G.-ANDREONI.  RIGOLETTO: LA DONNA E MOBILE                     E98
VERDI, G.-ANDREONI.  TRAVIATA, LA: DI PROVENZA IL MAR, IL SUOL        E98
VERDI, G.-ANDREONI.  TRAVIATA, LA: LIBIAM NE' LIETI CALICI            E98
VERDI, G.-ANDREONI.  TROVATORE, IL: DESERTO SULLA TERRA               E98
VERDI, G.-ANDREONI.  TROVATORE, IL: DI QUELLA PIRA                    E98
VERDI, G.-ANDREONI.  TROVATORE, IL: IL BALEN DEL SUO SORRISO          E98
VIDAL, P.  SOLO DE CONCERT #2                                          D36
VILLETTE, P.  FANTAISIE CONCERTANTE (OP)                              D36
VIVALDI, A.  PRAELUDIUM IN C MINOR                                    B85
VOXMAN, H.  CONCERT & CONTEST COLLECTION                              F07
WAGNER, R.-BUCHTEL.  EVENING STAR (TANNHAUSER)                        D18
WAGNER, R.-ROBERTS.  SONG TO THE EVENING STAR (TANNHAUSER)            C11
WAGNER, R.-DEDRICK.  SONG TO THE EVENING STAR                         D14
WAGNER, R.  WALTHER'S PRESLIED                                        D92
WAGNER, R.-BUCHTEL.  WALTHER'S PRIZE SONG                             D18
WALTERS.  SHINDIG (FOLK SONG FANTASY)                                 F07
WALTERS.  WHEN THE SAINTS GO MARCHING IN                              F07
WALTERS (ARR).  AMAZING GRACE                                         F07
WALTERS (ARR).  FAT BOY POLKA                                         F07
WASILJEW, S.  KONZERTSTUCK                                            C75
WEBER, A.  ALLEGRO                                                    D36
WEBER, C.M.V.-HOCH.  FANTASIE CONCERTANTE                             C11
```

WEBER, C.M.V.-LAUBE. ROMANZA APPASSIONATA   B53
WEBER, F. JULIA MAURINE WALTZ   A62
WEBSTER-BUGGERT. RETROSPECTION   F07
WEINER. PHANTASY, OP. 42   A71
WEISS, W.H. VILLAGE BLACKSMITH   B53
WEST, G. LARGO & ALLEGRO   E00
WHITNEY, M.C. CORTEGE   A84
WIGY, F. LEGENDE   D67
WILCKEN, E. BLAUER MOHN (OP)   C30
WILDER, A. 3 VIGNETTES FOR TROMBONE   D14
WILKENSCHILDT. CAPRICE   H30
WILKENSCHILDT. IMPROMPTU   H30
WILLIAMS, E. LITTLE CLASSICS   B31
WILLIAMS, E. ONTEORA   B31
WILLIAMS, E. RONDO CONCERTANTE   B31
WILLIAMS, E. TAHOE CHARNS   B31
WILLSON, M.-REED. 76 TROMBONES   C27
WOLFE, D. TURN YOURSELF AROUND   D14
WOOD, A. TROMBONE CAPERS   E83
WOOD, S.B. ALAMADA, FANTASY   D92
WRIGHT & STILLMAN. SMALL TOWN BLUES   D84
WURMSER, L.R. TENDRES MELODIES   A71
WURNSER, L.R. SOLO DE CONCOURS   A71
YARDIER. PALOMA, LA   D92
YOUMANS, V.-GOSSETTE. TEA FOR 2   C58
ZAGWIJN, H. ESQUISSE   B74
ZELLER. OBERSTEIGER, DER   D92
ZELLER. SCHENKT MAN SICH ROSEN IN TIROL   D92
ZIMMERMAN. AUTUMN DREAMS   G31
ZIMMERMAN. LEONA   G31
ZIMMERMAN. SOLOS FOR THE DOUBLE BASS PLAYER   F23
ZOBEL. AFTERGLOW   D18
ZOBEL. DESERT DREAMS   D18
ZOBEL. FOREST MOODS   D18
ZOBEL. MIDNIGHT SERENADE   D18
ZOBEL. SPRUCE SHADOWS   D18

0127 TROMBONE SOLOS, UNACCOMPANIED

ALSINA. CONSECUENZA   A83
ARNOLD, M. FANTASY   C05
BACH, J.S.-BROWN. 6 CELLO SUITES   C91
EACH, J.S.-LAFOSSE. SUITES FOR VIOLONCELLO SOLO   D36
BACH, J.S.-MARSTELLER. VIOLONCELLO SUITES (2 VOL)   F60
BASSETT, L.R. SUITE   G83
EAVICCHI, J. PRELUDES   B98
BEALE, J. MUSHROOM PIECE, OP. 36   A13
BERIO. SEQUENZA V   F97
BERNSTEIN, L. ELEGY FOR MIPPY II   F23
BORDOGNI, G.M.-COUILLAUD. 12 VOCALISES (2 VOL)   D36
CAGE. SOLO FOR SLIDING TROMBONE   E65
CHILDS, B. SONATA   F88
COPE, D. ETRB (THEATRE PIECE)   M80
COPE, D. PIECES FOR TRB WITH F ATTACHMENT   M80
COPE, D. 3 PIECES   B35
COUILLAUD, H. 24 PIECES MELODIQUES (3 VOL)   D36
CROLEY, R. MIES STRUCTURE #3   G83
CROLEY, R. VARIAZIONNI PICCOLA   G83

0131   BASS TROMBONE CONCERTOS AND CONCERTINOS

GOERGE. CONCERTO FOR BASS TROMBONE (P)	F02
LIEB. CONCERTINO BASSO (OP)	C11

0132   BASS TROMBONE SONATAS AND SONATINAS

HINDEMITH, P. SONATA (1941)	F31
LINK, J.D. SONATINA	C75
MARTELLI, H. SONATE	B92
MARTELLI, H. SONATE	E66
MC CARTY, R.P. SONATA (OP)	B98
OSTRANDER, A. SONATA IN G MINOR	B85

0133   BASS TROMBONE SOLOS WITH BAND ACCOMPANIMENT

HARTZELL, D. EGOTISTICAL ELEPHANT (BP)	F43
TANNER, P. ARIA (BP)	G21

0134   BASS TROMBONE SOLOS WITH ORCHESTRAL ACCOMPANIMENT

ANDRIX. FREE FORM (O)	F23
MC CARTY, R.P. SONATA (WITH STR QUARTET OR ORCH)	B98

0136   BASS TROMBONE SOLOS WITH PIANO ACCOMPANIMENT

BACH, J.S.-FIGERT. FOR HE THAT IS MIGHTY	D14
BARILLER, R. ENTERREMENT DE SAINT-JEAN, L'	D36
BARILLER, R. HANS DE SCHNOKELOCH	D36
BARTLES. ELEGY	C25
BELCKE, F.A. 7 ETUDEN	C75
BITSCH, M. IMPROMPTU	D36
BOUTRY, R. TUBAROQUE	D36
BOZZA, E. NEW ORLEANS	D36
BOZZA, E. PRELUDE ET ALLEGRO	D36
BOZZA, E. THEME VARIE; POUR TUBA OU TRB BASSE	D36
BROWN, C.L.G. RECITATIF, LIED ET FINAL	D36
CARPENTER, B. BLUES FOR BASS TRB	F74
CASTEREDE, J. FANTAISIE CONCERTANTE	D36
CLERISSE, R. PIECE LYRIQUE	D36
CLERISSE. R. VOCE NOBILE	D36

CROLEY, R. DIVERTISSEMENT	B98
DEDRICK. INSPIRATION	D14
DEDRICK. PETITE SUITE	M65
DEVOS, G. 2 MOUVEMENTS CONTRASTES	D36
DUBOIS, P.M. CORNEMUSE	D36
DUBOIS, P.M. PICCOLO SUITE	D36
FAYEULLE, R. BRAVACCIO	D36
GABAYE, P. TUBABILLAGE	D36
GARTENLAUB, O. ESSAI	N50
GAY. INTRODUCTION & ALLEGRO MODERATO	C00
HANDEL, G.F.-OSTRANDER. POLIFEMO'S AIR	D14
HARTLEY, W.S. ARIOSO	G70
HARTZELL, D. EGOTISTICAL ELEPHANT (BP)	F43
HENRY, O. PASSACAGLIA & FUGUE	D16
HOFFMAN, E. TRIGGER TREAT	F60
KAI, N. LEGENDE	D36
KREISLER, F.-LEIDZEN. LIEBESLIED	C18
KREISLER, F.-LEIDZEN. RONDINO UBER EIN THEMA VON BEETHOVEN	C18
LASSEN, E. DEVOTIONS, AT	B85
LEMAIRE. 3 EXERCICES DE STYLE	D36
LISCHKA. 3 SKIZZEN	C75
LULLY, J.B. DANCES FOR THE KING	B85
MARC-CARLES. INTRODUCTION ET TOCCATA	D36
MARGONI, A. APRES UNE LECTURE DE GOLDONIF FANTAISIE...	D36
MARINI, B.-BASSETT. SONATA (2 BTRB)	M80
MARTELLI. DIALOGUE	C01
MARTELLI, H. SUITE, OP. 83	C01
MILLARS-HAYDN. DREAM OF LOVE, THE	D92
MULLER, J.I. PRAELUDIUM, CHORALE, VARIATIONS & FUGUE	B85
OSTRANDER, A. CONCERT PIECE IN FUGAL STYLE	B85
PALA, J. GREEN HILLS	D92
PETIT, P.Y.M.C. FANTAISIE	D36
PETIT, P.Y.M.C. GRAVE	D36
PETIT, P.Y.M.C. WAGENIA	D36
PLANEL, R. AIR ET FINAL	D36
POOT, M. IMPROMPTUS	C01
RUEFF, J. CONCERTSTUCK	D36
SEMLER-COLLERY, J. SAXHORNIA	D36
SMITH, K. HAPPY MAN, THE	D92
SOLOMON. DRAMATIQUE	F60
SPILLMAN, R.A. 2 SONGS	B85
TANNER, P. ARIA (BP)	G21
TOMASI, H. ETRE OU NE PAS ETRE	D36
TUTHILL, B.C. FANTASIA	B98
VILLETTE, P. FANTAISIE CONCERTANTE	D36
WEBER, A. SOLILOQUE	D36
ZBAR. JEU 3	D36

0137 BASS TROMBONE SOLOS, UNACCOMPANIED

ADLER, S.H. CANTO II	E51
BLANK, A. 4 COMMENTS	A38
BLANK, A. SHORT SUITE, A	A13
BRINK. P. EXEGISIS	M80
CROLEY, R. VARIAZIONI PICCOLA	G83
DEDRICK. LYRIC ETUDE	M65

```
DEDRICK.  PRELUDE & MARCH                        M65
HARTLEY, W.S.  SONATA BREVE                      F80
JOHNSTON.  REVELSTOKE IMPRESSIONS                M80
RAHN.  PROGRESSIVE ETUDE                         G83
RAPH, A.  CAPRICE                                M70
RAPH, A.  ROCK                                   C11
ZBAR.  JEU 3                                     D36
```

0141   EUPHONIUM CONCERTOS
AND CONCERTINOS

AREND, D. CONCERTINO VOOR TUBA OF BARITON (B)	D92
CAPUZZI-CATELINET. ANDANTE & RONDO FR CONCERTO FOR DB (P)	C71
DAVID, F.V. CONCERTINO (P)	D92
DE SCHRIJVER. CONCERTINO (P)	F81
GARTH . CONCERT VOOR BARYTON (P)	D92
HANDEL, G.F.-BARR. ALLEGRO FR. CONCERTO IN F MINOR (P)	D52
HANDEL, G.F.-BARR. SARABANDE FR. CONCERTO IN F MINOR (P)	D52
HAYDN, J. ANDANTE FROM CONCERTO (P)	F62
HOVHANESS, A.S. CONCERTO #3 (DIRAN) (O)	D16
KLENGEL, J.-FALCONE. CONCERTINO IN B-FLAT MAJOR (P)	A62
KLENGEL, J. CONCERTINO #1 (1ST MVMT) (P)	A62
LEBEDEV, A. CONCERTO IN ONE MOVEMENT (P)	B85
MOZART, W.A.-MARSTELLER. CONCERTO IN B-FLAT (BSN) (P)	F60
MOZART, W.A.-FOTE. CONCERTO IN B-FLAT, K. 191 (RONDO)(P)	D14
MOZART, W.A.-OSTRANDER. CONCERTO, K. 191 (BSN) (P)	B85
MOZART, W.A.-BLAAUW. HOORN CONCERT NO. 4 (P)	D64
MOZART, W.A.-SURMUHLE. HOORNCONCERT NO.1 IN D MAJOR (P)	D92
MOZART, W.A.-BLAAUW. HORNSONATE (CONCERTO) #1 IN D	D92
MOZART, W.A. HORNSONATE (CONCERTO) NO.2 & 3 (P)	D92
MOZART, W.A. HORNSONATE (CONCERTO) NO.4 (P)	D92
MOZART, W.A. RONDO FR. HORN CONCERTO IN E-FLAT MAJOR (B)	A78
SPILLMAN, R.A. CONCERTO (P)	B85
TOWNSEND. CHAMBER CONCERTO #2 (P)	D74
WILLIAMS, E. CONCERTO #5	B31

0142   EUPHONIUM SONATAS AND SONATINAS

AMBROSIUS, H. SONATE	C75
ANNIE LAURIE.	D64
BEETHOVEN, L.V.-BLAAUW. SONATA, OP.17 (ORIG. HORN)	D64
BEETHOVEN, L.V. SONATE, OP.17 (ORIG HORN)	D92
CHERUBINI, L.-PALA. SONATE #2	D92
GEORGE, T.R. SONATA	B97
GEORGE, T.R. SONATA FOR BARITONE HORN OR CELLO	E87
HANDEL, G.F.-POWELL. SONATA #3	F60
HUTCHISON. SONATINA	C11
MOZART, W.A. HORNSONATE #2 AND #3	D92
SCHMUTZ, A.D. SONATINE	D52
SENAILLE, J.B. INTRODUCTION AND ALLEGRO SPIRITOSO	E59
TAKACS, J. SONATE, OP.59	C41
ULRICH. SONATA	F88

0143   EUPHONIUM SOLOS WITH
BAND ACCOMPANIMENT

BAUMANN, J. KLANGE DER FREUNDSCHAFT (B)	F10
BERLIOZ, H. SANCTUS AUS DEM "REQUIEM" (B)	F10

BIENE, V. BROKEN MELODY, THE (B)   A78
BIZET, G. TOREADOR SONG FR. CARMEN (B)   A78
DAVIS, A.O. DESERT STAR (BP)   D52
DEDRICK, A. (ARR). VIENNESE REFRAIN (B)   D14
ETHERINGTON . LEA RING, THE (B)   E83
FUCIK-MASTON. OUDE BROMBEER, DE (B)   D92
GEEHL, H.E. (ARR). WACHING THE WHEAT (B)   E59
GORDON, S. ICEBERG, THE (B)   A78
GOUNOD, C.F. VULCAN SONG (B)   F54
HANDEL, G.F. LARGO AUS "XERXES" (B)   F10
HANDEL, G.F. O RUDDIER THAN THE CHERRY (B)   A78
HARTZELL, D. BALLAD FOR YOUNG CATS (B)   F43
HIPPENMEYER, W.(ARR). MORGENGRUSS FOR TENORHORN (B)   F10
JACOB. FANTASIA (B)   A78
JARMAN, H.C. PRIVATEER (B)   A82
JECKER, W. HIRTEN ABENDGEBET, DES (B)   F10
LAKE, M.L. NAIDA (BP)   D52
MACDOWELL, E.A.-BALL. TO A WILD ROSE (B)   E59
MORATIN . MYSTERE, LE (B)   D64
MULLER, S. (ARR). ALTENGLISCHES MADRIGAL (B)   F10
NOVELLO . SHINE THROUGH MY DREAMS (B)   D92
RICHTER, H.E. ERINNERUNG (B)   F10
ROOY, D. 12 ROVERS, DE (B)   D92
ROOY, D. WATCHING THE WHEAT (B)   D92
ROSSINI, G. CAVATINA "LARGO AL FACTOTUM" FR. BARBER...   A78
ROTHLIN, A. AM BERGSEE (B)   F10
RUH, E. GLOCKENGELAUTE (B)   F10
RUH, E. HEIMAT (B)   F10
SCHUBERT, F.P. IM ABENDROT (B)   F10
SENAILLE, J.B.-WRIGHT. INTRODUCTION & ALLEGRO SPIRITOSO (B)   E59
SIEBERT, E. HUPERION (B)   A78
STORM, C.W. BOUQUET FOR BASSES (B)   G10
STREET, A.(CMPL). 4 SOLOS (B)   E59
SUTTON. CAVALIER, THE (B)   D92
THOME, F. SIMPLE AVEU (B)   A78
WALTERS, H.L. JABBERWOCKY (BP)   F07
WALTERS, H.L. TARANTELLE (BP)   D52
WATELLE. GRAND SOLO DE CONCERT (B)   D64

0144   EUPHONIUM SOLOS WITH ORCHESTRAL ACCOMPANIMENT

BUSSER, H.P. CHASSE DE SAINT-HUBERT (OP)   D36

0146   EUPHONIUM SOLOS WITH PIANO ACCOMPANIMENT

ALEXANDER. REQUIEM & CODA   A84
ARBAN, J.J.B.L.-LILLYA & ISAAC. ETUDE #11   C11
ARBAN, J.J.B.L. VARIATIONS SUR THEME DE MERCADANTE   D64
BACH, J.S.-SMITH. ARIOSO   A62
BACH, J.S.-FIGERT. FOR HE THAT IS MIGHTY   D14
BACH, J.S.-CLUWEN. JESU, JOY OF MAN'S DESIRING   D64
BACH, J.S.-MARSTELLER. SONATA #1 & 3   F60
BALFE, M.W.-HARTMANN. BOHEMIAN GIRL   A62
BARAT, J.E.-SMITH. INTRODUCTION & DANCE   F60

```
FIRST DIV BAND COURSE.  SONG OF THE EVENING STAR                A62
FIRST DIV BAND COURSE (12 SOLOS).                               A62
FLOTOW, F.V.-BLAAUW.  MARTHA                                    D64
FRAURE, G.U.-STOUTAMIRE.  AURORA                                D14
FROST, G.  GRAND FANTASIA                                       D92
GIORDANI-JORDAANS.  CARO MIO BEN                                D64
GIRLAMO-VINCENT.  BALLAD IN BLUE                                A62
GLIERE, R.M.-ISSAC.  RUSSIAN SAILOR'S DANCE                     C11
GLINKA, M.I.  ROMANCE MELODY                                    F62
GLUCK, C.W.-MEIJNS.  J'AI PERDU MON EURYDICE                    D64
GOLTERMANN, G.E.-BELL.  CONCERTO NO. 4, OP. 65 (EXCERPTS)       C11
GORDON, S.  ICEBERG, THE                                        A78
GOVAERT-BLAAUW.  AIR VARIE                                      D64
GOWER, W.  3 SHORT PIECES                                       F80
GRIEG, E.H.-BLAAUW.  CHANSON DE SOLVEJG                         D64
GRIEG, E.H.-BLAAUW.  DERNIER PRINTEMPS                          D64
GRIEG, E.H.-HOLMES.  IN THE HALL OF THE MOUNTAIN KING           A62
GRIEG, E.H.-BLAAUW.  JE T'AIME                                  D64
GRIEG, E.H.-BLAAUW.  POEME EROTIQUE                             D64
HANDEL, G.F.  AIRA FROM THE MESSIAH                             D92
HANDEL, G.F.-GEE.  ANDANTE AND ALLEGRO                          F60
HANDEL, G.F.  LARGO                                             B53
HANDEL, G.F.-BARNES.  SOUND AN ALARM                           F62
HANDEL, G.F.-OSTRANDER.  THUNDER, LIGHTING AND WHISTLING WIND   D14
HANDEL, G.F.-BLAAUW.  WHERE'ER YOU WALK                         D64
HARRIS, F.O.  FAIRY PRINCESS                                    D52
HARRIS, F.O.  LITTLE COMMANDER                                  D52
HARRIS, F.O.  OCEAN BEACH VALSE                                 D52
HARTMANN, J.-BOCHON.  ALEXIS, GRANDE FANTAISIE                  D64
HARTMANN, J.  FANTAISIE BRILLANTE SUR "THE CONQUERING HERO"     D64
HARTMANN, J.-BLAAUW.  FATHERLAND                                D64
HARTMANN, J.  GIPSY'S WARNING                                   D64
HARTMANN, J.-MOLENAAR.  RETURN, THE                             D64
HARTMANN, J.-MOLENAAR.  ROBIN ADAIR                             D64
HARTZELL, D.  BALLAD FOR YOUNG CATS                             F43
HAYDN, J.-VOXMAN.  AIRA & ALLEGRO                               F07
HAYDN, J.-SMITH.  GYPSY RONDO                                   A62
HAYDN, J.-MILLARS.  REVE D'AMOUR, LE                            D64
HERBERT, V.-HARRIS.  GYPSY LOVE SONG                            D52
HUME, J.O.  HARMONIOUS BLACKSMITH, INTRO & VARIATIONS           D64
JACOB.  FANTASIA                                                A78
JAKMA, F.  SANCTA LUCIA                                         D64
JARMAN, H.C.  PRIVATEER, THE                                    A82
JEANJEAN.  REVERIE DE PRINTEMPS                                 A71
KLUGHART, A.  ROMANCE                                           F62
LANGLOIS, L.  GRAND AIR VARIE                                   D92
LANTIER, P.  ANDANTE ET ALLEGRO                                 D41
LIAGRE.  SOUVENIR DE CALAIS                                     A71
LISZT, F.-BLAAUW.  REVE D'AMOUR                                 D64
LODEON.  CAMPAGNARDE                                            D36
LONG, LONG AGO.                                                 D64
LOVEC-BOSWELL.  REQUIEM                                         N62
MACDOWELL, E.A.-BLAAUW.  TO A WILD ROSE                         D64
MACDOWELL, E.A.-PALMER.  TO A WILD ROSE                         E59
MAES, J.  CONCERTSTEUCK                                         A96
MAHY, A.  SOLO DE CONCERT                                       D64
MARCELLO, B.-MERRIMAN.  ADAGIO AND ALLEGRO                      F60
MARCELLO, B.-MERRIMAN.  LARGO AND ALLEGRO                       F60
MARITANA.                                                       D64
MARTEAU, H.-BARNES.  MORCEAU VIVANT                             F62
MARTIN.  SUITE                                                  G88
MASSO, G.  SUITE FOR LOUISE                                     D14
```

MC BRIDE, R. WAY OUT, BUT NOT TOO FAR	A13
MC BRIDE, R. WAY OUT, BUT NOT TOO FAR	B36
MC KAY, G.F. SUITE FOR BASS CLEF INSTRUMENTS	G01
MENDELSSOHN, F.-BLAAUW. IF WITH ALL YOUR HEARTS	D92
MENDELSSOHN, F.-CLUWEN. MON CHANT TE BERCE MON ANGE	D64
MONTAGNE. AIR VARIE	D92
MOZART, W.A.-CLUWEN. AVE VERUM CORPUS	D64
MOZART, W.A.-VOXMAN. CONCERT ARIA	F07
MOZART, W.A.-BARNES. PER QUESTA BELLA MANO, K.612	F62
MULLOT. SIEBEL	D64
MULLOT. SIEBEL	D92
NEUKOMM, S.R.-KAPLAN. ARIA	F60
NEVIN, E.W.-BLAAUW. NARCISSUS	D64
NEVIN, E.W.-BLAAUW. NARCISSUS	D92
NEVIN, E.W. ROSARY, THE	D52
NEVIN, E.W.-HARRIS. ROSARY	D52
NIVERD, L. CHANT MELANCOLIQUE	D64
NIVERD, L. COMPLAINTE	A71
NIVERD, L. HISTORIETTE DRAMATIQUE	A71
NIVERD, L. HYMNE	A71
NIVERD, L. LEGENDE	A71
NIVERD, L. 6 PETITES PIECES DE STYLE	A71
NIVERD, L. ROMANCE SENTIMENTALE	A71
NIVERD, L. SCHERZETTO	A71
PAQUE, J. VARIATIONS BRILLANTES	D92
PERGOLESI, G.B.-BARNES. CANZONE	F62
PETIT, A.S. ETUDE DE CONCOURS	A10
PETRIE, H.W.-WALTERS. ASLEEP IN THE DEEP	F07
POLLA-BEELER. DANCING TAMBOURINE	C58
PORRET, J. PIECE DE CONCOURS #1	A87
PORRET, J. 15E SOLO DE CONCOURS	D92
PORRET, J. 16E SOLO DE CONCOURS	D92
PORRET, J. 21E SOLO DE CONCOURS	D92
PORRET, J. 22E SOLO DE CONCOURS	D92
PORRET, J. 25E SOLO DE CONCOURS	D92
PORRET, J. 26E SOLO DE CONCOURS	D92
PORRET, J. 29E SOLO DE CONCOURS	D92
PORRET, J. 30E SOLO DE CONCOURS	D92
PRESSER, W.H. RONDO	F80
PURCELL, H.-ZIMMERMAN. ARIA	C91
PURCELL, H. ARISE YE SUBTERRANEAN WINDS	B85
PURCELL, H.-VINCENT. 2 PIECES	A62
RAVEL, M. PIECE EN FORME DE HABANERA (ORIG. FOR BSN)	D36
ROSSINI, G. LARGO AL FACTOTUM	A78
ROSSINI, G.-OSTRANDER. LORD PRESERVE ME	B85
ROUGNON, P. VALSE LENTE: PRIERE	C46
SAVERIO-HARRIS. FLOWER OF THE ORIENT	D52
SCARLATTI, A.-BARNES. ARIA FROM OPERA TIGRAINE	F62
SCHUBERT, F.P.-MOLENAAR. AIR DE ROSAMUNDE	D64
SCHUMANN, R.-CLUWEN. LOTUSBLUME, DIE	D64
SEGERHAMMER. SIERRA SERENADE	E80
SEMLER¬COLLERY. CANTABILE ET DIVERTISSEMENT	C01
SENAILLE, J.B.-FALCONE. ALLEGRO SPIRITOSO	F60
SHISHOV. GROTESQUE DANCE	B85
SOUTHWELL, G.-DIIANNI. EXECUTION	G10
SPILLMAN, R.A. 2 SONGS	B85
STORM, C.W. BOLD & BRAVE	D33
STORM, C.W. BOUQUET FOR BASSES (BP)	G10
STOUTAMIRE, A.L. PRELUDE & FUGUE	D52
TANNER. DAWN IS THE BEGINNING	A62
TCHAIKOVSKY, P.I.-LAUBE. ANDANTE CANTABILE	B53
TCHAIKOVSKY, P.I. CHANSON TRISTE	D92

```
TELEMANN, G.P.-BARNES.  ARIE FROM "PIMPINONE"          F62
TEMPLETON, A.  ELEGIE                                  D71
TROJE-MILLER, N.  HEROIC EPISODE                       A62
UBER.  GOLDEN LEAVES                                   M65
UBER.  MONTAGE                                         B85
VERDI, G.  ATTILLA                                     D64
VERDI, G.  TROVATORE (FAVORITE AIRS)                   B53
VINCENT.  GALAXY                                       A62
VITALE.  5 DANCING ELEPHANTS                           E80
VOXMAN, H.  CONCERT & CONTEST COLLECTION               F07
WAGNER, R.-DEDRICK.  SONG TO THE EVENING STAR          D14
WAGNER, R.  WALTHER'S PREISLIED                        D64
WAGNER, R.-MASSO.  WALTHER'S PRIZE SONG                D14
WALTERS, H.L.  JABBERWOCKY (BP)                        F07
WALTERS, H.L.  ONE-FINGER POLKA                        F07
WARREN, D.  DANISH DANCE                               D52
WARREN, D.  SHAKOS ON PARADE                           D52
WHITE.  LYRIC SUITE                                    F23
WIESCHENDORFF.  THEMA MIT VARIATIONEN & TEMPO DE POLONAISE   F26
WOLPE.  TURN YOURSELF AROUND                           D14
WRIGHT, D.(ARR).  6 SOLOS FOR CORNET (BARITONE)        E59
WURMSER, L.R.  SOLO DE CONCOURS                        D64
WURMSER, L.R.  TENDRES MELODIES                        D64
```

0147   EUPHONIUM SOLOS, UNACCOMPANIED

```
DEFER.  ETUDE                                          C49
DUFOUR, O.  MORCEAU D'EXAMEN                           C49
GAUDERFROY.  PETITE PIECE D'EXAMEN                     C49
```

0151   TUBA CONCERTOS AND CONCERTINOS

AMELLER, A.C. TUBA KONZERT, OP.69 (P)	C01
AREND, D. CONCERTINO VOOR TUBA OR BARITON (B)	D92
BENCRISCUTTO. CONCERTINO (P)	F43
ELAAUW, L. CONCERTINO (P)	D64
BLAAUW, L. CONCERTINO VOOR TUBA (P)	D92
BOTTJE, W.G. CONCERTO (P)	A13
BOZZA, E. CONCERTINO (OP)	D36
DAUCE. CONCERTINO (P)	N66
FRACKENPOHL, A.R. CONCERTINO (P)	M98
FRACKENPOHL, A.R. TUBA CONCERTINO (O)	E87
GARTH-JOOSEN. CONCERT VOOR TUBA (P)	D64
GOLTERMANN, G.E.-BELL. CONCERTO #4, OP.65 (EXCERPTS) (P)	C11
GOLTERMANN, G.E. EXCERPTS FROM CONCERTO #4, OP. 65 (P)	C11
HANDEL, G.F.-BARR. ALLEGRO FR. CONCERTO IN F MINOR (P)	D52
HARTLEY, W.S. CONCERTINO (P)	F80
LEBEDEV, A.-OSTRANDER. CONCERTO IN ONE MOVEMENT (P)	B85
LEBEDEV, A. KONZERT FUR TUBA & KLAV. (P)	C75
MOZART, W.A.-JOOSEN. CONCERT, K.191 (P)	D64
MOZART, W.A.-BLAAUW. HOORNSONATE (CONCERTO) #1	D92
PRESSER, W.H. CONCERTO (P)	F80
SPILLMAN, R.A. CONCERTO (P)	B85
VAUGHAN-WILLIAMS, R. CONCERTO FOR BASS TUBA & ORCH (OP)	E51
VIVALDI, A.-OSTRANDER. CONCERTO IN A MINOR (P)	B85
WILLIAMS, E. CONCERTO NO.2 (P)	B31
WILLIAMS, E. CONCERTO NO.5 (P)	B31

0152   TUBA SONATAS AND SONATINAS

BARDWELL. SONATA	D16
BEETHOVEN, L.V. SONATA, OP. 17 (ORIG. FOR HORN)	D92
BEVERSDORF, T. SONATA	B52
BODA, J. SONATINA	N70
CUNNINGHAM, M.G. SONATA, OP. 55	G66
HARTLEY, W.S. SONATA	F80
HARTLEY, W.S. SONATINA	B52
HAYDN, J.-BOWLES. SONATA #7, 1ST MVMT	A62
HINDEMITH, P. SONATE	F31
HOGG, M.E. SONATINA FOR TUBA & PA	B98
KLAUSS, K. SONATA FOR SOLO TUBA (UNACC)	B35
KOETSIER. SONATINA	B74
LINK, J.D. SONATINE (1951)	C75
PASCAL, C. SONATE EN 6 MINUTES 30	B81
PRESSER, W.H. SONATINA	F80
PRESSER, W.H. SONATINA #2	F80
REYNOLDS, V. SONATA	C11
SEAR, W.E. SONATA FOR TUBA & PA	B44
SEAR, W.E. SONATA FOR TUBA UNACCOMPANIED	G21
SIBBING. SONATA	F80
STABILE. SONATA	N13
STEIN, L. SOLO SONATA	B36

```
STEVENS, H.  SONATINA                                        E68
TAKACS, J.  SONATA CAPRICCIOSA                               B73
TROJE-MILLER, N.  SONATINA CLASSICA                          A62
WILDER, A.  SONATA                                           C25
```

0153   TUBA SOLOS WITH BAND ACCOMPANIMENT

```
BENCRISCUTTO.  CONCERTINO (B)                                F43
BILIK.  INTRODUCTION & DANCE (B)                             C29
ERICCETTI, T.  ECLOGUE NO.4 (B)                              B42
BRIEGEL, G.F.  BASSO PROFUNDO (B)                            A91
CATOZZI.  BEELZEBUB (B)                                      C11
FILLMORE, H.  DEEP BASS (BP)                                 C09
FRACKENPOHL, A.R.  VARIATIONS FOR TUBA AND WINDS (B)         F43
HARTLEY, W.S.  CONCERTINO (B)                                F80
HARTLEY, W.S.  DOUBLE CONCERTO FOR TUBA & ALTO SAX (B)       G83
HARTZELL, D.  EGOTISTICAL ELEPHANT (BP)                      F43
HAYS.  SOLO POMPOSO (BP)                                     C09
HOLMES, G.E.  EMMETT'S LULLABY (B)                           F07
KLEINSINGER, G.-ROACH.  TUBBY THE TUBA (BO)                  F23
MC QUAIDE, G.-BARNES.  SAMSONIAN POLKA (BP)                  D52
NELHYBEL, V.  CONCERT PIECE (B)                              G68
PETRIE, H.W.-WALTERS.  ASLEEP IN THE DEEP (BP)              F07
PRESSER, W.H.  CAPRICCIO (B)                                 F80
SIEBERT.  BOMBASTIC BOMBARDON, THE (B)                       E59
SOUTHWELL, G.-DILANNI.  MY TUBA SOLO (B)                     G10
STORM, C.W.  BOUQUET FOR BASSES (BP)                         G10
WALTERS.  TARANTELLE (B)                                     D52
WALTERS, H.L.  CONCERTANTE (B)                               F07
WALTERS, H.L.  40 FATHOMS (B)                                A78
WALTERS, H.L.  SCHERZO POMPOSO (B)                           F07
ZANINELLI, L.  PEG LEG PETE (BP)                             A78
```

0154   TUBA SOLOS WITH
ORCHESTRAL ACCOMPANIMENT

```
ANDRIESSEN.  CONCERTINO (O)                                  B74
BILLETTE.  FANTAISIE CONCERTANTE (OP)                        D36
BOUTRY, R.  TUBAROQUE (O)                                    D36
DUBENSKI, A.  FANTASY (O)                                    B32
FRACKENPOHL, A.R.  CONCERTINO (O)                            M98
LEVY.  DIALOGUE (O)                                          G66
```

0156   TUBA SOLOS WITH PIANO ACCOMPANIMENT

```
ABSIL, J.  SUITE, OP.78                                      F21
ALETTER, W.-KNIGHT.  DEEP SEA STORIES                        C11
AMELLER, A.C.  HAUTERIVE                                     D36
ARBAN, J.J.B.L.  OBERTO                                      D92
BACH, J.S.-BELL.  AIR & BOUREE                               C11
```

BUCHTEL, F.L.	GOLDEN DREAMS		D18
BUCHTEL, F.L.	HARLEQUIN		D18
BUCHTEL, F.L.	HERCULES		D18
BUCHTEL, F.L.	HERMES		D84
BUCHTEL, F.L.	HOLY CITY		D18
BUCHTEL, F.L.	INTRODUCTION & RONDO		A55
BUCHTEL, F.L.	JOLLY SAILOR		D84
BUCHTEL, F.L.	KING MYDAS		C09
BUCHTEL, F.L.	PENSEROSA E L'ALLEGRO, IL		C09
BUCHTEL, F.L.	PIED PIPER		D18
BUCHTEL, F.L.	RELUCTANT CLOWN, THE		D84
BUCHTEL, F.L.	SALAMANDER, THE		A55
BUCHTEL, F.L.	SONG OF THE SEA		D18
BUCHTEL, F.L.	WOTAN		D18
BURGSTAHLER.	CHANSONNOIR		E80
BURGSTAHLER.	TUBA CAPER		E80
BURGSTAHLER.	TUBALOW		E80
CAPUZZI-CATELINET.	ANDANTE & RONDO FROM DOUBLE BASS CONCERTO		C71
CARISSIMI, G.G.-BARNES.	HEART VICTORIOUS		F62
CARLES, M.	INTRODUCTION ET TOCCATA		D36
CASEY-BUCHTEL.	HONEYSUCKLE POLKA		D18
CASEY-BUCHTEL.	REMEMBRANCE OF LIBERATI		D18
CASTELLUCCI, L.S.	INTERMEZZO CAPRICCIOSO		D84
CASTEREDE, J.	FANTAISIE CONCERTANTE		D36
CATOZZI.	BEELZEBUB		C11
CECCONI.	TUBA-1		N50
CHALLAN.	INTERMEZZO		D36
CHAMBERS, W.P.-BUCHTEL.	COMMODORE, THE		D18
CHARLES.	CORTEGE ET DANSE		F87
CHARPENTIER, J.	PRELUDE & ALLEGRO		D36
CHILDS, B.	MARY'S IDEA (WITH HPCD)		G66
CHILDS, B.	SEAVIEW		B30
CHRISTENSEN, J.	BALLAD FOR TUBA		D14
CLERISSE, R.	CHANT D'AMOUR		D64
CLERISSE, R.	IDYLLE		D36
CLERISSE, R.	MARINE		N66
CLERISSE, R.	PIECE LYRIQUE		D36
CLERISSE, R.	PRELUDE ET DIVERTISSEMENT		D64
CLERISSE, R.	ROMANCE		D36
CLERISSE, R.	SOIR		D34
CLERISSE, R.	VOCE NOBILE		D36
COHEN, S.E.	ROMANCE & SCHERZO		A62
CORELLI, A.-HALL.	PRELUDIO & ALLEMANDA FR. VLN SONATA NO.10		A94
CROLEY, R.	TRE ESPRESSIONI		G83
DE JONG, M.	MORCEAU DE CONCERT.CONCERTSTUK, OP.50		A96
DE LAMATER, E. (ARR).	ROCKED IN THE CRADLE OF THE DEEP		F07
DE LAMATER, E. (ARR).	TRAMP! TRAMP! TRAMP!		F07
DE LAMATER, E. (ARR).	AULD LANG SYNE		F07
DEBAAR, M.	LEGENDE ET CAPRICE		A96
DEDRICK, A.	TOUCH OF TUBA, A		D14
DEL NEGRO, L.	POLKA GRAZIOSA		A91
DELBECQ, A.	AIR VARIE POUR CONTREBASSE		D64
DELGIUDICE, M.	10 PETITS TEXTES		C01
DELHAYE.	GRAND AIR VARIE		D64
DELHAYE.	THEME VARIE		D64
DEMERSSEMAN.	1ST CONCERT SOLO		F16
DESENCLOS, A.	SUITE BREVE DANS LE GOUT CLASSIQUE		D36
DESMOND, W.	SEA GONG		A62
DEVOS, G.	2 MOUVEMENTS CONTRASTES		D36
DIERCKS, J.	VARIATIONS ON A THEME OF GOTTSCHALK		F80
DOWLING, R.	HIS MAJESTY THE TUBA		A62
DOWNEY.	TABU FOR TUBA		D73

DUBOIS, P.M.   CORNEMUSE   D36
DUBOIS, P.M.   PICCOLO SUITE   D36
DURAND-AUDARD.   DIALOGUE   D36
FAYEULLE, R.   BRAVACCIO   D36
FILLMORE, H.   DEEP BASS (BP)   C09
FIRST DIV BAND COURSE.   ANDANTE CON MOTO   A62
FIRST DIV BAND COURSE.   CACTUS JACK   A62
FIRST DIV BAND COURSE.   CHALLENGER   A62
FIRST DIV BAND COURSE.   CHEERIO   A62
FIRST DIV BAND COURSE.   CHEYENNE   A62
FIRST DIV BAND COURSE.   CONCENTRATION   A62
FIRST DIV BAND COURSE.   CONQUERER   A62
FIRST DIV BAND COURSE.   ELECTRA III   A62
FIRST DIV BAND COURSE.   FIDELITY   A62
FIRST DIV BAND COURSE.   HOLIDAY WALTZ   A62
FIRST DIV BAND COURSE.   MELODY FR QUARTET IN D MINOR   A62
FIRST DIV BAND COURSE.   SONG OF THE EVENING STAR   A62
FOTE.   TUBADOUR   D14
FRACKENPOHL, A.R.   VARIATIONS (THE COBBLER'S BENCH)   F43
FRANGKISER, C.   CAVERN IMPRESSION   A62
FRANGKISER, C.   MELODIE ROMANZA   A62
FRESCOBALDI-CERHA.   CANZONI (2 BKS)   B73
FROST, G.   GRAND FANTASY OBLIGATO   D92
GABAYE, P.   TUBABILLAGE   D36
GARLICK.   FANTASIA   G66
GEIB, F.   CAPRICE IN B-FLAT MINOR, OP.4   D84
GEIB, F.-FORST.   CAVATINA, OP.6   D84
GEIB, F.-FORST.   HEROIC TALE, A,OP.25   C11
GEIB, F.   IN THE DEEP FOREST, OP.20   A91
GEIB, F.   JOYOUS DIALOGUE, A   D84
GEIB, F.-MOORSE.   MELODY, THEME & VARIATIONS   C11
GEIB, F.   POLKA PIQUANT   D84
GEIB, F.-FORST.   SERENADE   D84
GEIB, F.   SONG WITHOUT WORDS   C11
GERSCHEFSKI, E.   "AMERICA" VAR. FOR WINDS, OP.45/1   E68
GERSCHEFSKI, E.   "AMERICA" VARIATIONS, OP. 45, NO. 1   A13
GLANTZ, H.   6 GREAT MODERN SOLOS   B31
GODFREY, F.   LUCY LONG   B53
GOODE.   TUNE FOR TUBA   E80
GOTKOVSKY, I.   SUITE FOR TUBA   F16
GOUNOD, C.F.-OSTRANDER.   CALF OF GOLD, THE   B85
GOUNOD, C.F.-WALTERS.   MARCH OF A MARIONETTE   F07
GOUNOD, C.F.-BELL.   VALENTINE'S SONG FROM FAUST   A62
GRANT, P.   CONCERT DUO, OP.48   E68
GRETCHANINOFF.   SLUMBER SONG   A62
GRIEG, E.H.-HOLMES.   IN THE HALL OF THE MOUNTAIN KING   F07
GUENTZEL, G.   MASTODON   D84
HADDAD, D.   SUITE FOR TUBA   F43
HALEVY, J.F.-CLARK.   CARDINAL'S AIR, THE   B85
HALL, H.H.(ARR).   MENUET   A94
HANDEL, G.F.-BARR.   ALLEGRO FROM CONCERTO IN F MINOR   D52
HANDEL, G.F.-HALL.   ARIA (JUDAS MACCABEUS) & MENUET (ALCINA)   A94
HANDEL, G.F.-OSTRANDER.   ARM, ARM,YE BRAVE   B85
HANDEL, G.F.   ART THOU TROUBLED?   D92
HANDEL, G.F.-HARVEY.   HONOR & ARMS (SAMSON)   F23
HANDEL, G.F.-O'NEILL.   RECITATIVE & AIR (MESSIAH)   G13
HANDEL, G.F.   SARABANDE FROM CONCERTO IN F MINOR   D52
HANDEL, G.F.-BARR.   SARABANDE FROM CONCERTO IN F MINOR   D52
HANDEL, G.F.-BARNES.   SOUND AN ALARM (MACCABEUS)   F62
HANDEL, G.F.-MORRIS.   THRICE HAPPY THE MONARCH   D52
HANDEL, G.F.-SWANSON.   WHERE'ER YOU WALK   A62
HARTLEY, W.S.   ARIA   B92

```
HARTLEY, W.S.   SONORITIES                                        G83
HARTLEY, W.S.   SUITE                                             B92
HARTMANN, J.   AULD LANG SIJNE                                    D92
HARTMANN, J.   BELLE AMERICAINE, LA                               D92
HARTMANN, J.   RETURN, THE                                        D92
HARTMANN, J.   SEHNSUCHT NACH DER HEIMAT                          D92
HARTZELL, D.   EGOTISTICAL ELEPHANT (BP)                          F43
HASSE, J.A.-GOWER.   MENUET & BOURREE                             F07
HAUSER, E.   TWILIGHT THOUGHTS                                    C11
HAYDN, J.-BELL.   MEDLEY FROM SYMPHONY #94                        A62
HAYS.   SOLO POMPOSO                                              C09
HENRY.   MOUVEMENT                                               D36
HOLMES, G.E.   CARNIVAL OF VENICE                                 F07
HOLMES, G.E.   CARRY ME BACK TO OLD VIRGINNY                      F07
HOLMES, G.E.   EMMETT'S LULLABY                                   F07
HOLMES, P.   LENTO                                                F43
HUBERT.   DANS LES PINS                                           D64
HUDADOFF.   MARCHES, MARCHES, MARCHES                             E80
HUPFELD, B.-MACLEAN.   WHEN YUBA PLAYS THE RUMBA ON THE TUBA      C58
ISAAC, M.   JOLLY DUTCHMAN                                        C11
JACOB.   TUBA SUITE                                               A78
JAFFE.   CENTONE BUFFO CONCERTANTE                                F60
JAKMA, F.   DANS DER TEDDYBEREN                                   F81
JAKMA, F.   HERFSTBLOEMEN                                         F81
JAKMA, F.   PARADE DER OLIFANTEN                                  D92
JAKMA, F.   SANCTA LUCIA                                          D92
JAKMA, H.   BASSENPARADE                                          F81
JEANJEAN.   REVERIE DE PRINTEMPS                                  D64
JENNE.   RONDO                                                    F88
JUDE-DEVILLE.   MIGHTY DEEP, THE                                  C11
KAI, N.   LEGENDE                                                 D36
KESNAR, M.   PRELUDE                                              B53
KING, K.L.   OCTOPUS & THE MERMAID                                A55
KINYON, J.L. (ARR).   RECITAL PIECES FOR TUBA (2 VOL)            G31
KREISLER, A.V.   ALLEGRETTO GRAZIOSO                              F60
KREISLER, A.V.   RONDO                                            F60
KROEPSCH.   DOWN IN THE DEEP CELLAR                               C11
KROTOV-BLAZHEVICH.   CONCERT ETUDE                                D81
LANGLOIS, L.   GRAND AIR VARIE                                    D92
LANTIER, P.   ANDANTE ET ALLEGRO                                  D41
LAVALLE & TARTO.   BIG JOE, THE TUBA                              C25
LEBEDEV, A.-SMITH.   CONCERT ALLEGRO FOR TUBA                     G01
LIAGRE.   SOUVENIR DE CALAIS                                      A71
LISCHKA.   3 SKIZZEN                                              C75
LLOYD.   3 SKETCHES                                               F80
LODEON.   CAMPAGNARDE                                             D36
LODEON.   TUBA SHOW                                               D36
LOTZENHISER, G.W.   HORNPIPE                                      A62
LOTZENHISER, G.W.   SOLITUDE                                      A62
LOUVIER.   CROMAGNON                                              D36
MACDOWELL, E.A.-MASSO.   DESERTED FARM, A,OP.15                   E83
MAGANINI, Q.   APRES-MIDI D'UNE CROCODILLE, L'                    B85
MAHY, A.   CANTILENE                                              D92
MARGONI, A.   APRES UNE LECTURE DE GOLDONI                        D36
MARTEAU, H.-BARNES.   MORCEAU VIVANT                              F62
MARTELLI, H.   SUITE, OP.83                                       C01
MARTIN.   POMPOLA                                                 C11
MASSENET, J.-OSTRANDER.   HEROD'S AIR FR HERODIADE                B85
MASSO, G.   SUITE FOR LOUISE                                      D14
MATTEI, T.-WALTERS.   MARINER, THE                                F07
MC KAY, G.F.   SUITE FOR BASS CLEF INSTRUMENTS                    G01
MC QUAIDE, G.-BARNES.   SAMSONIAN POLKA (BP)                      D52
```

```
MENDELSSOHN, F.-BLAAUW.  ELIAS                                   D64
MENDELSSOHN, F.-OSTRANDER.  IT IS ENOUGH                         B85
MERLE.  DEMETRIUS                                               C11
MERLE.  MUMMERS                                                 C11
MERLE.  QUINTERO                                                C11
MERLE.  QUINTERO (THE FARMER)                                   C11
MONROE-ISAAC.  IN THE GARDEN                                    C11
MOQUIN, A.  KING OF THE DEEP                                    CC9
MOQUIN, A.  SAILING THE MIGHTY DEEP                             C09
MOQUIN, A.  SOUSAPHONIUM                                        C09
MOREAU.  COULEURS EN MOUVEMENTS                                 D36
MOZART, W.A.-MORRIS.  ISIS AND OSIRIS (F MAJOR)                 M80
MOZART, W.A.-SWANSON.  MENUETTO                                 A67
MOZART, W.A.-MORRIS.  O ISIS AND OSIRIS                         M80
MOZART, W.A.-LEMARC.  PAPEGENO ARIA                             F81
MOZART, W.A.-BARNES.  PER QUESTA BELLA MANO, K.612              F62
MOZART, W.A.-OSTRANDER.  SERENADE FROM DON GIOVANNI             B85
MOZART, W.A.  ZAUBERFLOTE, DIE                                  D92
MUELLER, F.  CONCERT MUSIC FOR BASS TUBA                        G01
MULLER, J.I.-OSTRANDER.  PRAELUDIUM, CHORALE... & FUGUE         B85
MULLOI.  SIEBEL                                                 D92
MURGIER, J.  CONCERTSTUCK                                       F87
MUSSORGSKY, M.P.-OSTRANDER.  SONG OF THE FLEA                   B85
NELHYBEL, V.  CONCERT PIECE                                     G68
NELHYBEL, V.  SUITE FOR TUBA & PA                               C40
NESSLER, V.-LUREMAN.  DE RATTENVANGER VAN HAMELN                F81
NEULING, H.  KONZERT-KADENZ                                     C59
NIVERD, L.  LEGENDE                                             D64
NIVERD, L.  6 PETITES PIECES DE STYLE                          D64
CLD HOME DOWN ON THE FARM.                                      D18
OSTRANDER, A.  CONCERT ALBUM                                    B85
OSTRANDER, A.  CONCERT PIECE IN FUGAL STYLE                     B85
PAINPARE, H.-VOXMAN.  CONCERTPIECE                              F07
PALA, J.  CERBERUS                                              D64
PARES, G.P.C.  CREPUSCULE                                       D64
PERGOLESI, G.B.-BARNES.  CANZONA                                F62
PETIT, P.Y.M.C.  1RE ETUDE DE CONCOURS                          D64
PETIT, P.Y.M.C.  FANTAISIE                                      D36
PETIT, P.Y.M.C.  GRAVE                                          D36
PETIT, P.Y.M.C.  THEME VARIE                                    D36
PETIT, P.Y.M.C.  WAGENIA                                        D36
PETRIE, H.W.-WALTERS.  ASLEEP IN THE DEEP (BP)                  F07
PETRIE, H.W.-TEAGUE.  ASLEEP IN THE DEEP                        G31
PHILLIPS, H.  8 BEL CANTO SONGS                                 F43
PLANEL, R.  AIR ET FINAL                                        D36
POOT, M.  IMPROMPTU                                             C01
PORRET, J.  1RE PIECE DE CONCOURS                               D64
PORRET, J.  15E SOLO DE CONCOURS                                D64
PORRET, J.  16E SOLO DE CONCOURS                                D64
PORRET, J.  21E SOLO DE CONCOURS                                DE4
PORRET, J.  22E SOLO DE CONCOURS                                D64
PORRET, J.  22E SOLO DE CONCOURS                                D92
PORRET, J.  23E SOLO DE CONCOURS                                D64
PORRET, J.  23E SOLO DE CONCOURS                                D92
PORRET, J.  24E SOLO DE CONCOURS                                D64
PORRET, J.  24E SOLO DE CONCOURS                                D92
PORRET, J.  25E SOLO DE CONCOURS                                D64
PORRET, J.  26E SOLO DE CONCOURS                                D64
PORRET, J.  29E SOLO DE CONCOURS                                D64
PORRET, J.  30E SOLO DE CONCOURS                                D64
PORRET, J.  31E SOLO DE CONCOURS                                D64
PORRET, J.  32E SOLO DE CONCOURS                                D64
```

PAGE 144   (0156)

TOURNIER. RECIT ET RONDO	N50
TUTHILL, B.C. FANTASIA	B98
UBER, D.A. PANTOMIME	B31
VANDERCOOK, H.A.-BUCHTEL. ARBUTUS	D18
VANDERCOOK, H.A. BEHEMOTH	F07
VANDERCOOK, H.A. BOMBASTOSO	F07
VANDERCOOK, H.A.-BUCHTEL. CHRYSANTHEMUM	D18
VANDERCOOK, H.A. COLOSSUS	F07
VANDERCOOK, H.A.-BUCHTEL. COLUMBINE	D18
VANDERCOOK, H.A.-BUCHTEL. DAISIES	D18
VANDERCOOK, H.A.-BUCHTEL. DEWDROPS	D18
VANDERCOOK, H.A.-BUCHTEL. HYACINTHE	D18
VANDERCOOK, H.A.-BUCHTEL. IVY	D18
VANDERCOOK, H.A.-BUCHTEL. LILY	D18
VANDERCOOK, H.A.-BUCHTEL. MAGNOLIA	D18
VANDERCOOK, H.A.-BUCHTEL. MARIGOLD	D18
VANDERCOOK, H.A.-BUCHTEL. MORNING GLORY	D18
VANDERCOOK, H.A.-BUCHTEL. MOSS ROSE	D18
VANDERCOOK, H.A.-BUCHTEL. PANSIES	D18
VANDERCOOK, H.A.-BUCHTEL. PEONY	D18
VANDERCOOK, H.A.-BUCHTEL. ROSEBUDS	D18
VANDERCOOK, H.A.-BUCHTEL. TULIP	D18
VANDERCOOK, H.A.-BUCHTEL. WILD ROSE	D18
VAUGHAN. CONCERTPIECE NO. 1	B52
VERDI, G.-OSTRANDER. ARIA FR. DON CARLOS	B85
VERDI, G.-OSTRANDER. GRAND AIR FR. THE MASKED BALL	B85
VILLETTE, P. FANTAISIE CONCERTANTE	D36
VIVALDI, A.-SWANSON. ALLEGRO FROM SONATA #3	A62
VIVALDI, A.-MAGANINI. PRAELUDIUM IN C MINOR	B85
WADOWICK, J. 2 FOR THE TUBA	G90
WAGNER, R.-MASSO. WALTHER'S PRIZE SONG	D14
WALTERS, H.L.(ARR). BLOW THE MAN DOWN	F07
WALTERS, H.L.(ARR). CHRISTMAS NOCTURNE	F07
WALTERS, H.L.(ARR). CONCERTANTE	F07
WALTERS, H.L.(ARR). DOWN IN THE VALLEY	F07
WALTERS, H.L.(ARR). FORTY FATHOMS	F07
WALTERS, H.L.(ARR). LANCER, THE	F07
WALTERS, H.L.(ARR). LEPRECHAUNS PATROL	F07
WALTERS, H.L.(ARR). SCHERZO POMPOSO	F07
WARREN, D.(PSEUD). MANTIS DANCE	D52
WATELLE-BILLAULT. CARNIVAL OF VENICE, THE	F16
WATELLE. GRAND SOLO DE CONCERT	F16
WEBER. SOLILOQUE	D36
WEBER, F. BIG BOY	A62
WEBER, F. 3 FAVORITES	A62
WEEKS. TRIPTYCH	D16
WEISS, W.H. VILLAGE BLACKSMITH	B53
WEKSELBLATT, H. FIRST SOLOS FOR THE TUBA PLAYER	F23
WEKSELBLATT, H.(CMPL). SOLOS FOR THE TUBA PLAYER	F23
WHEAR, P.W. MANTIS DANCE	D52
WILDER, A. SUITE #1 (EFFIE SUITE)	H09
WILLIAMS, E. LITTLE CLASSICS	B31
WORTH, G.E. SERPENT OF THE BRASS	F07
WURMSER, L.R. SOLO DE CONCOURS	A71
WURMSER, L.R. TENDRES MELODIES	A71
ZANINELLI, L. PEG LEG PETE (BP)	A89

0157   TUBA SOLOS, UNACCOMPANIED
STUDY MATERIALS

ADLER, S.H. CANTO VII	A78
ANTONICU. 6 LIKES	A51
ARNOLD, M. FANTASY	C05
BAKER, C. CANZONET	F60
BAMERT. INCON-SEQUENZA	F23
COPE, D. BTRB (THEATRE PIECE)	M80
CROLEY, R. VARIAZIONI	A43
DUBOIS, P.M. SOLI EN FORME D'ETUDES, TUBA	D36
FULKERSON. PATTERNS III	N29
GABRIELI, D.-MORRIS. RICERCAR	F43
HANKS. SOLO #1	N92
HARTLEY, W.S. MUSIC FOR TUBA SOLO	N62
HARTLEY, W.S. SUITE FOR UNACCOMPANIED TUBA	B92
JOB, M. (CMPL). SCHOOL FOR CANTABILE AND STYLE	D36
KINNEY. LITTLE SUITE	N61
KINNEY. RICERCAR	N61
KLAUSS, K. SONATA FOR SOLO TUBA	B35
KRAFT. ENCOUNTERS II	D71
KUHN. IMPROVISATION	N92
MC CARTHY, F. COLOR-ETUDES	N29
MUCZYNSKI. IMPROMPTUS, OP. 32	F23
PERSICHETTI, V. SERENADE NO.12 FOR SOLO TUBA, OP.88	B92
POWELL. MIDNIGHT REALITIES	N79
POWELL, M. MIDNIGHT REALITIES	M80
PRESSER, W.H. SUITE FOR TUBA	B98
RECK. 5 STUDIES	E65
SACCO. TUBA MIRUM	N38
SEAR, W.E. SONATA FOR TUBA UNACCOMPANIED	G21
SPILLMAN. 4 GREEK PRELUDES	B85
STEIN, L. SOLO SONATA	B36
TUTHILL, B.C. TINY TUNES FOR TUBA	F80

COMPOSER INDEX

COMPOSER INDEX

KEY TO PUBLISHERS

KEY TO PUBLISHERS

Alphabetization is by publisher code. American agents or distrubutors for foreign firms are indicated in parentheses.

A02   Accura Music, Box 887, Athens, Ohio 45701

A03   Henry Adler, Inc. (G85-Belwin-Mills)

A04   Advanced Music Corp. (H06-Warner Bros)

A07   A.G.M. Music Publishers (G85-Belwin-Mills)

A08   Ahn & Simrock, Bühnenverlag, Taunusstrasse 66, 6200 Wiesbaden, Germany

A10   Alfred Music Co., Inc., 75 Channel Drive, Port Washington, N.Y. 11050

A11   Allan & Co., Ltd., 276 Collins Street, Melbourne, Australia

A13   American Composers Alliance, 170 W. 74th Street, New York, N.Y. 10023

A15   American Music Edition, 263 E. 7th Street, New York, N.Y. 10009 (C11-C. Fischer)

A16   Amphion Editions Musicales, 9 Rue d'Artois, Paris 8e, France (G85-Belwin-Mills)

A18   Amsco Music Publishing Co., 33 W. 60th Street, New York, N.Y. 10023

A20   Johann Andre, Postfach: 141, 605 Offenbach Am Main, Germany

A25   Appleton Music Publishers (C11-C. Fischer)

A26   Arcadia Music Publishing Co., 10 Sherlock Mews, Baker Street, London W.1, England

A31   Ars Polona, Krakowskie Przedmiescie 7, 00-068 Warsaw, Poland

A33   Artia, Ve Smeckach 30, Prague I, Czechoslovakia (A78-Boosey)

A35   Ascherberg, Hopwood & Crew, Ltd., 16 Mortimer Street, London W.1, England

A36   Edwin Ashdown, Ltd., 19 Hanover Square, London W.1, England

A37   Ashley Dealers Service, Inc., 263 Veterans Blvd., Carlstadt, N.J. 07072

A38   Associated Music Publishers, Inc., 866 Third Ave., New York, N.Y. 10022

A39   Astoria Verlag, Brandenburgische Strasse 22, Berlin-Wilmersdorf, Germany

A42   Augener, Ltd., (C33-Galaxy)

A43   Avant Music (G21-Western Int. Music)

A44   Axelrod Publications, Inc. (F43-Shawnee)

A51   Bärenreiter Verlag, Heinrich Schütz Allee 29, 500 Kassel-Wilhelmshöhe, Germany

A52   Bärenreiter & Neuwerk, Heinrich Schütz Allee 35, 35 Kassel-Wilhelmshöhe, Germany

A55   C.L. Barnhouse Co., 110 B Avenue East, Oskaloosa, Iowa 52577

A56   Maurice Baron Co., P.O. Box 149, Oyster Bay, Long Island, N.Y. 11771

A58   M.P. Belaiff (E65-C.F. Peters)

A62   Belwin-Mills Publishing Corp., 25 Deshon Drive, Melville, N.Y. 11746

A63   Anton J. Benjamin, Werderstrasse 44, Hamburg 13, Germany

A65   Claude Benny Press, 1401 State Street, Emporia, Kan. 66801

A67   Berkeley Publishing Co., 952 Shattuck Avenue, Berkeley, Calif. 94707

A69   Besson & Co., Ltd, 295 Regent Street, London W.1., England

A70   Big 3 Music Corp., 729 Seventh Avenue, New York, N.Y. 10019

A71   Editions Billaudot, 14, rue de l'Echiquier, Paris 10e, France (E77-Presser)

A78   Boosey & Hawkes, Inc., P.O. Box 130, Oceanside, N.Y. 11572

A79   Borups (H30-W.Hansen)

A80   Gustav Bosse Verlag, Postfach 417, 84 Regensbu 2, Germany

A81   Boston Music Co., 116 Boylston Street, Boston, Mass. 02116 (C27-Frank Music Corp.)

A82   Bosworth & Co., Ltd., 14-18 Heddon St., Regent St., London W.1, England (G85-Belwin-Mills)

A83   Bote & Bock, Hardenbengstrasse 9A, 1 Berlin 12, Germany (A38-AMP)

A84   Bourne Co., 1212 6th Avenue, New York, N.Y. 10036 (B20-Chappell)

A87   Editions Braun (A71-Billaudot)

A89	Breitkopf & Härtel Musikverlag, Karlstrasse 10, Leipzig C1, Germany
A90	Breitkopf & Härtel, Walkmühlstrasse 52, D 6200 Wiesbaden 1, Germany (A38-AMP)
A91	George F. Briegel, Inc., 4 Summit Court, Flushing, N.Y. 11355
A93	Broadcast Music, Canada (A38-AMP)
A94	Brodt Music Co., P.O. Box 1207, Charlotte, N.C. 28201
A96	Editions Musicales Brogneaux, 73 Ave. Paul Janson, Bruxelles 7, Belgium (B91-H. Elkan)
A98	Broude Bros., 56 West 45th Street, New York, N.Y. 10036
B02	Buffet-Crampon (D36-Leduc)
B07	Carisch S.P.A. 20124, Via General Fara 39, Milan, Italy
B12	Centre Belge De Documentation Musicale (CeBeDeM), rue de l'Hopital, 31, B-1000 Bruxeles, Belgium (B91-H. Elkan)
B13	Century Music Publishing Co., Inc., 263 Veterans Blvd., Carlstadt, N.J. 07072
B14	CFG Publishing Co., Box 26, Cold Spring Harbor, N.Y. 11724
B15	Chamber Music Library (C25-Fox)
B17	Le Chant du Monde (G85-Belwin-Mills)
B20	Chappell & Co., Inc., 810 Seventh Avenue, New York, N.Y. 10019
B23	J. & W. Chester, Ltd., Eagle Court, London EC1, England (D58-Magnamusic)
B24	Edition Choudens, 38, rue Jean Mermoz, Paris 8e, France (E65-C.F. Peters)
B26	The John Church Co. (E77-Presser)
B30	M.M. Cole Publishing Co., 251 East Grand Avenue, Chicago, Ill. 60611
B31	Charles Colin Music Publishers, 315 W. 53rd Street, New York, N.Y. 10019
B32	Franco Colombo, Inc. (G85-Belwin)
B34	Published by the Composer
B35	Composers' Autograph Publications, Box 671, Hamilton, Ohio 45012
B36	Composers' Facsimile Edition, 170 W. 74th Street, New York, N.Y. 10023
B38	The Composers Press, Inc., 177 E. 87th Street, New York, N.Y. 10028 (G66-Seesaw)
B40	Concordia Publication House, 3558 S. Jefferson Avenue, St. Louis, Mo. 63118
B41	Consolidated Music Publishers, Inc., 33 W. 60th St., New York, N.Y. 10023
B42	Contemporary Music Publishers
B44	Cor Publishing Co., 67 Bell Place, Massapequa, N.Y. 11758
B46	Editions Costallat, 60, rue de la Chausse-d'Antin, Paris 9e, France (A71-Billaudot)
B47	Editions Cousin, 116, Ave. Franklin Roosevelt, Bruxelles, Belgium
B50	Editions A. Cranz Musikverlag, Adelheidstrasse 68, 62 Wiesbaden, Germany (B91-H. Elkan)
B52	Crescendo Music Sales Co., Box 395, Naperville, Ill. 60540
B53	Cundy-Bettoney Co., Inc. (C11-C. Fischer)
B55	Dania (E65-C.F. Peters)
B66	Georges Delrieu et Cie, 45, Ave. de la Victoire, Nice, France (C33-Galaxy)
B69	Deutscher Verlag fur Musik, Postfach 147, 701 Leipzig, East Germany
B72	Oliver Ditson Co. (E77-Presser)
B73	Ludwig Doblinger, Dorotheergasse 10, Vienna, Austria (A38-AMP)
B74	Stichting Donemus, Jacob Obrechtstraat 51, Amsterdam-Z, Holland (E65-C.F. Peters)
B81	Durand et Cie, 4 Place de la Madeleine, Paris 8e, France (B92-Elkan-Vogel)
B84	Editio Musica Budapest, Pf. 322, Budapest 5, Hungary (A78-Boosey)
B85	Editio Musicus-New York, Inc., Box 1341, Stanford, Conn. 06904
B90	Ehrling Förlagen, Linnégatan 9-11, Box 5268, Stockholm 5, Sweden
B91	Henri Elkan Music Publisher, 1316 Walnut St., Philadelphia, Pa. 19107
B92	Elkan-Vogel Co., Inc. (E77-Presser)
B95	Enoch & Cie, 27 Boulevard des Italians, Paris 2e, France (A38-AMP)

B98	Ensemble Publications, Inc., P.O. Box 98, Bidwell Station, Buffalo, N.Y. 14222
B99	Rudolph Erdmann, Postfach 471, Wiesbaden, Germany
C00	Eriks Musikhandel & Förlag AB, Karlavägen 40, Stockholm, Sweden
C01	Editions Max Eschig, 48 rue de Rome, Paris 8e, France (A38-AMP)
C03	Edition Eulenburg KG (E65-C.F. Peters)
C04	Evette & Schaeffer (D36-Leduc)
C05	Faber Music Ltd., 38 Russell Square, London WC1B5DA, England (F23-G. Schirmer)
C09	Fillmore Music Co. (C11-C. Fischer)
C10	A.E. Fischer (A63-Benjamin)
C11	Carl Fischer, 62 Cooper Square, New York, N.Y. 10003
C13	H.T. FitzSimons Co., Inc., 615 North La Salle St., Chicago, Ill. 60610
C16	Edition Maurice et Pierre Foetisch, rue de Bourg 6, Lausanne, Switzerland
C18	Charles Foley (C11-C. Fischer)
C19	Robert Forberg Musikverlag, Mirbachstrasse 7, 53 Bonn-Bad Godesberg, Germany (E65-C.F. Peters)
C25	Sam Fox Sales Corporation, 1540 Broadway, New York, N.Y. 10036
C27	Frank Music Corp. 116 Boylston St., Boston, Mass. 02116
C29	Samuel French, 25 W. 45th Street, New York, N.Y. 10036
C30	Friedrich W. Fröhlich, Ansbacher Strasse 52, Berlin W. 30, Germany
C33	Galaxy Music Corporation, 2121 Broadway, New York, N.Y. 10023
C38	Editions E. Gaudet (F16-Salabert)
C39	Carl Gehrmans Musikförlag, Vasagatan 46, Box 505, 101 26 Stockholm 1, Sweden (A78-Boosey)
C40	General Music Publishing Co., P.O. Box 267, Hastings-On-Hudson, New York, N.Y. 10706
C41	Hans Gerig Musikverlag, Drususgasse 7-11, D-5, Cologne, Germany (D71-MCA)
C42	Gervan (B91-H. Elkan)
C45	Gordon Music Company, 2680 Chrokee Way, Palm Springs, Calif. 92262
C46	David Gornston Music, c/o Charter Publications, Box 850, Valley Forge, Pa. 19482 (C25-Sam Fox)
C49	Ch. Gras, 12 Rue Faidherbe, Lille, France
C50	S.A.R.L. Gras Frères, 36 Rue Pape-Carpentier, 72-La Flêche, France (A56-M. Baron)
C54	Philipp Grosch Musikverlag, Lisztstrasse 18, 8000 München 8, Germany
C55	J. Hamelle & Cie, 24 Boulevard Malesherbes, Paris 8e, France
C56	Charles Hansen Publishing, 1842 West Avenue, Miami Beach, Fla. 33139
C58	T.B. Harms Co., c/o Cimino Publications, 1646 New Highway, Farmingdale, N.Y. 11735
C59	Harth-Pro Musica Verlag, Karl-Liebknecht-Strasse 12, 701 Leipzig, Germany
C60	Heinrichshofen Verlag, Liebigstrasse 4, Wilhelmshaven, Germany (E65-C.F. Peters)
C61	Editions Henn-Chapuis, 8 rue de Hasse, Geneva, Switzerland
C65	Heugel et Cie, 2 Bis Rue Vivienne, Paris 2e, France (E77-Presser)
C67	Max Hieber Musikverlag, Kaufingerstrasse 23, 8 München 2, Germany
C71	Hinrichsen Edition, Ltd., 10 Baches Street, London N. 1, England (E65-C.F. Peters)
C75	Friedrich Hofmeister-Verlag, Ubierstrasse 20, 6238 Hofheim Am Taunus, Germany
C78	Hornists' Nest, Box 2713, Buffalo, N.Y. 14226
C80	Hug & Co., Musikverlag, Limmatquai 26-28, CH-8022 Zürich, Switzerland
C91	International Music Co., 511 Fifth Ave., New York, N.Y. 10017
C93	Israel Music Institute, P.O. Box 11253, Tel Aviv, Israel
C94	Israeli Music Publications, c/o Alexander Broude, 1619 Broadway, New York, N.Y. 10019
C95	Israel Publishers Agency
D00	Jobert & Cie, 44 rue de Coleseé, Paris 8, France (B92-Elkan-Vogel)
D08	Edwin F. Kalmus, Opa Locka, Fla. 33054
D11	KaWe, Brederodestraat 90, Amsterdam 13, Holland

D14	Kendor Music, Delevan, N.Y. 14042
D16	Robert King Music Co., 112A Main Street, North Easton, Mass. 02356
D17	Kistner & Siegel & Co., Postfach 101, 5 Köln 7, Germany
D18	Neil A. Kjos Music Co., 525 Busse Highway, Park Ridge, Ill. 60068
D20	Johann Kliment Musikverlag, Kolingasse 15, 1090 Vienna, Austria
D21	Edition Kneusslin, Amselstrasse 43, Basel 24, Switzerland (E65-C.F. Peters)
D22	Koff Music Co., P.O. Box 1442, Studio City, Calif. 91604
D23	S. Kovar, 4974 Noeline, Encino, Calif. 91316
D26	Ludwig Krenn, Reindorfgasse 42, Vienna 15, Austria
D29	Kultura, P.O. Box 149, Budapest 62, Hungary (A78-Boosey)
D32	Knud Larsen Musikforgal, Graabrødretorv 7, Copenhagen K, Denmark
D33	Lavell Publishing Co., P.O. Box 717, Omaha, Neb. 68101
D34	Leblanc Publications, 7019 30th Ave., Kenosha, Wisc. 53141 (F60-Southern Music)
D35	Lacour (A71-Billaudot)
D36	Alphonse Leduc, 175 rue Saint-Honoré, Paris 2e, France
D37	Leeds Music Corporation (G85-Belwin-Mills)
D41	Henry Lemoine & Cie, 17 rue Pigalle, Paris 9e, France (B92-Elkan-Vogel)
D42	Alfred Lengnick & Co., Purley Oaks Studios, 421A Brighton Road, South Croydon, Surrey DR2 6YR, England
D44	F.E.C. Leuckart Musikverlag, Nibelungenstrasse 48, Munich 19, Germany
D46	Musikverlag Robert Lienau, Lankwitzer Strasse 9, 1 Berlin 45 (Lichterfelde), Germany (E65-C.F. Peters)
D48	H. Litolff's Verlag, Forsthausstrasse 101, Frankfurt, Germany (E65-C.F. Peters)
D52	Ludwig Music Publishing Co., 557-567 East 140th Street, Cleveland, Ohio 44110
D55	McGinnis & Marx, 201 West 86th Street, New York, N.Y. 10024
D61	Mannheimer Musikverlag, Mollstrasse 35, Mannheim 2, Germany
D62	Edition Marbot, Bornstrasse 12, Hamburg 13, Germany
D63	Edward B. Marks Music Corp., 1790 Broadway, New York, N.Y. 10019 (G85-Belwin)
D64	Editions Robert Martin, 106 Grande-rue de la Coupée, 71, Charnay-les-Macon, France
D67	J. Maurer, Avenue de Verseau 7 Watermanlaan, Brussels 15, Belgium
D71	MCA Music (G85-Belwin-Mills)
D73	Mentor Music Inc., Broadview Drive, Brookfield, Conn. 06804 (C25-Fox)
D74	Mercury Music Corporation (E77-Presser)
D78	Karl Merseburger Verlag, Alemannenstrasse 20, 1 Berlin 38, Germany
D80	Muziekuitgaven Metropolis, Frankrijklei 24, Antwerp, Belgium
D81	Mezhdunarodnaya Kniga Editions (F23-G. Schirmer)
D82	M-F Company, Box 351, Evanston, Ill. 60204
D84	Belwin-Mills Publishing Corp., 25 Deshon Drive, Melville, N.Y. 11746
D92	Molenaar's Musiekcentrale, Zuideinde 18, Wormerveer, Holland (B91-H. Elkan)
D93	Mondia, Paris, France
D96	Edwin H. Morris & Co., Inc., 810 7th Ave., New York, N.Y. 10019
D97	Moscow (A38-AMP)
D98	Möseler Verlag, 3340 Wolfenbütel, Germany
E00	MS Publications, 946 S. Wesley, Oak Park, Ill. 60304
E02	Willy Müller-Süddeutscher Musikverlag, Marzgasse 5, Heidelberg, Germany (E65-C.F. Peters)
E03	Neuer Münchner Musikverlag, Franz Pollak, Imkerweg 42B, 8 München 60 Germany
E10	Music Press Inc. (E77-Presser)
E11	Music Publishers Holding Corp. (H06-Warner Bros.)

E14	Musica Rara, 2 Gt. Marlborough Street, London, W.1, England
E19	Muzika USSR Publishing House (A38-AMP)
E27	Nauka I Izkustva, Sofia, Bulgaria (D11-KaWe)
E30	New Music Edition (E77-Presser)
E31	New Sounds in Modern Music (B31-Colin)
E33	New Wind Music Co., 23 Ivor Pl., London, N.W.1, England
E34	New World Music (H06-Warner Bros.)
E36	Pierre Noel, 24 Boulevard Poissonniere, Paris 9e, France
E37	Otto Heinrich Noetzel, Liebigstrasse 4, Wilhelmshaven, Germany
E41	Novello & Co., Ltd., Borough Green, Sevenoaks, Kent, England or Box 1811, Trenton, N.J. 08607
E43	Louis Oertel, Eichenweg 11a, 3006 Grossburgwedel/Hanover, Germany
E47	Omega Music Co., 353 E. 52nd, New York, N.Y. 10022
E51	Oxford University Press, Inc., 200 Madison Ave., New York, N.Y. 10016
E54	Panton, Rieni 12, Prague, Czechoslovakia
E58	Paterson's Publications Ltd., 38-40 Wigmore Street, London, W. 1 HOEX, England (C11-C. Fischer)
E59	W. Paxton & Co., Ltd. (E41-Novello)
E61	Peer International Corp., 1740 Broadway, New York, N.Y. 10019
E65	C.F. Peters Corp., 373 Park Ave. South, New York, N.Y. 10016
E66	Philippo-Combre, 24 Boulevard Poissonnière, Paris 9e, France (E77-Presser)
E67	Piedmont Music Co., Inc. (D63-Marks)
E68	American Composers Alliance, 170 West 74th Street, New York, N.Y. 10023
E70	Plymouth Music Co., Inc., 17 West 60th Street, New York, N.Y. 10023
E72	Polskie Wydawnictwo Muzyczne, Krakowskie Przedmiescie 7, 00-068 Warsaw, Poland
E77	Theodore Presser Co., Presser Place, Bryn Mawr, Pa. 19010
E80	Pro Art Publications, Inc., 469 Union Ave., Westbury, N.Y. 11591
E81	Pro Musica Verlag, Karl-Leibknecht-Strasse, 701 Leipzig 1, East Germany
E83	Providence Music Press, Box 2362 East Side Station, Providence, R.I. 02906
E87	Pyraminx Publications, 358 Aldrich Road, Fairport, N.Y. 14450
E89	D. Rahter (A38-AMP)
E93	Remick Music Corp. (H06-Warner Bros.)
E98	G. Ricordi & Co., Viz Salomone 77, Rome, Italy (G85-Belwin-Mills)
F01	Robbins Music Corp. (A70-Big 3)
F02	Rochester Music Publishers, 358 Aldrich Road, Fairport, N.Y. 14450
F03	Rongwen Music, 56 W. 45th Street, New York, N.Y. 10036 (A98-Broude)
F05	Rouart, Lerolle, Et Cie (F16-Salabert)
F07	Rubank, Inc., 16215 N.W. 15th Ave., Miami, Fla. 33169
F10	Emil Ruh Musikverlag, Zürichstrasse 33, CH-8134 Adliswil, Zürich, Switzerland
F16	Editions Salabert, 22 rue Chauchat, Paris 9e, France or 575 Madison Ave., New York, N.Y. 10022
F21	Scherzando, 41 Transvaalstreet, Berchem-Antwerp, Belgium
F23	G. Schirmer, Inc., 866 Third Ave., New York, N.Y. 10022
F24	Schlesinger'sche Musikhandlung (E65-C.F. Peters)
F26	C.F. Schmidt (E65-C.F. Peters)
F27	Schmitt Music Center 110 N. 5th Street, Minneapolis, Minn. 55403
F30	Schott Freres, 30 rue Saint-Jean, Bruxelles 1, Belgium (E65-C.F. Peters)
F31	B. Schott's Söhne Weihergarten 1-9, 6500 Mainz, Germany (G85-Belwin)
F33	Edward Schuberth & Co., New York, N.Y.
F34	J. Schuberth & Co., Zietenring 3, Wiesbaden, Germany

F36	Science and Art, Boul. Ruski Nr. 6, Sofia, Bulgaria
F37	Walter Sear (B44-Cor)
F39	Editions Musicales Selmer, 18 rue de la Fontaine-au-Roi, Paris, France
F42	Shapiro, Bernstein & Co., Inc., 10 East 53rd Street, New York, N.Y. 10022
F43	Shawnee Press, Inc., Delaware Water Gap, Pa. 18327
F50	Hans Sikorski Musikverlag, Johnsalle 23, 2 Hamburg 13, Germany (G85-Belwin-Mills)
F52	N. Simrock, Werderstrasse 44, Hamburg 13, Germany (A38-AMP)
F53	Sirius-Verlag, Wiclefstrasse 67, 1 Berlin 21, Germany
F54	R. Smith & Co., Ltd, 210 Strand, London W.C.2, England
F59	Southern Music Publishing Co., Inc., 1740 Broadway, New York, N.Y. 10019
F60	Southern Music Co., 1100 Broadway, P.O. Box 329, San Antonio, Tex. 78292
F62	Spratt Music Publishers, 17 W. 60th Street, New York, N.Y. 10023
F64	Staff Music Publishing Co., 17 West 60th Street, New York, N.Y. 10023
F65	Stainer & Bell, Ltd (C33-Galaxy)
F69	STIMS Informationscentral för Svensk Musik (B90-Ehrling)
F72	Summy-Birchard Co., 1834 Ridge Ave., Evanston, Ill. 60204
F74	Swing Lane Publications, P.O. Box 128, Beverly, N.J. 08010
F78	Templeton Publishing Co. (F43-Shawnee)
F79	Tempo Music Publications, P.O. Box 392, Chicago, Ill. 60690
F80	Tenuto Publications (E77-Presser)
F81	Tierolff-Musiekcentrale, Markt 90/92, Roosendaal, Holland (B91-H. Elkan)
F87	Editions Musicales Transatlantiques, 14 Avenue Hoche, Paris 8E, France (E77-Presser)
F88	Tritone Press, Box 158 Southern Station, Hattiesburg, Miss. 39401 (E77-Presser)
F95	Union Musical Espanola (A38-AMP)
F97	Universal Edition, Karlsplatz 6, Wien 1, Austria
F98	Universal Musical Instrument Co., 732 Broadway, New York, N.Y. 10003
G01	University Music Press, P.O. Box 1267, Ann Arbor, Mich. 48103 (C25-Fox)
G03	USSR State Music (A38-AMP)
G09	Voggenreiter Verlag, Potsdam, Germany
G10	Volkwein Brothers, 117 Sandusky Street, Pittsburgh, Pa. 15212
G13	Waterloo Music Co., 3 Regina Street North, Waterloo, Ontario, Canada (A38-AMP)
G16	Joseph Weinberger, Oederweg 26, Frankfurt, Germany
G17	Weintraub Music Co., 33 West 60th Street, New York, N.Y. 10023
G18	Weltmusik Edition International, Seilergasse 12, Wien 1/15, Austria
G21	Western International Music, Inc., 2859 Holt Ave., Los Angeles, Calif. 90034
G26	Joseph Williams, Ltd. (C33-Galaxy)
G27	Willis Music Co., 7380 Industrial Road, Florence, Ky. 41402
G28	Wind Music, Inc., 1014 South Goodman Street, Rochester, N.Y. 14620
G31	M. Witmark & Sons (H06-Warner Bros.)
G38	G. Zanibon, Piazza Dei Signori, 24, 35100 Padova, Italy (E65-C.F. Peters)
G41	Edizioni Suvini Zerboni, Corso Europa 5/7, Milan, Italy
G43	Wilhelm Zimmermann Musikverlag, Zeppelinallee 21, 6000 Frankfurt, Germany (E65-C.F. Peters)
G58	J. Curwen and Sons Ltd., 20 Maiden Lane, London, W.C.2, England
G66	Seesaw Music Corp., 177 East 87th Street, New York, N.Y. 10028
G68	Joseph Boonin, Inc., P.O. Box 2124, S. Hackensack, N.J. 07606
G70	Fema, Box 395, Naperville, Ill. 60540
G81	Editio Supraphon, Palackého 1, Praha 1, Czechoslovakia
G83	Autograph Editions, c/o Atlantic Music Supply, 152 W. 42nd Street, New York, N.Y. 10036

G85	Belwin-Mills Publishing Corp., 25 Deshon Drive, Melville, N.Y. 11746
G88	Canadian Music Centre, 33 Edward Street, Toronto 2, Ontario, Canada
G89	CMP Library Editions, University Microfilm, 300 North Zeeb Road, Ann Arbor, Mich. 48106
G90	Concert Music Publishing Co. (A84-Bourne)
G95	Edizioni Curci, Galleria Del Corso 4, Milan, Italy
H03	Schweizerisches Music-Archiv, Bellariastrasse 82, 8038 Zurich, Switzerland
H05	University of Missouri Press, Columbia, Missouri 65201
H06	Warner Brothers, 75 Rockefeller Plaza, New York, N.Y. 10019
H09	Wilder Music Incorporated (C25-Fox)
H26	Edizioni Internazionale, Milan, Italy
H27	H. Flammer (F43-Shawnee)
H30	Wilhelm Hansen Musik-Forlag, Gothersgade 9-11, 1123 Copenhagen, Denmark (D58-Magnamusic)
I36	Hooper Co., P.O. Drawer C, Denton, Tex. 76201
J39	Metropolis (B91-H. Elkan)
M63	Alfred E. Weissman (B31-Colin)
M65	Almitra Enterprises (D14-Kendor)
M67	Edition Andel Uitgave (B91-H. Elkan)
M68	Autopress Publications, c/o Atlantic Music Supply, 152 W. 42nd Street, New York, N.Y. 10036
M69	Appleyard Publications, Box 111, Durham, N.H. 03824
M70	AR Publishing Co., 756 7th Ave., New York, N.Y. 10019
M72	Argee Music Press, Box 436, Greencastle, Ind. 46135
M76	Edizioni Musicali Berben, Ancona, Italy
M77	Berklee Press Publications, 1140 Boylston Street, Boston, Mass. 02215
M79	Brightstar Music Publications (G21-Western Int. Music)
M80	The Brass Press, 159 Eighth Ave. North, Nashville, Tenn. 37203
M92	Crown Music Press, 4119 N. Pittsburg, Chicago, Ill. 60634
M93	Date Music, c/o Educulture, Inc., Box 1932, Santa Monica, Calif. 90406
M98	Easton Music Co. (D16-King)
M99	Les Editions Ouvrieres, 12 Ave. Soeur-Rosalie, Paris 13E, France (C33-Galaxy)
N05	Musikverlag Wilhelm Hatter, Karlsruhe, Germany
N06	Harold T. Brasch, 2707 South June Street, Arlington, Va. 22202
N07	Harold Branch Publications, 42 Cornell Drive, Plainview, N.Y. 11803
N10	Highland Music Co., 1311 W. Highland Ave., Hollywood, Calif. 90028
N11	High Note Studios, Box 429, Hollywood, Calif. 90028
N13	Honour Publications (G21-Western Int. Music)
N16	Musikforlaget Imudico, Colbjornsensgade 19, 1652 Copenhagen, Denmark
N21	Luther Publisher, Box 179, Ansonia Station, New York, N.Y. 10023
N23	Maher Publications (B31-Colin)
N26	Musica Islandica
N27	M.M. Cole Publishing Co., 251 E. Grand Ave., Chicago, Ill. 60611
N28	Moeseler Verlag, Wolfenbuettel, Germany
N29	Media Press, Box 895, Champaign, Ill. 61820
N37	Okra Music Corp., 177 E. 87th Street, New York, N.Y. 10028
N38	Ostara Press (G21-Western Int. Music)
N40	Paolo Baratto, Wiesenstrasse 4, CH 8008 Zürich, Switzerland
N42	Philharmusica Corp., Box 180, West Nyack, N.Y. 10994
N43	Pillon Music (G21-Western Int. Music)
N45	Podium Music Inc., 4 Broadway, Valhalla, N.Y. 10595

N47	Roger Dean Publishing Co., 324 W. Jackson, Macomb, Ill. 61455
N49	Roslyn Publications. Box 128. Malverne, N.Y. 11565
N50	Rideau Rouge (E77-Presser)
N56	Schilke Music Products, 529 S. Wabash Ave., Chicago, Ill. 60605
N57	Carl B. Schulz Corp., 305 E. 4th Street, Waterloo, Iowa 50703
N61	Studio P/R, 224 S. Lebanon Street, Lebanon, Ind. 46052
N62	Richard Stegmann, Wald Kugelweg 5A, 87 Wurzburg, Germany
N63	Stevens-Costello (N07-Branch)
N66	Tromba Publications, 1859 York Street, Denver, Colo. 80206
N68	Union Europeene D'Editions, Monaco
N70	W.D. Stuart Music (D16-King)
N74	David Zauder (A78-Boosey)
N75	June Emerson, Ampleforth, York, England
N76	Aeolus Publishing Co., 60 Park Terrace West, New York, N.Y. 10034
N79	Brass Music Ltd. (M80-Brass Press)
N84	Saul B. Groen, Ferdinand Bolstraat 6, Amsterdam, Holland
N85	Thames Publishing, 14 Barlby Road, London W.10 6AR England
N91	Smith Publications, 906 E. Water Street, Urbana, Ill. 61801
N92	Tomorrow Brass Series, c/o Tuba-Euphonium Music Publications, Box 524, Muncie, Ind. 47305
N95	Silvio Coscia (D16-King)
N96	Rayner Brown (G21-Western Int. Music)
P23	Eble Music Co., P.O. Box 1171, Iowa City, Iowa 52240
P24	Bayley & Ferguson (F23-G. Schirmer)
P31	Blixt Publications, 15795 Poppy Lane, Los Gatos, Calif. 95030